D1285059

Homer William Smith, Sc.D.

Photograph by Fabian Bachrach

Homer William Smith, A.B., Sc.D., M.S. (Hon.)
Scientist, Teacher, Explorer, Philosopher, Novelist, and Perennial Student

Homer William SMITH

Sc.D.

His Scientific & Literary Achievements

EDITED BY

Herbert Chasis, M.D.
Professor of Medicine
New York University School of Medicine

AND

William Goldring, M.D.
Professor of Medicine
New York University School of Medicine

NEW YORK UNIVERSITY PRESS · 1965

LIBRARY OF CONGRESS CATALOG CARD NUMBER: 65–10765

MANUFACTURED IN THE UNITED STATES OF AMERICA
DESIGNED BY ANDOR BRAUN

TO ALL THOSE SCHOLARS AROUND THE WORLD

WHO WERE ASSOCIATED WITH

Homer Smith

IN HIS SCIENTIFIC ACTIVITIES

PREFACE

Homer William Smith received wide acclaim during his life for his scientific medical achievements, but those of us who worked closely with him, feel nevertheless that the recognition was inadequate. There is little doubt that Smith, as he was affectionately called, would have been in violent opposition to this book, particularly those portions with laudatory overtones. However, our wish to present a lasting memorial outweighed his likely opposition and we sincerely hope that when he reads it on some lofty perch in Scientists' Heaven he will find it not too difficult to forgive.

To the many scientists, teachers, and physicians who were associated with Smith, the material in this book should serve to recall experiences of their early training. We also hope that it will recreate the man for students and young investigators who know of his scientific contributions but who did not have the good fortune to have personal contact with him.

This book will be of particular interest to scientists in the field of normal and abnormal renal physiology, and will also interest a much wider group of readers because of the literary contributions through which Smith achieved an international reputation as writer, philosopher, and naturalist. Among his well-known publications are Kamongo, Man and His Gods, and From Fish to Philosopher. Wherever possible we have allowed Smith to speak for himself.

He conceived and organized a division of the New York University School of Medicine Library devoted to books dealing with "Man's Place in Nature," in the strong belief that medical scientists should be familiar with a broad base of scientific thought. We have included a list of titles which Smith selected as the nucleus of the Library.

Early in his approach to the problems of renal physiology, the Commonwealth Fund encouraged and largely supported the laboratory. The scientific effort of Smith and his associates culminated in the "bible" for all investigators, students, and physicians interested in renal physiology and renal diseases, The Kidney: Structure and Function in Health and Disease (New York, Oxford University Press, 1951).

Our collaboration with Smith began in 1928 when we brought to him for interpretation puzzling renal functional data obtained from patients on the New York University Medical Division of Bellevue Hospital. He promptly recognized the inadequacy of existing knowledge on normal renal functions in man and the need for new approaches before attempting to interpret aberrations in disease. He realized that collaboration between the departments of physiology and medicine was essential and required elimination of the barrier which traditionally had existed between the preclinical sciences of the first two years of the medical school curriculum and the clinical sciences. In this connection, Sir George Pickering, Regius Professor of Medicine in the University of Oxford said, ". . . Smith saw that the scientific method had been developed by the laboratory sciences, but that clinical science had not yet accepted it. He had a clear and practical idea of how science could be brought into the clinic and how clinicians could be trained as scientists. He succeeded in taking young men into his laboratory and training them in the kinds of methods they could use in the clinic, whither they went. Once there, he did not abandon them, as so many physiologists do, but continued to take an interest in their problems and to bring to them his unique qualities of mind. He was one of the most attractive writers in the field of medical research of my generation. He combined a clear mind, imagination and precision of thought; and these were all evident in his writings. I would say that he was one of the great men of our generation."

In 1944, when at our request Smith wrote the introduction to a monograph we were preparing on Hypertension and Hypertensive Disease (New York, Commonwealth Press, 1944), he saw an opportunity to emphasize his personal views on the importance of training in basic scientific disciplines to those who care for patients. His conviction of the need to apply the scientific method to bedside clinical problems, he expressed as follows: "Collaboration between the Department of Medicine and the Department of Physiology of New York University College of Medicine has been the product of *a broader plan whereby in successive years various junior members of the medical faculty have returned to physiology for a period of a year or more, during which time they have usually assumed the routine duties of instruction as well as the privileges of investigation. Facilities have been made available for certain of these men on their return to the Department of Medicine to carry on investigative work along the lines of their chief clinical interests; and as certain phases of this investigative work have assumed increasing clinical importance, special effort has been made to aid it by supervision and criticism and above all by integration in relation to normal physiology.*

"The impetus to this cooperative program was afforded by the late John Wyckoff. As Associate Professor of Medicine, then as full Professor, and finally as Dean, Dr. Wyckoff ever defended the thesis that those who would reap the maximal benefits from their medical training should return at some time during this training, or shortly thereafter, to one or more of the preclinical departments for additional experience.

"William Goldring and Herbert Chasis are of the men who have brought their clinical experience to physiology and thus enriched this subject, and whom physiology in turn has been able to help. For fifteen years they have given generously of their time to investigations on the physiology of the normal and the diseased kidney, and it is a pleasure to acknowledge this indebtedness and to acknowledge with them that the opportunities for these collaborative studies stem from the foresight of our mutual friend, John Wyckoff."

This concept of the need for collaboration between clinical and preclinical departments was the means by which we were introduced to Smith. As young members of the Department of Medicine we were fortunate to be among the first, with Norman Jolliffe and Jim Shannon, to have been offered the opportunity to collaborate. Our association lasted 34 years. It was a milestone in our lives and an unforgettable experience to have known Homer Smith intimately as scientist, teacher, and friend. Compiling this information about Smith has been a source of great satisfaction for us.

On July 1, 1961, Homer William Smith, Professor and Chairman of the Department of Physiology in New York University School of Medicine, reached the age of retirement. Plans were made for the customary farewell dinner and for a portrait in oil. As we had anticipated, however, he rejected both with great vehemence. "A formal dinner is equivalent to an obituary, for which I am not ready," he protested. "My desk is filled with materials for several years of writing, for which I now will finally have the time. As for the portrait, I will not sit for it, and moreover I will sue anyone who authorizes a painting from a photograph. I have seen enough to know that although a portrait is first hung in the main lobby, it is soon transferred to the library and eventually to a dust bin in the cellar. Several years later, it is completely unidentifiable by anyone and discarded."

Some of us felt that Smith's scientific achievements and his enormous value to the school made it imperative that we show some token of esteem in spite of his opposition. Accordingly, we arranged a surprise for him on the occasion of the New York University School of Medicine annual Alumni Day, February 22, 1962. Two of his illustrious former research associates were chosen to reminisce. Dr. Stanley E. Bradley, Bard Professor and Chairman of the Department of Medicine at the College of Physicians and Surgeons, Columbia University, spoke to the general Alumni of the School, and Dr. Robert Pitts, Professor and Chairman of the Department of Physiology, Cornell University Medical School, spoke at an informal dinner after the day-long meeting. The element of surprise to Homer Smith was the content of both talks, which dealt with him personally, his importance to the School and the world-wide influence of his scientific achievements in renal physiology. It is doubtful that he would have been present had he known in advance. As the climax to a pleasant surprise, we had invited to the dinner all of his past and present scientific associates, from all parts of the country. As we anticipated, he did not speak at the dinner, but on the way home he admitted to one of us that it had been a wonderful experience and that he was happy we had lured him to the dinner against his will.

New York, 1965

Herbert Chasis
William Goldring

CONTENTS

Homer William Smith, Sc.D.

1.

Three Decades of Progress in Knowledge of the Kidney

We reproduce below an address delivered by Dr. S. E. *Bradley at an informal dinner on the occasion of the New York University School of Medicine annual Alumni Day, February* 22, 1962. (*See* Preface, *p.* x.)

In returning here *to speak briefly of some of New York University's contributions to our knowledge of the kidney, I am acutely aware of my presumption. Dr. Farber assured me that this would be a gathering of old friends pleased to participate in a tribute to Alma Mater, to savor old triumphs, and to recall some of the vicissitudes and blunders along the way. But as I look around, I find myself quailing before a group of steely-eyed experts who know as well as I how faulty my judgments are. You have just conferred your highest honor upon Bob Pitts, of whom you may well be proud, because his way of thought and his contributions, stemming clearly from your tradition of critique, have immeasurably enhanced the prestige of the College of Medicine. Certainly the fact that he began his work in the Department of Physiology is of particular significance, because Homer Smith of Physiology and the school Homer Smith has nurtured have been responsible for the major discoveries that link New York University and the kidney in men's minds the world over. I know, however, that Dr. Smith himself would be the first to stress his dependence upon the College of Medicine as a whole, and upon the spirit which the College embodies.*

The major contributions have been conceptual, solid, difficult, puzzling, irritating ideas that made one think, that have been accepted reluctantly, but once accepted have become part of the common intellectual heritage. Thirty years ago we were deep in controversies about kidney function. Though Cushing had brought some semblance of order into the field by his critical appraisal of current notions and data, the ideas of glomerular filtration and of tubular processing of filtrate were at best vague, partial, and vitiated by complementary views that obscured and often contradicted the fundamental concepts. Here at New York University these uncertainties were first realized most poignantly, I think, by Bill Goldring in the Department of Medicine in the course of studies of changes in urea clearance during febrile disease. You all undoubtedly remember those days in midwinter when the beds in Bellevue Hospital came down the middle of each ward and on into the hall, filled with the indigent, the indignant, and the indigenous patients with pneumonia, sepsis, etc., beyond the counting. What a crowded, colorful, vital place it was and is still today! And in this setting young Bill, at the suggestion of John Wyckoff, consulted the new young Professor of Physiology who was known to be interested in the renal functions of fish. In fact it was even said in Charlottesville where Homer Smith worked before coming to New York University that he had persuaded the management of a visiting circus to let him follow the camels around, pot in hand, to collect samples of urine. Surely a man like this should be able to read the urine of patients dried out by fever, and shortly indeed there began to emerge those papers in which the clearance concept was first spelled out as a quantitative tool for the measurement of glomerular filtration rate and renal blood flow.

As with all complexities, the basic concept is simple. In essence, it is what the circulatory people here had called the "Fick Principle," for the same approach had been used before to estimate volumes in the cardiovascular system. The principle states merely that a volume of fluid may be determined after a known quantity of some substance is thoroughly mixed in it by dividing the total quantity added by the amount added to each milliliter. In the case of glomerular filtration rate, Smith, Shannon, Jolliffe, and their associates found that inulin could be used, and since it appeared neither to return to the blood by tubular absorption nor to enter the glomerular filtrate by any route other than filtration, the total quantity put out each minute (UV) could be divided by the plasma concentration per milliliter (or the amount in each ml of filtrate) to yield the volume of filtrate formed each minute. Similarly the amount of some substance, first Diodrast, later p-aminohippurate, which is removed completely from all the blood perfusing the kidney, put out each minute when divided by the amount per ml of blood yields the renal blood flow. These two methods have proved powerful tools indeed, for they have provided a yardstick by which tubular cellular function may be evaluated in terms of the load placed upon them and of their performance in transfers of various kinds. Thanks to this seminal idea, it is customary today everywhere in the world to think of urine formation in terms of glomerular filtration. No one thinks of azotemia and other evidences of renal failure except as manifestations of diminished filtration. And the work of Smith, Shannon, Goldring, Chasis,

Ranges, and many others here at the College of Medicine has proved conclusively that filtration and renal perfusion are inseparably linked.

It is of course entirely appropriate that elucidation of the behaviour of the circulation of the kidney should have occurred in New York University. When Bellevue Hospital Medical College opened its doors in 1861, Austin Flint was Professor of the Principles and Practice of Medicine. Flint's work on cardiac murmurs and on the techniques of auscultation and percussion established him as the "American Laennec," inaugurating a vigorous tradition of interest in heart and the circulation which was kept alive through the century that has passed by his assistants and successors, including William Henry Welch, Edward Janeway, and John Wyckoff. To this galaxy of stars and their satellites we can attribute a sharpening and clarification in the definition of heart disease today, embodied in the criteria of the New York Heart Association. In shaping this approach, I think, New York University established its own singular branch of critical appraisal, a scientific scepticism that has done much to determine the direction and soundness of its contributions in many spheres.

Many departments of the school participated in using the technique of Diodrast or PAH clearance to measure renal blood flow under a variety of conditions and in testing its validity as a guide to the effects of disease and therapy. Rovenstine and Papper in the Department of Anesthesiology, for example, collaborated in studies of the effects of spinal anesthesia and narcotics, and Welsh, Wellen, and Taylor in the Department of Obstetrics in an investigation of the changes associated with pregnancy and eclampsia. A joint program was set up in the early days of World War II between Columbia University and New York University to study shock, a study in which Medicine, Surgery, Physiology, and Pharmacology participated. More recently Baldwin, Chasis, and others have applied these methods in the evaluation of the role of the kidney in hypertensive disease. The fact emerging from all these studies, and which is now universally accepted, is that the renal circulation contributes importantly in nearly all cardiovascular adjustments, sometimes to the detriment of the kidney's role as an excretory organ in regulating the composition and volume of body fluids.

The method for estimating renal blood flow proved important also in the evaluation of tubular function, since the load of any material brought to the tubules for excretion depends upon blood flow. The measurement of GFR provides a similar measure of the load imposed upon tubular reabsorptive mechanisms. From these measurements emerged the data that led Smith and James Shannon and their co-workers to the concept of Tm, the maximal rate at which a substance is taken up by the renal cells from blood or tubular urine for transfer. The work of Shannon, Farber, and Troast on glucose Tm proved to be particularly important as an approach to the question of glomerular intermittency. This concept and the methods for its study are still today, some 30 years later, occupying the thought and energies of hundreds of workers all over the world.

A measure of GFR also opened the door to precise evaluation of urea, electrolyte, and water excretion, serving as a basis for the classical studies of Dr. Pitts. Important new views of the tubular handling of water and electrolytes were also developed here in the past 15 years by Smith, Wesson, Anslow, Zak, Brun, and many others. In the course of this work the concept of the free water clearance emerged, a clarifying notion that has made it much easier to define the mechanisms of changes in water excretion. In stressing the importance of collecting tubule function in determining urinary concentration and of distal tubular reabsorption of sodium, these studies led the way to the exciting recent developments in which Wirz, who worked here as a Fellow in Physiology has figured so prominently. Wirz has called attention to the peculiar structure of the renal medulla that makes it possible for a countercurrent multiplier system to operate in raising and maintaining the osmotic pressure of the medullary interstitial fluid as the means of reabsorbing water from urine passing down the collecting tubules along an osmotic gradient. A host of others have brought forward a mass of persuasive supporting evidence.

So far we have concentrated upon those major contributions of New York University to renal physiology which have been largely dependent upon the genius of Homer Smith; but we must not forget to acknowledge contributions to our knowledge of the kidney by others in the school. In Anatomy, of course, you have Doctor Rhodin, whose electron microscopic studies of the ultramicrostructure of the renal tubular cells are already classic; in Therapeutics, the work of Dr. DeGraff and his associates upon the diuretic action of digitalis and the various specific diuretic agents; in Pathology, the work of Dr. Graef in the juxtaglomerular apparatus, to which attention in this country was first drawn by workers in this school; and in Medicine, of course, the studies made here by Drs. Goldring, Chasis, Shannon, Earle, Taggart, and others upon the renal manifestations of glomerulonephritis and hypertensive disease. It was here that the first split-function studies were done by Chasis and Redish in studies of unilateral renal disease that have become such a focus of interest in the last few years. And in closing this sketchy and incomplete survey, I must mention also the studies of streptococcal disease, of the amino-acidurios, of tissue reactions in which the kidney participates—contributions linked with the names of McLeod, McCarty, Tillett, McEwen, Thomas, and Holt.

A remarkable spirit of cooperation, loyalty, and scientific critique has made New York University School of Medicine an outstanding institution of learning in the medical sciences. In the years ahead we may confidently expect sweeping changes in the pattern of medical practice, the organization and ordering of medical teaching, and the character of medical knowledge. With its traditions, New York University will continue to play a formative and leading role in these changes. Certainly this would be little to expect from the institution in which we have witnessed the apotheosis of the kidney.

2.

Homer William Smith: A Memoir

The National Academy of Sciences honored Homer Smith by publishing a tribute to him. Because of his close scientific and personal relationship to Smith over a period of many years, Robert F. Pitts was asked to prepare the following memorial for Volume 39 of the National Academy Memoirs.

HOMER WILLIAM SMITH died in his sleep of a cerebral hemorrhage on March 25, 1962 at his home in New York City. For some time he had been occupied with the revision of his textbook, Principles of Renal Physiology, a classic of supplementary reading for students of medicine. He was active and productive until the end.

His death brought to a close what has been aptly termed the Smithian Era of renal physiology. For over thirty years he had dominated his chosen field in a way that few if any have dominated other fields. His personal investigations, his broad and inclusive concepts, the methods of study of function which he developed and popularized, the texts which he wrote, and the many investigators and students of medicine whom he trained or influenced established him as the acknowledged master of all things renal. Although not a physician, he has been widely recognized by clinicians for his contributions to an understanding of functional alterations in renal disease as well as by physiologists for his contributions to knowledge of the functional properties of glomeruli, tubules and the renal vascular bed.

Although such a thumb-nail sketch might satisfy those who knew him only through his publications on renal function, it fails to indicate the scope and catholicity of his interests. Even as a scientist, he was as much a biologist as a renal physiologist, with, at one extreme, a profound occupation with the problems of consciousness of man and of his role in the universe, at the other, a penetrating inquisitiveness concerning the properties and structure of the plasma membrane of cells. He was a voracious reader, not only in the realms of biological and physical sciences but also in those of philosophy, religion, art, music and literature. He had a remarkably retentive memory and could converse intelligently with authorities in many fields. But the characteristic which, to me, set him apart from his peers was the rapidity with which he could grasp an involved concept, examine its several facets, marshall a variety of arguments in favor of and against it, and quickly return it to its proponent, simplified and stripped of inconsequential trappings. His was the ultimate of logical reason; it was an unforgettable experience to observe his mind at work.

If there is any real purpose to be served by a memorial such as this, it lies in an attempt to analyze the factors which shaped and developed him into the man he was. Sheer sentimentality would have been anathema to him. A group of those who, at some time in their careers, were close to him wished to have him sit for a portrait to be presented to the Library of New York University College of Medicine at the time of his retirement from the Professorship of Physiology. It was to have been hung in the section on Man's Place in Nature which he had been instrumental in establishing. He refused to sit for a portrait. Another thought was to have a dinner in his honor, to be attended by the many who had worked with him. This he vetoed; he would not attend. Only by the subterfuge of honoring one of his students and former associates at the Medical College Alumni Day, was the dinner finally engineered with Dr. Smith in attendance. Rather grudgingly he admitted to a friend, who had long known him well, that he had enjoyed it. To most of us, he never acknowledged the fact that he knew the dinner had really been in his honor.

By those who did not know him, this refusal to permit personal recognition by friends and colleagues might be interpreted as indicating resentment of the fact of retirement. It was not. He had gracefully and graciously accepted many honors throughout his distinguished career. He simply did not want any demonstration as his active professorial career drew to a close. Furthermore, he had no intention of retiring to a state of passive scientific inactivity. Why recognize the mere transition from Professor to Professor Emeritus? He aimed to remain active and productive. Less than two weeks before he died, he wrote to me asking for my considered guess as to the volume of fluid reabsorbed in the various segments of the nephron; this, in connection with the revision of his textbook.

However, his refusal to permit his friends to pay him homage stemmed in part from personality traits of independence and, shall we say, distance. He was self-sufficient; he could handle his own problems; a fact reflected in many ways but perhaps most disturbingly in recent years in his complete disregard of the advice of his personal physician. He was not an outwardly warm individual. Most of us kept our distances, a bit in awe of the master. Yet many of us, when faced with some personal problem, *ultimately found that he was cognizant of it and had taken steps which made it easier for us to solve it. He never obviously intruded; he would never permit intrusion by others.*

His personal life was not notably happy. His first marriage ended in divorce, his second in the tragic death of his wife. In the decade from 1932 to 1942 when I was an instructor and medical student and was most closely associated with him, he was frequently moody. However, flashes of wit and humor leavened his contacts with those who worked for him and with him. He was always kindly, the perfect gentleman. Later as he began to receive the recognition which he so richly deserved and when his home life was more pleasant, he became a warmer, mellower and more outgoing person. The great joy of his life in later years was his son, Hudi (Homer Wilson Smith), born of his second marriage in April 1951. Smith's way of life, his hopes and plans were centered around the boy. The two were drawn even closer together by the death of Mrs. Smith.

Dr. Smith was an indefatigable worker, seemingly at all times in library or office, reading, writing or, with slide-rule in hand, calculating and plotting data of his most recent experiments. Despite his concentration on his work, he was always available for the discussion of an idea or an experiment. Furthermore, he would quickly sense flaws in experimental design or argument and suggest appropriate changes. He demanded precision in analytical work and insisted on justification of methods by extensive chemical recoveries. He took pride in the work which originated in his laboratory and would countenance nothing but the best in execution and presentation of experiments.

When one of his associates brought a paper for review, it received the most thoroughgoing editorial criticism possible, to the point of complete reorganization and rewriting, if necessary. When the shock of reading what seemed to be a new paper on a different subject had passed, there was no doubt in the writer's mind that his contribution had been vastly improved. Smith was a master of lucid, logical and exciting scientific prose. By this laborious process of revision, he taught a number of his associates to write lucidly and logically, although none attained the quality which characterized his expression. Writing was important to

Smith and he appreciated that the efforts of his junior associates were important to them. A paper was never placed at the bottom of a pile of accumulated work; it received prompt consideration.

Philosophy was important to Smith throughout his scientific career, not an avocation to which he turned in later years. Kamongo, published in 1932, was an expression of his views of man's place in nature, a synthesis of the scientific, humanistic and philosophic traditions which have influenced the development of man as a biological, social and creative being. He was concerned with consciousness as the awareness of environment and self, coupled with the time binding quality of persistence in perception. He recognized its minimal existence in the simplest of cellular organisms and its greatest development in man. His early scientific investigations of the comparative physiology of the body fluids led through his study of paleontology to his erudite essays on the evolution of the kidney, contained in his Porter Lectures and expanded into his book From Fish to Philosopher. He summarized his views in the statement: "the human kidney manufactures the kind of urine that it does, and it maintains the blood in the composition which that fluid has, because this kidney has a certain functional architecture; and it owes that architecture not to design or foresight or to any plan, but to the fact that the earth is an unstable sphere with a fragile crust, to the geologic revolutions that for six hundred million years have raised and lowered continents and seas, to the predaceous enemies, and heat and cold, and storms and droughts; to the unending succession of vicissitudes that have driven the mutant vertebrates from seas into fresh water, into desiccated swamps, out upon the dry land, from one habitation to another, perpetually in search of the free and independent life, perpetually failing, for one reason or another, to find it."

Smith's science and philosophy were never far separated. To quote again: "mental integrity is a sine qua non of the free and independent life. As intermittent rays of light blend into moving images on the cinematographic screen, so the multiform activities within the brain are integrated into images of consciousness, and brought into an unstable focus to form that fleeting entity which we call personality, or Self. But let the composition of our internal environment suffer change, let our kidneys fail for even a short time to fulfill their task, and our mental integrity, our personality, is destroyed." To continue the theme with another quotation: "Superficially, it might be said that the function of the kidneys is to make urine; but in a more considered view one can say that the kidneys make the stuff of philosophy itself."

Three of Dr. Smith's scientific monographs have exerted a tremendous influence on the development of renal physiology and on investigators in the field. His first, entitled The Physiology of the Kidney and published in 1937 by the Oxford University Press, was a masterful summary of the then existing body of knowledge of renal function. It was an extremely readable book and provided an accurate and up to date summary of inestimable value for both students and investigators. No comparable summary had been attempted since Cushny published The Secretion of Urine in 1917. It is interesting that The Physiology of the Kidney was written as one of a series to be combined into a medical textbook of Physiology. The only other monograph of the series to be published was Dr. Fulton's Physiology of the Nervous System. These two volumes undoubtedly influenced many young men to take up careers of investigation in the fields of renal physiology and neurophysiology. His second and really monumental treatise, entitled The Kidney; Structure and Function in Health and Disease, was published by the Oxford University Press in 1951. This book was a far more detailed and exhaustive treatment of renal function than was his first monograph and encompassed both the normal and pathological states. Its increased scope reflected the great advances in knowledge which had been made in the intervening 14 years, largely based on the methods and concepts which Smith himself had introduced. Because of its encyclopedic coverage, extensive documentation and authoritative treatment, it became known in common parlance as the Bible. It was, however, more a reference work and less suited as a general supplementary text for students. To fill the needs of students for more information on kidney function than that contained in the usual textbook of Physiology, Smith wrote his Principles of Renal Physiology, published in 1956 by the Oxford University Press. This small monograph was an excellent summary, lucidly written. It at once became a classic for the student as well as the investigator who wished a concise, accurate and readable discussion of current concepts of renal function. Dr. Smith was in the process of revising and updating this book when he died.

Homer William Smith was born in Denver, Colorado, on January 2, 1895, the son of Albert C. and Margaret E. (Jones) Smith. He was the youngest of six children. His grade school and the first two years of his high school education were received in Cripple Creek, Colorado, where he lived till the age of 14. The last two years of high school and his collegiate education were obtained in Denver, Colorado, the latter at the University of Denver, from which he received the A.B. degree in 1917. He described his early environment as economically poor but culturally as broad or broader than that of the average middle class family which migrated west in the '70's and '80's. From the beginning he was interested in science and devoted his free time to amateur chemical, electrical and biological experiments. His juvenile predilections for gadgets and experiments unquestionably were the forerunners of his adult scientific interests.

Shortly after graduation from the University of Denver he joined the armed forces and was assigned to a battalion of engineers. Fortunately he was soon transferred to the Chemical Warfare Station of the American University in Washington, D.C. A unit under Dr. E. K. Marshall had been given the task of investigating the biological effects of war gases. Marshall was in urgent need of chemists to participate in his project and by a stroke of good fortune, Smith was assigned to him. The first of Smith's scientific publications, which appeared in 1918, was concerned with this work.

This strictly accidental association of Smith and Marshall developed into a lifelong friendship and loose scientific collaboration. Here indeed the element of chance seems to have played a major role in shaping Dr. Smith's career. One wonders what his subsequent course of action would have been had he remained an engineer throughout the war. With cessation of hostilities, Marshall arranged for Smith to undertake graduate study under Dr. William H. Howell of The Johns Hopkins University School of Hygiene and Public Health, from which institution he received his D.Sc. in 1921. The titles of the publications which resulted from his graduate studies are interesting in that they reflect his early interest in chemistry, an interest which he maintained throughout his subsequent scientific career.

For a period of two years after receiving his degree, Smith worked in the research laboratories of Eli Lilly and Co. (1921–1923), then became a Fellow of the National Research Council at Harvard University in the laboratory of Dr. Walter B. Cannon (1923–1925). During this period he was offered and accepted the Chairmanship of the Department of Physiology of the University of Virginia School of Medicine. After three years in Charlottesville (1925–1928), he was appointed Professor of Physiology and Director of the Physiological Laboratories at the New York University College of Medicine, posts which he held until his retirement in 1961.

One may trace Smith's scientific development through phases of more or less pure physical chemistry and cellular physiology to descriptive chemical physiology of the body fluids. In consequence of these latter studies he became interested in the kidneys as the Master Builders of the internal environment. His investigations now became analytical rather than descriptive. Prior to this time Van Slyke and his associates had formulated the clearance concept and Rehberg had used the creatinine clearance in an empirical fashion as a measure of glomerular filtration rate in man. However, it is my opinion that Smith was the first to understand what renal clearance really meant and to appreciate what a powerful tool the clearance concept could be if properly justified. He realized that a precise measure of glomerular filtration rate was central to the study of all renal functions in the intact animal, including man. His knowledge of the comparative physiology of the kidney made him doubt the validity of the creatinine clearance as a measure of filtration rate in man. After all, if the aglomerular fish can secrete creatinine, is it valid to assume that man cannot? Thus began the hunt for an adequate measure of filtration rate which led through a series of studies on the non-metabolizable sugars to culminate in the justification of the inulin clearance.

From his observations on the clearance of phenol red, a substance first introduced by Rowntree for the clinical assessment of renal function, and from his subsequent studies on the excretion of a series of iodinated urological contrast agents he developed the methods for measurement of both effective renal blood flow and tubular mass. From titrations of the renal tubules with these latter substances Smith was able to assess the dispersion of tubular blood perfusion relative to tubular mass, and from titrations with glucose, to measure the dispersion of glomerular filtration relative to tubular mass. In the normal kidney he observed a remarkable balance between filtration, blood perfusion and tubular mass of individual nephrons, even though these nephrons vary markedly in length and diameter. In the diseased kidney, he noted a far greater dispersion of filtration and of blood perfusion, a fact which correlates well with the morphological changes of hypertrophy, atrophy and replacement fibrosis affecting glomeruli, tubules and blood vessels.

These studies on the human kidney in health and disease were begun shortly after his coming to New York University in 1928 and continued to occupy a major proportion of his time and thought for the rest of his life. He was fortunate in finding early in this phase of his career such able and devoted associates as Drs. Goldring, Chasis, and Shannon and there rapidly developed a degree of intellectual exchange and stimulation between clinic and basic science rare in medical schools of the time or indeed of any time. The evident value, productivity and excitement of this association of clinic and basic science attracted to him a succession of young physicians who have subsequently attained eminence as investigators in their own right and who have gone on to positions of responsibility in other institutions.

However, Smith was not one to specialize narrowly in clinical physiology; he maintained interests in comparative physiology, paleontology and evolution. He spent his summers in Salisbury Cove, Maine, dividing his time between studies of renal function in marine animals at the Mount Desert Island Biological

Laboratory and the writing of papers, books and essays at his nearby cottage. His broad biological interests were responsible for his associations with the American Museum of Natural History (1930–1938), the New York Zoological Society (1938–1962), the Mount Desert Island Biological Laboratory (1926–1962), the Bermuda Biological Station for Research (1938–1962) and for his travels as a Guggenheim Fellow to Central Africa (1928) and to Siam and Malaya (1930). His publications on the lungfish and on body fluid composition of fresh water sharks resulted from these latter scientific expeditions.

In the Department of Physiology of New York University College of Medicine he provided research opportunity and guidance for many young men who have since attained stature in Physiology, Medicine, Urology and Surgery. He also provided an opportunity for others to study medicine while working in the Department of Physiology as instructors or technicians. I am personally indebted to him and to the late Dean Wyckoff for my own medical education.

Smith lived for research. Furthermore he wanted others to experience for themselves the satisfactions which he himself had found in investigation. To achieve this end he made it possible for a number of bright young students to spend a summer in his laboratory in Maine, this long before summer fellowships became the commonplace they now are. Recently a fund known as the Homer W. Smith Fund for Training in Biological Research has been established by a gift from the Science and Arts Foundation of Dedham, Massachusetts, to the Mount Desert Island Biological Laboratory. Its purpose is to "introduce young people to the joys and frustrations of scientific research," a singularly appropriate memorial. Other no less fitting memorials include the Homer W. Smith Award in Renal Physiology established by the New York Heart Association and the Homer W. Smith Lectureship of the Honors Program of the New York University College of Medicine.

Despite his obvious relish for personal involvement in research and for the training of young medical scientists at both undergraduate and postgraduate levels he somehow found time to accept and discharge with distinction numerous advisory and consultative responsibilities. During World War II, he was a member of the Chemistry Division of the National Defense Research Committee, Chairman of its Chemical Warfare Section, and a Consultant on Biological Warfare to the Chief of the Chemical Warfare Service. For this service, Mr. Truman awarded him the President's Medal for Merit in 1948. As a member of the Committee on Medicine, he participated in preparation of the Bush report entitled "Science—The Endless Frontier"; and thereafter, as Secretary to the Browman Committee Supporting the Bush Report, worked actively for the legislation which culminated in the establishment of the National Science Foundation. From 1938 until 1953, he was a member of the Postdoctoral Fellowship Board in Medical Sciences of the National Research Council and Chairman (1948–1951) of the NRC-AEC Postdoctoral Fellowship Board (Medicine). He was also Chairman (1951–1954) of the NRC-Fulbright Advisory Committee on Medicine. He was, from 1956 until 1959, a member of the Cardiovascular Study Section of the National Institutes of Health. In addition to these generous services to governmental or quasi-governmental agencies, he also served in an advisory capacity to the Sloan Kettering Institute for Cancer Research, the Jackson Memorial Laboratory and the Russell Sage Institute of Pathology. In 1948 he received the Lasker Award for his distinguished achievements in research on diseases of the cardiovascular system and in 1954 was given the Passano Award for his outstanding contributions to research in clinical medicine.

Dr. Smith was elected to membership in many scientific societies, including the National Academy of Sciences, The American Physiological Society, The American Society of Biological Chemists, The Society for Experimental Biology and Medicine, The Association of American Physicians, The Harvey Society, The New York Academy of Medicine, The Society of General Physiology, Phi Beta Kappa, and Alpha Omega Alpha.

Among the innumerable lectureships which he discharged with distinction, the Belfield (1938), Porter (1939), Harvey (1940), Kober (1958), and National Institutes of Health (1960) should be mentioned. From 1936 on, he held, among others, visiting appointments at Yale (1936), Hadassah (1950), Bowman-Gray (1953), the University of Washington (1955), and the University of Indiana (1958).

Dr. Smith was a truly great man, a leader, a creative and imaginative investigator, a wise counselor and a gifted teacher. Although he will continue to live through his scientific papers, books and monographs as the preeminent renal physiologist of his time, his greatest contributions to medical science will no doubt come through the combined efforts of the many students and investigators whom he trained and influenced. His gentleness, his tact and his innate generosity will cause him to live on in the hearts of those who knew him well. Those who knew him at all were the richer for the experience.

3.

Autobiography: Boyhood Years

We reproduce below the story, told in Smith's own words, of his boyhood years in Cripple Creek. This autobiographical sketch he appended to Man and His Gods, *published in 1952, to explain the beginnings of some of the scientific and philosophical interests that fascinated him throughout life.*

I WAS THE LAST OF SIX CHILDREN—my father was forty-five, my mother forty-two, when I was born—and separated by seven years from my youngest sister, data that are pertinent chiefly to the circumstance that I grew up in the company of siblings much older than myself. Of more immediate significance is the fact that when I learned to talk I turned my *r*'s into *l*'s, and consequently, to the amusement of all visitors, "The lat lan lound the loom." There is no evidence that I ever showed any tendency to left-handedness, and I believe that I am intrinsically right-handed, but in any case by the age of five or thereabouts I began to stutter and thereafter all my efforts at speech culminated only in a series of painful lingual paralyses, broken at interminable intervals by a forcibly ejected word. I continued to stutter until I was thirty years old, but the handicap has long since been mastered and for twenty-five years I have, with few exceptions, faced audiences however large or small with an almost arrogant confidence. But stuttering probably drove me as a child into silence and introspection.

The family fortune, such as it was, had gone in the panic of 1893, and I was born two years later. When I was three years old we moved from Denver to Cripple Creek, the fabulous place that boasted that it was the geographical center of Colorado and the "Greatest Gold-Mining Camp on Earth." Located ten miles southwest of Pikes Peak, the District, as it was called, was an ancient volcanic pockmark in the Rampart Range of the Rocky Mountains, it eroded hills ranging from timber line at 10,000 feet to the perpetual snow line at 11,000 feet. Below timber line the mountain had once been covered with yellow and lodgepole pines, red fir, cottonwoods and aspen, and had sheltered silvertip and black bears, elk and deer; the streams had been rich with rainbow trout. However, by 1905, when I was ten years old and interested in these things, the great mines, the Portland, Elkton, Independence, Vindicator, Hall City and Sacramento, were in operation and gold production had risen to $15,000,000 a year. The mountainsides had been pitted with open mines or deep shafts from the mouths of which vast dumps of granite, dug from miles of underground workings—the Portland alone had more than 25 miles of tunnels above the 1100-foot level—fell away in gray-white cones into the valleys, in some places spilling across the sidewalks. For every big mine there were a hundred little ones, many of them long since abandoned. It would be hard to say whether the scene was terrifying, bizarre, or just plain ugly.

The houses in Cripple Creek ranged from unpainted pine shacks, usually covered against the rigors of winter with black tar paper, to mansions of brick, or white or yellow clapboard. Only a few persons boasted a lawn because nearly all newly turned ground was composed of sterile, decayed granite that would not support a blade of grass. The streets everywhere were dirt roads rutted by wagon tracks, the sidewalks whatever hard-packed trails might be left between the wagon tracks and the wavering property lines. The main business street, Bennett Avenue, consisted of a few blocks of two-story brick buildings, some of them pretending by a false front to be half a story higher, with uneven flagstones or more generally boards for sidewalks. There were, I would think, at least one dance hall and three saloons to a block on either side of Bennett Avenue, and I can remember Carry Nation breaking the plate-glass window in several of the latter. The era was before drinking in the home became widespread, and the saloon was where men went to escape life, or to engage it, under the blessed levitation of alcohol. My father rarely drank, but my brother stoutly defended his right to "go to town" on Saturday night. However, I never knew him to be drunk.

Violence was basically foreign to Cripple Creek, despite the fact that the District had seen violence in the labor strikes of 1894 and 1903–1904. Historians of the labor movement record the latter as one of the most arbitrary and unjustified applications of power in the history of trade unionism. The Western Federation of Miners had attempted to organize the refining mills at Colorado City and, failing in only one mill, had called nine men out on strike. When the mill continued to operate, the union called out all its members in the entire District, intending to force the issue by shutting down the supply of ore to all the Colorado City mills, although thousands of men in the District had no grievance against the mine owners and were opposed to the strike. But they were forced to lay down their tools. In the ensuing friction union pickets resorted to force, and one episode led to another until union agitators, imported for the purpose, were fighting the mine owners, independent operators, innumerable deputy sheriffs and finally state troops with violence and dynamite. It was then that antiunion men got out their guns, and for months my father and brother went about with six-shooters strapped on their hips.

This labor crisis was, however, an exception that proved the rule. Men gambled on long odds, sank their money into the ground to lose it, followed a hunch on borrowed money to turn up a seam worth millions. Six days a week they crowded, ten or more on each platform of a double-decker stage, to be lowered a thousand feet into the earth, and rode ore cars through miles of lateral tunnels to reach the workings where they drilled, blasted and shoveled out the gold-bearing rock. Pay dirt began with stuff that assayed only $50 a ton, and under favorable conditions two men could blast and cart out a ton in an ordinary working day; but a really rich strike might bring $100 a pound and large-sized pockets of almost pure gold were known. It was a gambler's paradise. The priceless thing about it was that what a man earned was his, and if he wanted to gamble it on digging another hole in the already pock-marked earth, that was his God-given privilege. Or he could damn well take the Short Line over the hill and go back to his farm in Missouri. Uneducated laborers, chemists, mining engineers, professional gamblers, guys with divining rods, ignoramuses who mistook iron pyrites, fool's gold, for the real stuff, wiseacres who had made and lost several fortunes, all had one golden rule: you let me alone and I'll let you alone. As a gesture to prudence we locked the door when we left home, but we put the key under the mat, as everyone else did. Violence was abhorrent to Cripple Creek, and the labor agitators, because of their use of it as much as because of the unfairness of the strike, were as popular as Carry Nation. For nearly a year the District was, by proclamation of the governor, in "a state of insurrection and rebellion," and the end result was that large numbers of union sympathizers were thrown into the "bull pen" and subsequently "ridden out of town"—forcibly deported to Kansas or New Mexico and told never to come back. The Western Federation of Miners sowed class consciousness in a community where class consciousness did not exist, and it rose up and destroyed them. Thereafter to be identified with a union was to be branded as an anarchist, and from 1904 until I left it in 1910, Cripple Creek was a one-class town.

It seems something of a paradox that a mushroom mining camp, typical of its kind in respect to its large floating population, its saloons and less respectable dives—Cripple Creek boasted the largest number of cribs per capita of any town in Colorado—should afford a superior opportunity for primary and secondary education. Progressive schools had not yet been invented, or if they had, we did not have them. We went to school to learn in the old-fashioned sense. However, for youngsters the cultural atmosphere of Cripple Creek was a mixed blessing. In winter, when we were in school, we were occupied by school activities and the requirements of homework, with some snowballing and sledding to relieve the monotony of daily chores, and in the spring and fall, when the ground was bare of snow, there would be an hour of twilight for games before study. But as the days lengthened, and particularly when school came to an end, the streets and empty lots, in all their dusty, weedy barrenness, the hills with their abandoned, dangerous, open-mouthed shafts, received us.

My mother died when I was nearly seven, after a protracted period of invalidism. I have no recollection of her although I can remember that during this period I slept alone in a large tent in the yard—it was in midwinter—and that in the early morning my father would wrap me in warm blankets and carry me into the house. After my mother's death there were left six children, myself, aged seven; Alice, fourteen; Helen, seventeen; Harry, nineteen; Margaret, twenty-one; and Alberta, twenty-six. Some neighbors offered to divide us but the family, after lengthy deliberation, decided to stick it out together.

The family was, in a manner of speaking, a clan of intellectual snobs who emphasized three things: you can be clean, you can hold your own, and you can be educated. When my education began, the rest of the family were in a position to be very superior about theirs and yet to imply that I carried their reputation on my shoulders. I did not particularly want to be educated but I was, in effect, scared into a middling performance. At home, when I had nothing to do, I was supposed to be reading. My juvenile literary consumption included *Black Beauty*, *At the Back of the North Wind*, *Wild Animals I Have Known*, *The Girl of the Limberlost* (with whom I fell in love), *The Little Colonel* and numerous others long since forgotten. I was not supposed to read dime novels; most of the other boys had them, with or without parental approval, and I remember their lurid covers, but I do not remember reading any of them. I think they bored me. With apologies to Little, Brown and Company (to whom Louisa May Alcott had much the same relation as oil to Mr. Rockefeller), neither did I like *Little Women* and its companion volumes. Juvenile fiction was abandoned when, under the tree on Christmas just preceding my ninth birthday, I received a book, title now unknown, on chemical experimentation. I read it in bed before breakfast. It told how to do everything, how to make gunpowder and *aqua regia* (which would dissolve platinum) and hydrofluoric acid (which would dissolve glass and had to be kept in wax bottles); how to make black powder, gun cotton, dynamite, mercury fulminate (the highly explosive detonator used in the center of gun shells); how to dye fabrics; how to make colorless water turn blood-red and then turn colorless again. At least I think that all these things were in the same book. I am slightly confused because there were several books of this nature, including a biography of Thomas Alva Edison with a frontispiece, in color, of the great inventor, his apron and hands besmeared by half a dozen aniline dyes; and yet another: a dog-eared, coverless volume of yellowed pages, dating probably from the '70's or '80's, and containing, as I judge now, rather more alchemical mystery than verifiable science but nonetheless expounding, within the limits of the author's wisdom, which seemed unlimited, the answers to everything from thunder and lightning to the fermentation of malt and the distillation of spirits.

Then, as the seeds of this literature were germinating in the spring of my eleventh year (six weeks before school was out), I came down with measles. After weeks in a darkened bedroom, I became aware of strange voices and the noises of sawing and hammering in the back yard. The family, forced to offer some explanation, said that my father was building a chicken house. When the great day came that I could get out of bed, the chicken house was, of course, what I wanted to see first. But there were no chickens. It was an unfinished one-room shed of pine, on the east side of the yard, opposite the sweet peas, perhaps 8 x 12 feet, with two steps and a four-inch stove pipe sticking out of the peaked roof, and a window in the north end. Inside I can still smell stove polish mixed with the fragrant odor of pine shavings. Along one wall were a heavy workbench with a carpenter's vise, a toolbox with saw, plane, hammer, square, and chisels. A little potbellied stove stood at one end in front of the window, and along the other wall was a pile of pine boards. There had not been time to sweep up the curled shavings left by the carpenter, and they supplied the kindling for my first fire. My father had decided that the time had come to get me off the streets, and the entire family had probably decided that the time had come to get me out of the house. I was beginning to clutter the place with retorts and crucibles.

My world had been given to me. I never learned to saw a board straight, either cross-grained or lengthwise, and I abandoned the tool box as soon as I had erected shelves on all four walls and put up a couple of cabinets. I set up an alcohol-heated, stationary steam engine that had come as a Christmas present, and in subsequent years it never once let me down by failing to operate. I installed a hand-operated vacuum pump and bell jar that I acquired heaven knows where, and demonstrated how a lighted candle beneath the jar grew feeble and slowly died as the air was evacuated. I demonstrated to my satisfaction, and to the satisfaction of a few visitors, that, as the book said, a mouse did the same thing under the same conditions. When electricity came our way, I helped install the wires and hung a 16-candle-power carbon-filament lamp square in the middle of the room. I lacked either the aesthetic vision or the necessary permission to put in two outlets or a table lamp, but I was not outclassed by the professional electricians of the age, who thought that one naked, glaring bulb in the middle of the room was the hallmark of the Electrical Era.

I collected minerals, gold, silver and copper ores, turquoise, feldspar, asbestos, garnets, amethysts, tourmaline; and then, inevitably, butterflies, and moths (with a backward thought towards the girl of the Limberlost). I once thought of going into taxidermy and set out over the hills with a .22 rifle to kill my specimens for myself but when I shot my first bird I was so hurt that I buried it in the woods.

It was never called anything but my "shop." It was my sanctum sanctorum and none of the family ever came into it unless invited. It gave me a privileged position because, apart from the electric light, the stove, the tools that had now grown rusty, the steam engine, and the vacuum pump, it permitted me to accumulate miscellaneous riches that would be the envy of any boy. The "book" contained instructions on how to make a telegraph key and sounder, and zinc-copper sulfate wet batteries; and a telegraph set was fabricated (to be replaced later by commercial instruments) and a single wire strung on the telephone (or it may have been electric light) poles for nearly three blocks to the home of a friend. We laboriously spelled out the latest news in the Morse code at least once a day until open communication palled and then we spelled everything in a concealed code just in case the wire should be tapped.

Now the family began to have cause to regret the Christmas of 1903, when they had given me the books on chemistry. In those days a knowledgeable boy of eleven could buy anything he wanted at the drugstore, from arsenic to saltpeter, and my dimes began to go into chemical experiments. Homemade gun cotton reposed casually in my trousers pocket; black powder could be compounded at any time from stock reagents on the shelves; turning water into blood by pouring it from one beaker to another, and vice versa, was kid stuff; and nitric acid stained my fingers until I looked, rather proudly, like Edison. As a matter of courtesy I was taking the warts off my friends' hands by the judicious application of a drop of that fuming corrosive. Since no laboratory science was then taught in the public grade schools, I was the object of the rather skeptical envy of the classmates who visited the shop. Most of them were scared of gun cotton and dynamite, and had never even heard of nitric acid. No doubt I seemed queer to many of them, who possibly looked at me askance because of my stuttering and, when I could talk, probably could not understand what I was talking about.

I have no idea where I got it, possibly from Dr. King, the family physician, but shortly the choice piece of apparatus in the shop came to be a Wimshurst machine for generating static electricity. In dry weather and under the application of sufficient muscular energy to the driving gear, fat, noisy, two-inch sparks discharged between the brass ball electrodes and filled the room with the odor of ozone. My machine generated only some 15,000 or 20,000 electron volts, but this was a miniature lightning storm that terrified the uninitiated, and was powerful enough to ignite gun cotton and alcohol, to puncture holes in cardboard or to fragment a piece of thin glass. I did not have imagination enough to dream that one day, with 10 billion electron-volt machines, men would split atoms into smithereens and manufacture new elements even more unstable than radium (I had a small piece of pitchblende from the Colorado lode and had repeated Becquerel's experiment of making a radioautograph on a paper-covered film), but the Atomic Energy Commission has not had any more fun, or enjoyed any greater local prestige, than I did when the thunder and lightning were cracking properly.

Along with the static machine came a small X-ray tube which, in conjunction with a fluorescent screen, enabled me to see the bones of the fingers, hand and wrist, the entire skeleton of a mouse. Not many people, however, wanted to see the skeleton of a mouse, or even the bones in their own fingers, but were prepared to take their bones on faith. The X-ray tube led to the construction of a spark coil, because activation of the tube by means of the static machine involved the expenditure of excessive muscular energy on my part and prevented me from looking at the fluorescent screen while I was operating the machine; with a spark coil plugged into the 110 volt A.C. lighting circuit all I had to do was to snap a switch and the X-ray tube was in continuous operation. Then, since any spark coil is an effective generator of radio waves, a friend and I were soon flashing wireless messages to each other, using a primitive iron-filing coherer on the receiving end.

I reached the pinnacle of my electrical engineering efforts when, to supplement the spark coil, I built a three-foot Tesla coil: all over the world audiences have paid admission to see the death-defying, breath-taking performance of the wizard who, with this prop, generates genuine lightning upon the stage and, through a short iron rod, takes its foot-long million-volt (but harmless) flashes into his very body, lights an electric light bulb with the circuit flowing entirely through his arm and causes his gloved fingers to spark at every chair and table, and at any lady or gentleman who will accommodate by volunteering. My homemade Tesla coil worked magnificently and gave off twelve-inch and very noisy flashes of lightning.

I came close to inventing the neon light long before someone else obtained a patent on it; or, more accurately, I foresaw the practical application of what had, for four decades, been an interesting scientific gadget, the Geissler tube. This is a glass tube with electrodes sealed in it at either end, evacuated of air and filled with one or another excitable gas. When activated by a high-voltage, high-frequency current, these tubes emit a soft light of a color characteristic of the gas with which they are filled, and elaborate patterns of color can be obtained by alternating bulbous expansions and narrow constrictions in the tube and by playing changes in the composition of the glass. In a set of Geissler tubes the rainbow has been trapped so that one can hold all its colors between the fingers. I saw how the soft, fluorescent light might be substituted for the glaring carbon-filament lamp, and in my dreams I was sometimes the owner-superintendent and expert electrical engineer of a plant that controlled the patents on this new system of universal lighting. My spare time was used for searching out new inventions in the manner of Thomas Alva Edison, assisted, in the more complicated and delicate operations, by the girl of my dreams.

The girl of the Limberlost had turned into one whose disturbing (but fully clothed) beauty was portrayed in an advertisement that I carried in my wallet. She was also a true helpmeet in every chemical and physical experiment. I was as yet scarcely interested in girls in a practical sort of way—only on the idealistic level. My two older sisters had married and left home, and I had twice become an embarrassed Uncle Homer by the age of ten. My younger sisters, Helen and Alice, were teaching in the local high school. It was perhaps for this reason that I came by the Geissler tubes and various chemical apparatus and books from Mr. Lory, the high school superintendent. I am on more certain ground in recounting that there was a constant stream of beaux at the house—it was the Gibson Girl era when women wore shirtwaists of elaborate hand embroidery and spent an hour doing their hair, and men sent them long-stemmed American Beauty roses and five-pound boxes of the most delicious bittersweet chocolate creams, the like of which I have never since tasted. It was one of Helen's beaux who led me into perdition, a newly graduated physician and assistant to Dr. King, named Dr. Brittain. I had long possessed a microscope of the push-pull type, with a box of microscope slides, each holding beneath its circular cover glass a cross section of some plant stem or other specimen appropriately stained with aniline dyes—the geometric, polychromatic beauty of such preparations has inspired many a modern fabric designer. There was also in the collection, I remember, a perfectly mounted flea, the transparency of which permitted one to see all the vital organs; and I believe the intricate leg and foot of a spider, though I may have made that preparation myself because I obtained microscope slides, cover glasses and oil of balsam from Dr. Brittain and went into microscopy on my own. Having no microtome for making optically thin sections of plants or animal tissues, I had to confine myself to amoebae, paramecia and other water animalcules that could be raised in hay infusions, and hay infusions inevitably led to bacteria. A discarded textbook of bacteriology quickly gave me a bird's-eye view of Pasteur and of pathogenic and nonpathogenic organisms and the elements of their culture, fixation and staining. However, I still suffered the deficit of the incubator that is necessary to propagate some of the more delicate species and shortly test tubes filled with culture media were surreptitiously being incubated in the warming oven over the kitchen range. The family tolerated me until specks of aniline dyes began to appear in the biscuits and apple dumplings and then they served the ultimatum: I and my dangerous bacterial cultures could just damn well get out of the house! Thus, again, I was driven back upon myself. For lack of an incubator, another career was closed to me. When I begged for a culture of tuberculosis and diphtheria, the door of destiny was slammed in my face. I saw that I was not to become a bacteriologist.

I do not recall how the other matter started. Dr. Brittain spent considerable time in the shop, possibly as a blood price because, where others were concerned, I had as yet no understanding of the intricacy of the affairs of the heart, and I was old enough to be quite a nuisance. I suppose that one question led to another, about the lungs, liver and kidneys, and so on. It was no great passion to know how the insides of an animal worked that led to the dissection of our first cat, but probably mere curiosity on my part and a matter of fair exchange on the part of the doctor. Needless to say, it was in the dark of night, certainly after eight o'clock, when nobody would come nosing in. In a primitive community there are always an abundance of abandoned cats—the general practice is to drown them but there was no water within miles of Cripple Creek—so that the cat supply presented no difficulty. Nor was there any difficulty about getting chloroform because by now I could buy almost any article I requested at the drug store, and I was quite frank about the matter because the customary way to dispose of excess cats in Cripple Creek was to chloroform them. I had some scissors, and Dr. Brittain supplied a sharp dissecting scalpel and showed me how to make a cardboard anesthetic cone, how to apply it adroitly and firmly to the head that protruded from a hole in the gunny sack, and how to tell by the respiration and heart beat when the cat was quite dead. Then the warm body was explored, its organs identified and their functions expounded. By ten o'clock the remains had been buried in a faraway field, the shop had been scrubbed, the instruments cleaned, the odor of cat and chloroform removed by thorough ventilation, and my colleague in crime had gone into the house to call upon my impatient sister, I to bed to dream of better and better dissections assisted by the girl of the Limberlost. I did not long require Dr. Brittain's professional guidance because I soon learned to handle the scalpel alone. The crisis came when the family discovered, not the bald fact, but that I was using the household's best turkey platter.

When one considers the thousands of cats that are drowned, gassed or otherwise disposed of, the millions of other animals that are slaughtered for commercial markets, shot for sport or exterminated because of their nuisance value, the half dozen or so stray felines that died a quick and painless death in the shop dwindle into the trivial. I am not recommending the exercise as a routine item in secondary education, but it has pedagogical possibilities that exceed the more aesthetic study of bees and flowers. The experience can be likened to Alice's adventure down the rabbit hole; it is not one to be shared by everybody, but to be enjoyed only by those who have something of Alice's curiosity as well as her common-sense approach to things. One simply cannot explore the insides of a cat and emerge with the same naïve philosophy with which one entered the adventure. The experience shatters certain basic premises frequently encountered in the philosophy of existence, and notably the premise that creation is intrinsically anthropocentric. He who has dissected the warm body of a cat emerges a philosophic rebel prepared, like Alice, to denounce the whole pack of cards including the King and Queen of Hearts.

I was not a religious child, nor was I reared in a particularly religious atmosphere. Cripple Creek had its Catholic, Episcopal and sectarian churches, architecturally and dogmatically primitive, where the straight and narrow path was expounded every Sunday, and on a week night the Epworth League held forth with ringing hymns and desultory prayers to complement the Sunday school lessons. I believe that the Epworth League served chiefly as an excuse for the sexes to walk out together, and that it was frequently an outlet for what, in those days, the parson called sinful if natural tendencies. So far as young people were concerned, scarcely more can be said for formal church attendance. There were, of course, among the oldsters many devout persons, but the adjective was certainly not applicable to the bulk of the younger generation, who participated in devotions under the mixed impulsion of convention and for what they could get out of the Sunday gathering as a social opportunity. As an intellectual institution, the church had become the transparent hypocrisy which Emerson had denounced a generation earlier. Occasionally a revivalist, such as Billy Sunday, came to town and stirred the gamblers, the chronic alcoholics, the lonely and weary among the adults, and among the youths those who were torn by an adolescent sense of guilt or sex frustration, into a hymn-singing orgy of repentance; but the sinners who were healed in front of the pulpit generally quickly repented of the healing and were more or less embarrassed for some weeks thereafter. Without statistics I would venture that the Greatest Gold-Mining Camp on Earth lay far north of what Mencken subsequently dubbed the Bible Belt. Religion was something that you took unostentatiously. It had a quaint stigma about it, and the farther you moved away from any public display of religiosity without actually leaving the pale of piety, the better. I am here, of course, expressing an attitude peculiar to the family, and perhaps even within that area rendered somewhat inaccurate by the lapse of time.

Had it been otherwise, however, I think I would remember. My father did not die until I was sixteen, and I have many clear recollections of him. I would say that he was of the generation that had one foot still planted in religious tradition, the other planted in irreligious rationalism; but that in his mind there was no question as to which general direction he, and his children, were going. The only issue was not to hurry the transition, or to be unpleasant about it. He and my mother carried away with them from Maryland five children (I was born in Denver), a "mammy" left over from prewar days, a strong tradition of respectability that was probably enhanced by the seeming uncouthness of the West, a deep sense of the responsibilities of hospitality, and a dedication to the aristocracy of the intellect. The last expression is, however, to be taken modestly. As for the past, his attitude was summed up in the aphorisms, probably dull with age when he was a boy, that we all go back to Adam—or

Cain, and that it did not pay to look too closely at the family tree lest you find somebody hanging from a limb.

* * *

THE MEN who poured into the District seeking to redress their fortunes were a motley lot. Many were uneducated, but among them were men whose background embraced broad reaches of literature, poetry, music, philosophy and politics. It was scarcely more surprising for a man to reveal an acquaintance with the pragmatism of William James than to pull a rich chunk of sylvanite out of his pocket, and in the intervals that separated the long, silent chess games that my father loved, he and his opponents argued, to my edification, the merits of Andrew Lang as a psychologist, of Tennyson as a poet, or the significance of the Curies' discovery of radium. He (and I surreptitiously) read the *Smart Set* when Mencken was first laying about him with a sardonic flail.

Nevertheless until I reached the rebellious age I was dutifully sent to Sunday school in the local Wesleyan chapel and listened to all the stories with childish indifference, and once, without assistance, I won a $10 prize for the best Christmas story: it had something to do with Jesus, and I must have laid to with imagination as earnestly as Renan because I can remember the family's startled reaction when they read my prize-winning essay. This early success at deliberate fabrication may have sown the ferment of later skepticism, since I thereby learned how easily the trick was done.

* * *

IT WAS thus that I grew up, apparently secure in the home, obviously insecure in all other directions. The Greatest Gold-Mining Camp on Earth did not offer much assurance of security in its streets and alleys, its cribs and saloons, its deep shafts with open mouths, or its long, black tunnels. At the pole of security was an emphasis on common sense, criticism, reserved opinion (experienced rather than intellectually appreciated, of course);

at the other pole was a world confused by variety, harsh contrasts, irreconcilable contradictions, and one also significantly expanded by literature. As I have said, I was told that when I was not doing anything I was supposed to be reading. I recall no public library in town, but there was a fair substitute for one operated by an incredibly old woman who suffered, by my present guess, the mixed catastrophe of heart failure, cirrhosis of the liver, dyspepsia, borborygmus, and strong body odor. She owned and operated the town's reading room, which contained perhaps (another guess) 3500 volumes and a fair supply of magazines and local newspapers. When I came to know her, she had for reasons of nature retired to a back room to which I paid an occasional but reluctant courtesy visit because the family had a charitable affection for her. The front door of her reading room was rarely locked except on Sundays and at night, and her clients entered and left without her knowledge, depositing, if they were so inclined, a dime in an open cigar box. From browsing among the partially alphabetized, partially chaotic collection I acquired a primitive library habit that still leads me to study the titles in any row of books, though I doubt that there were many on her shelves that received my attention; I visited the reading room to obtain novels for my sisters, and it is chiefly the mixed smell of cigar smoke, dyspepsia and old books that lingers in my memory, and the impression of the multiplicity of literature. I saw that there were many books in the world, more than one man could read in his entire lifetime, and my reaction was one of alarm: the remembrance of the books that I had read and enjoyed in the presence of rows and rows that presumably I should but obviously never could read for sheer lack of time, gave me a sense of futility.

The experience was counteracted by two elderly spinsters (or so they seemed to me), who lived a short distance from our house, an understanding pair whose names are lost but who occupy a warm corner in my heart. Their household furnishings had probably been moved *in toto* from the East: the Turkey red carpet, the carved walnut sofa covered with black horsehair with rocking chair and side chairs to match, the chromo prints in walnut frames, the knitted antimacassars, the mahogany pier glass in the hall, the big Chinese vase that held umbrellas, even the Swiss clock in a porcelain case decorated with pink rosebuds. There was no cigar smoke and little other odor because the house was aired every day, holding only the scarcely detectable perfume associated with ladies. They were the possessors of many books arranged around the sitting room walls, some of them in "sets" that may have been purchased locally because much of the world's literature traveled West in the form of "special editions, beautifully bound and most reasonably priced," peddled from door to door by young men who said that they were working their way through college. I was urged by the family to be particularly careful of these "sets" with their gold-embossed covers. But many of the books were just dog-eared volumes in tattered covers, first editions that had been read by two, perhaps three generations.

For a boy to come browsing through these shelves, wanting to borrow another book, must have given delicious meaning to the vellum and tooled-leather covers that were dusted once a week but so rarely removed from their position. I learned that the cover is not very important, and I have no idea of the sequence: *The Old Curiosity Shop*, *Oliver Twist*, *A Tale of Two Cities*, and *David Copperfield*, *Twenty Thousand Leagues under the Sea*, *Kim*, and *The Jungle Books*, *The House of the Seven Gables*, and *The Scarlet Letter*, *Ben Hur*, *Ivanhoe*, *The Conquest of Mexico*, *Quo Vadis*, *Vanity Fair*, and *The Virginians*, *The Little Minister*, *Les Misérables*, *Wuthering Heights*, and *Jane Eyre*, *The Last of the Mohicans*, and *The Pathfinder*, *The Trail of the Lonesome Pine*, *Robinson Crusoe*, *Lorna Doone*. . . . If I was too young to appreciate them all, they remained so uniquely my own, so private, so mined from a rich lode of my own discovery, that singly and collectively they became for me a magic carpet. I have never outgrown my early belief that a good book is man's most precious creation.

What I do believe is that most of the boys of Cripple Creek spent a good part of their lives downtown, or playing marbles, throwing pennies, or more generally, talking, just talking. Since I could not talk without embarrassment, I indulged in it to a minimal extent and instead retreated into the shop during free daylight hours, and, at night, into the world of literary imagination. Yet I was not a bookworm. My reading was somehow edged in between the shop and school, and, in the spring, between hikes into the hills to search for purple anemones, just coming up where the snow had melted or, later in the summer, to gather large handfuls of white Mariposa lilies and blue columbines, or to climb the smooth, steep slopes of conical Mount Pisgah or the dangerously vertical cliffs of other mountains. Or, in the company of other venturesome kids, not all of them boys, each with a flickering candle in hand, to explore for nearly a mile the black cavern of some horizontal tunnel long since abandoned, the walls glistening with moisture, the roof decorated with stalactites each hanging precisely above its stalagmite on the rock below, water dripping, dripping in the darkness between them. We were not supposed to go into abandoned mines, but anyone with half a grain of sense could have told from the mud on our shoes and clothes in perfectly dry weather that we had been deep in the heart of the cold, dark earth.

Cripple Creek supplied ample realism to accent, or counter-accent, the life of the imagination. Boys cheated and lied and used force to extort nickels and dimes out of smaller boys, but some of them did kind and heroic things. Girls were of exactly two kinds: nice girls, and girls that were not nice (this was, of course, initially an adult categorization, but readily confirmed and generally anticipated in experience), but somehow their charms as individuals did not correlate with this absolutist division. Life was sometimes as muddy as the streets when the winter snow was melting, sometimes it had the colors of the Sangre de Cristo Range seen against the sky through nearly a hundred miles of dry and utterly transparent air. But always it was charged with danger, not the kind that necessarily frightens but the kind that induces caution. Like creeping to the edge of a black, uncovered hole that went so far down that a rock took an unbelievable time to reach the bottom and send up its faint echoes; or the rolling stones and great boulders, the slippery shingle on a mountainside over which one had to find a way to reach the top, where one could look out upon miles upon miles of blue mountain ranges, the tips white with snow. Too many such adventures at too early an age left me with nightmares of climbing over endless miles of hills, or of struggling along a vertiginous height with the certain knowledge that I was going to fall, symbols of minor frustrations and the source of delayed migraine for many years until I saw the sequence and learned to wake myself up from such cold sweats. I have never dreamed of anemones in the snow, or Mariposa lilies and columbines, because they were attained with undangerous effort. But faraway, snow-capped mountains, their blue slopes and white tops so nearly transparent as almost to melt into the sky, to which I was about to set out, or for some reason was not able to set out, frequently recurred in dreams until, thirty years later, I returned and took a close look at them and found them to be more solid and a little more prosaic than the Maxfield Parrish vision which childhood memory had bequeathed to me. Thereafter there were fewer such dreams, and now I can take my mountains or leave them.

Mountains can mean many things in dreams, but in mine they probably symbolize the excessive measure of anxiety (I still cannot command the word when I want it) that Dr. Anne Roe read into the routine psychometric tests she gave me a few years ago. That the one certain thing about life is its uncertainty must have been an early lesson. My father and sisters gave unselfishly to my care, but they were too busy and too preoccupied with their own lives to enter deeply into my emotional domain, and I grew up, as perhaps all children should grow up, more or less alone, with ample opportunity for that "divine idleness" so necessary to maturation, but with the responsibility of figuring things out for myself. In the shop I could take things to pieces and learn what made them tick, and acquire a measure of self-confidence with which to fend against the precariousness of the pattern as a whole. I had the desire to understand them, and the conviction that, invariably, if one tried to understand them, they made sense.

Most things made sense, that is, but not everything. Among my earliest literary experiences was Dante's *Divine Comedy*. We possessed the work in two large volumes illustrated with full-page steel engravings by Gustave Doré. Sometime between the Grimm brothers' *Fairy Tales* and *Oliver Twist* I spelled my way through the Inferno and Purgatory (Paradise must have bored me) while lying face downward on the floor of the living room, struggling to discover why these tortured souls were being punished by God with devised cruelties that I would not conceivably inflict on a cat. The writhing, naked men and women connected remotely with the moral strictures as I knew them, with the Ten Commandments and the not very exciting lessons of Sunday school, but they failed to connect with anything else that I had either read or heard discussed or learned from direct experience. It just did not make sense. It must have been at this time that I came to the suspicion that the family, in spite of all evidence to the contrary, did not really approve of parsons because parsons really thought that this stuff might be true. I asked no questions because it seemed a silly and embarrassing thing to ask questions about. In the end I just left Dante on the bookshelf and passed into a mild state of philosophic confusion which lasted until the morning of April 15, 1912.

I had for the last two years been going to high school in Denver, but had returned to Cripple Creek at intervals, and was there, presumably during spring vacation, on the morning the news was flashed around the world by telegraph that the *Titanic* had gone down, with the loss of hundreds of lives. Magnificent beyond description, the finest ship ever built, she had been racing across the Atlantic Ocean trying to break the speed record. She had gone to the north to shorten her course and in the dark of night had crashed at full speed into an iceberg. I retrieved the *Cripple Creek Times* after breakfast and took it to the shop where I read the full-page story in every repetitious passage. I was sickened–not by the magnitude of the catastrophe, because if men would build bigger and bigger ships and race them across the ocean at faster and faster speeds, catastrophes were bound to happen–but sickened by the statement played up in big headlines that, as the sinking ship rolled slowly on her side to pour over two thousand frightened men and women into the dark water, the band played "Nearer, My God, to Thee." *That* did not make sense did not make sense did *not* make sense. . . . I do not know what I expected the band to do, certainly not jump into the water. The band was trying heroically to still the panic that filled the passengers, and it may have succeeded in part because nearly a quarter of them were saved in the few remaining lifeboats. But it was too late for the band to do any good. The band should not be in the picture. I have never liked brass bands. I don't even know now that it was a brass band. What I did know then, as I lay on my back in the yard, staring at the heavens, was that the band had nothing to do with it. It was a false note, a pitfall, a deception. Why had the captain of a great ship raced her across the ocean at night at the risk of running into icebergs? Why had the allegedly watertight compartments given way? Why was there not a better method of getting people into lifeboats? Why was there not some means of following icebergs, of knowing where they were? Why were men so stupid as to play up the band as the high point of the picture?

I went back to the Beginning. I wrestled, in my own terms, with the Meaning of Things. I took a sharp scalpel and took the wrappings off life and took a close look at its insides. I went downtown to listen to what people were saying. I came back home to stare into the sky and watch the clouds sailing across the bridge of heaven. I went into the shop and looked at the nonsensical toys around the walls, the fossils and minerals and dried flowers, the vacuum pump, the static machine, the X-ray tube, the Tesla coil—and an electric motor which my father had long before built for me but which, for mysterious reasons, had refused to turn a fraction of an inch, and I cried a little at how much he had been hurt by this, his failure, because he knew (and I knew in a dim way) that he was ill—when this defeat and the knowledge of his illness had been added to other misfortunes, he had tried to kill himself in the back yard with his six-shooter and was stopped by one of my sisters after a struggle the noise of which almost reached the neighbors—and in the motor that wouldn't turn, and on which he had spent so much labor, I saw a symbol, first of futility, then of frustration, then of comprehensible defeat, and I hurled it into the corner and went out of the shop, not caring a damn what became of anything in it. Nor do I know now. In a few hours it was all over. On that April 15, 1912, this book was begun.

4.

Renal Physiology between Two Wars

In 1928 one of us presented Smith with renal functional data obtained from Bellevue Hospital patients with acute infections. Interpretation of these data was limited because the methods available at that time did not quantitate and separate the specific functions involved in the elaboration of urine. Smith was consulted because for some years his primary scientific contributions had been in the field of experimental renal physiology. His work had included the renal excretion of nitrogen in the camel and the metabolism of the lung fish (Protopterus Aethiopicus). It was immediately apparent to him that new methods were necessary for interpreting aberrations of renal function in man. In his Welch lecture entitled "Renal Physiology between Two Wars," from which the following is an excerpt, he traces the history of modern renal physiology that served as a background for his own pioneering contributions to knowledge of the kidney in health and disease.

THE RENAL PHYSIOLOGY WHICH I HAVE REVIEWED up to this point has been rather more qualitative than quantitative. For the quantitative approach we must transfer to another field of investigation, and cut back again to the early part of the century. Strauss in 1903 and Widal and Javal in 1904 had introduced the determination of blood urea into clinical medicine for diagnostic purposes. But this datum by itself was untrustworthy, since it was contingent not only upon the capacity of the kidney to excrete urea but also upon the protein intake. Gréhant in 1904 had tried to use the urine/blood concentration ratio as an index of functional capacity; but this was worse than the blood urea alone, since the concentration of urea in the urine varied with the urine flow, which was of course not only an uncontrolled, but clinically an uncontrollable variable.

Ambard and Weill in 1912 attempted to relate the rate of urea excretion to the blood urea in a dynamic sense, but it so happens that because of back-diffusion the excretion of urea at varying urine flows is a rather complex affair, and Ambard and Weill ended up with an equation that contained two square root radicles. When used empirically, a square root radicle is a mathematician's device to squeeze a correlation out of data in which a simple correlation is not present, and Ambard and Weill's resort to this device did not serve appreciably to clarify renal physiology.

In 1914 Franklin C. McLean, who had been professor of Pharmacology at Oregon, had been studying the blood sugar in diabetes and was on his way to Breslau to work with Minkowski when the abrupt declaration of war stopped him on the Atlantic Seaboard. He went instead to the Rockefeller Institute as a resident. Mathematically minded, McLean had already been intrigued by Ambard's formula, and now he sought to rearrange it into a more rational urea excretion index. Conceiving that this index should be constant in the diseased as well as the normal kidney, he studied two cases of chronic nephritis over a two months' period, while the patients were kept on a low and a high protein diet. He found that the nephritic kidney responds with increased urea excretion in the face of an elevated blood urea just

Reprinted from Lectures on the Kidney, *Welch Lectures, Journal of Mount Sinai Hospital, 10: 59, 1943.*

as does the normal kidney, the mechanism of excretion remaining the same, the only difference between the two being that the nephritic kidney, to use the terms current in the period, shows a greater resistance to the passage of urea. Had McLean said that the capacity to excrete urea relative to the blood concentration is reduced in the diseased kidney, the description would have been essentially modernized. McLean abandoned this study when he was called to China to organize the Peking Union Medical School, and left renal physiology behind him with his chief, Donald D. Van Slyke.

At about this same time Thomas Addis and D. R. Drury demonstrated that the rate of urea excretion divided by the urea content of the blood was fairly constant if the urine flow was maintained at high levels by water diuresis. Addis thought that the administered water increased the excretory capacity for urea by a nervous or humoral mechanism; actually the diuresis itself, by reducing the back-diffusion of urea, appears to be the chief factor in explaining the constancy of the Addis index under these conditions. But the administration of water apart, the constancy of the Addis ratio still had no explanation in renal physiology. The situation was not inaccurately summed up when, at about this time, on addressing the Academy of Medicine, he closed his remarks with an emphatic "All we know *for certain* about the kidney, is that it makes urine."

One of the chief results of Addis's observations was to force the quantitative mode of thinking into experimental renal physiology in this country. Paradoxically, Addis has good-naturedly deplored to me the invasion of the quantitative and experimental method into clinical medicine: "There was a time, not so long ago, when physiology was the handmaid of medicine, and you know how disastrous was that bondage. But today there seems to me a danger that medicine may be sterilized by becoming an appendage of physiology. . . . Young clinicians, dazzled by new experimental methods, are in danger of becoming poor doctors, and they should remember that they are doctors, first, last and all the time." To this I would reply that if the use of quantitative methods and quantitative thinking ends in making poor doctors, it would indeed be tragic, but such need not be the case. I think that quantitatively-minded doctors can be better doctors than qualitatively-minded ones. And I can also retort that my friend Thomas Addis is in considerable measure responsible for the alleged "sterilization" process, in consequence of his pioneer work in this and other problems in renal physiology.

After McLean left the Rockefeller Institute, Van Slyke, working with Austin and Stillman, and later with Möller and McIntosh, showed that the excretory efficiency of the kidney could be expressed simply as *the volume of blood cleared of urea by one minute's excretion.* They called this volume of blood the *urea clearance.* With moderate or abundant diuresis, they found that the kidneys of a normal man excreted on the average the amount of urea contained in 75 cc. of his blood. If the urea content of the blood was increased by urea feeding, the rate of excretion rose parallel with the blood concentration, so that the same 75 cc. of blood were cleared per minute. If the kidneys were damaged by disease, they cleared less blood of urea per minute: in uremia only 3 or 4 cc. or less. The urea clearance was found to be a sensitive clinical measure of renal function. Visualizing, as in a measuring cylinder, the volume of blood which represents the clearance, makes it possible to use a mental photograph in place of a mathematical formula.

The clearance is calculated as (mg. urea excreted per minute)/(mg. urea in 1 cc. of blood). If 15 mg. of urea, e.g., are excreted per minute and the blood urea is 0.2 mg. per cc., the clearance is $15/0.2 = 75$ cc. of blood per minute.

Expressed in terms of the analytical observed values, urine urea concentration, U and urine volume flow, V, the urea excretion rate is the product UV. Indicating blood urea concentration as B, the clearance assumes the familiar form ordinarily used in its calculation:

$$\text{Clearance} = \frac{UV}{B}$$

If the urine flow fell below about 2 cc. per minute, Van Slyke and his collaborators found that the clearance began to decrease, and between flows of 2 and 0.5 cc. fell approximately in proportion to the square root of the urine volume. In order to use clearances observed with low urine flows as practical measures of renal function, it was necessary to correct the observed clearances by multiplying with the correction $1/\sqrt{V}$, when V was less than 2. Multiplying by this factor gives the volume of blood cleared of urea per minute when the urine flow is 1 cc. per minute. Möller, McIntosh, and Van Slyke called this the "standard clearance," because it applied to a standard urine flow of 1 cc. per minute. It averages 54 cc. of blood in normal men.

$$\text{Standard clearance} = \text{observed clearance} \times \frac{1}{\sqrt{V}} \qquad [A$$

$$= \frac{UV}{B} \times \frac{1}{\sqrt{V}} \qquad [B$$

$$= \frac{U\sqrt{V}}{B} \qquad [C$$

To differentiate the higher clearance obtained with abundant urine flows, Möller, McIntosh, and Van Slyke called it the "maximal clearance," since it is the maximum obtainable by accelerating the urine flow.

If in retrospect the square root sign over the V term in Austin, Stillman and Van Slyke's equation for low urine flows was a compromise with the then inexplicable vagaries of urea excretion, Möller, McIntosh and Van Slyke fully compensated in the direction of rationalism when they borrowed, perhaps from economic bankruptcy, the now familiar term "clearance." Like many good things, this term was born of necessity. In 1926 Van Slyke had been on his way to Baltimore to give an address on kidney function, and on the train his courage failed him when he thought of facing an audience again with a mathematical equation. He had learned what every lecturer must ultimately learn, that only experts can visualize and comprehend the true realities which the unreal symbols of a mathematical equation are intended to represent; the simplest equation has the fearsome power of completely dispelling the comprehension of an audience, at least in the fields of medicine. As Van Slyke sat on the train seeking a solution of how to dispense with mathematics for the benefit of the medical profession, it occurred to him that all that the equation for high urine flows said was that in effect some constant volume of blood was being "cleared" of urea in each minute's time.

In my opinion this word has been more useful to renal physiology than all the equations ever written. In recent years it has broken loose from the excretion of urea and, taking conceptual wings, has become a generalized notion applicable to all aspects of renal excretion. We glibly say that the kidneys *clear* the blood of a large variety of substances: in a particular subject and one minute's time 1.0 cc. of blood may be cleared of water, 10 cc. of sulphate, 20 cc. of potassium, 75 cc. of urea, 130 cc. of inulin, 760 cc. of phenol, 1200 cc. of diodrast, without knowing *a priori* how the kidneys clear the blood of these substances, whether by filtration plus tubular reabsorption, filtration without tubular reabsorption, or filtration plus tubular excretion. Urea is cleared first by separation of some approximately constant quantity of glomerular filtrate, and the reason that the urea clearance decreases with decreasing urine flow is because the more the tubular urine is concentrated the more urea diffuses back into the blood. Glucose is also filtered, but the *glucose clearance* is normally zero because all the glucose in the tubular urine is reabsorbed; but phlorizin completely blocks the tubular reabsorption of glucose, and in the phlorizinized animal the glucose clearance rises to a large and relatively constant value. If no glucose is secreted by the renal tubules, and if tubular reabsorption is completely blocked, then the rate at which glucose is cleared in the phlorizinized animal must be equal to the rate at which the glomerular filtrate is formed. But the glucose clearance in the phlorizinized animal is identical (in simultaneous observations!) with the *mannitol clearance*, the *sorbitol clearance*, the *dulcitol clearance*, the *creatinine clearance*, the *sucrose clearance*, and the *inulin clearance;* except for glucose and creatinine, these clearances are also identical in the normal animal: hence the conclusion that in the normal animal, mannitol, sorbitol, dulcitol, sucrose and inulin are excreted by filtration alone, and without tubular reabsorption or tubular secretion. Phlorizin blocks the reabsorption of glucose and brings the glucose clearance up to the level of the filtration rate. The creatinine clearance in both the normal and phlorizinized dog is identical with the simultaneous inulin clearance, but in normal man (and apes) the former is about 30 per cent higher, indicating that in addition to filtration, some creatinine is cleared from the blood by the tubules, as is the case in many of the lower animals. Phlorizin blocks this tubular excretion and brings the total creatinine clearance down to the level of the filtration rate.

If, as in the case of creatinine, the clearance of any substance, such as phenol red or diodrast, is greater than the simultaneous inulin or mannitol clearance, it can only be because some of that substance is cleared by the tubules, in addition to that which is cleared through the glomeruli. But there must be a limit even to the process of tubular clearance: we cannot clear any substance from a larger volume of blood than actually perfuses the kidneys. The clearance of diodrast in normal man, calculated as whole blood, is approximately 1200 cc. per minute—one fourth of the total cardiac output. Obviously, this must be close to the total renal blood flow: i.e., the extraction of this compound from the renal blood must be very nearly complete, and for practical purposes we may take the diodrast clearance as identical with the renal blood flow.

No elaborate equations are involved in this brief summary—only the notions of filtration plus tubular reabsorption, or filtration plus tubular excretion. The only mathematical operation required is simply to multiply $U \times V$ and divide by P.

Paradoxically, Möller, McIntosh and Van Slyke confused the issue by calling $U\sqrt{V}/B$ a "clearance," since in fact it is the product of a mathematical operation wherein UV/B is multiplied by $1/\sqrt{V}$, as shown in equations (A), (B) and (C) above; hence in the strict sense it is not a real clearance but a presumed clearance predicated on the assumption that below 2.0 cc. per minute UV/B will decrease in proportion to $1/\sqrt{V}$, and calculated to the value of $V = 1.0$. The widespread use of the calculation without general recognition of its derivation has served to confuse many workers. The "standard clearance" remains a physiological enigma so long as the V term is under a square root radicle. One of the hardest things students of physiology have to learn is that the two terms: UV, as they occur in the clearance expression, *must never be divorced;* for by joining them in multiplication they become an integer standing for some *quantity* of a substance excreted per unit time, and you cannot without offence to reason break a *quantity* of anything into two dissimilar parts. Neither can you put a square root sign over half of it.

This, I think was my own first lesson in renal physiology.

William Goldring, who was interested in the etiology of nephritis, had gone to the Rockefeller Institute one day in 1928 to meet Dr. Addis in order to discuss with him the Addis count. He could not find Addis and happened to drift into Van Slyke's laboratory, where he was asked to sit down and wait. He and Van Slyke fell to talking about renal function tests, and Van Slyke suggested that Goldring ought to do some urea clearances on patients with erysipelas, of which there were a large number in the Bellevue wards. The results, which have never been published, were very confusing.

During the febrile phase of the disease, the urea clearance might be as much as 200 per cent of the Van Slyke normal standard, and then during the afebrile recovery period they might fall to 30 or 40 per cent of the normal standard. Dr. Goldring could not make any sense out of it, and brought the data to me, knowing that I had been interested in the renal physiology of fishes, turtles and the like. This proved to be poor preparation, and I wrestled with his ever-changing standard clearances and maximal clearances, and got nowhere. Sometimes the patient's standard clearance was greater than his maximal clearance on another occasion, and vice versa. I tried some high-flying mathematics of my own (unable to interpret the physiological significance of the square root radicle in the standard clearance) but to no avail. Perhaps three months elapsed before I fully realized that the maximal clearance might mean something quite simple physiologically, but the standard clearance, because of its square root radicle, was an unphysiological and empirical calculation. The standard clearance apart, I began to think of the maximal clearance simply in terms of filtration rate and tubular reabsorption, as Van Slyke had no doubt thought of it when he first used the term. It was soon evident enough that no physiological interpretation could be forthcoming until there was contained in the experiment some thoroughly reliable, simultaneous measurement of the filtration rate.

This led, in 1929, to experiments by Norman Jolliffe showing that xylose is not excreted by the aglomerular fish, and then to further experiments on the dog and man with Jolliffe and subsequently with James A. Shannon. Our first essay on the measurement of the filtration rate using xylose, sucrose and raffinose proved to be wrong, but we were never wholly content with it, and had sought among other carbohydrates for still larger molecules where there could be no possibility of back diffusion. Sometime in 1933 I hit upon the inulin idea, but a laboratory sample proved to be relatively insoluble and I momentarily discarded it. Fresh inulin was ultimately procured, and in the latter part of the year we got down to work with inulin in a serious manner. We discovered then that we were wrong about xylose as a substance suitable for the measurement of the filtration rate, but we were now more than ever convinced that we were right about inulin.

In October of 1934 Richards came to New York to read a paper on kidney function before the Society of Experimental Biology and Medicine, and we discovered that we were working on the same problems and with the same motives and with the same substance. As far back as 1900 when he had been a student under Philip Hiss, the bacteriologist at Columbia, Richards had suggested inulin to Hiss as a polysaccharide which might yield only levulose for fermentation. If I am not mistaken, an inulin medium is still in use which is based on that suggestion. Thirty years later when he was racking his brain for a substance suitable for the measurement of glomerular filtration, inulin had recurred to him.

With the introduction of the inulin clearance the way was open to study tubular reabsorption and tubular excretion in a quantitative manner. In 1935 Shannon, studying phenol red excretion in the dog, showed, in accordance with the surmise of Marshall and Crane, that at high plasma levels the tubules do indeed become "saturated" and excrete the dye at a constant maximal rate. This maximal limitation in tubular excretion has subsequently been demonstrated for diodrast and a number of other substances in both dog and man, and may be considered to be a characteristic feature of tubular activity.

It was also in 1935 that Goldring, Clark and Smith pointed out that the phenol red clearance at low plasma levels (where the tubules are not approaching saturation) afforded a close approximation to the renal blood flow. At this point Herbert Chasis joined our group, and a little later, Hilmert Ranges. In 1937 Goldring, Chasis and myself showed that the clearance of diodrast, the tubular excretion of which had been demonstrated by Elsom, Bott and Shiels in Richards' laboratory, afforded a closer and indeed quite satisfactory measure of the renal blood flow; and further, that the maximal rate of tubular excretion of diodrast (or diodrast Tm) could be used to characterize the total quantity of functional tubular tissue in the kidneys, independently of the blood flow or filtration rate. In 1938 Shannon, Farber and Troast showed that a similar, limiting maximal rate characterized the reabsorption of glucose by the tubules and, in line with diodrast Tm, they called this term glucose Tm.

The newly described methods by Smith and his associates for the quantitative measurement of blood flow and filtration rate together with the saturation methods (diodrast Tm and glucose Tm) for the first time made available new avenues of approach to the study of the distribution of blood and glomerular filtrate among the functional units of the kidney.

5.

Renal Excretion of Sodium and Water

During his later years, from the close of World War II until the end of his scientific career, Smith devoted himself to a study of the mechanism of renal excretion of water and solutes and their integration with the composition and volume of the body fluids. In conjunction with Lawrence Wesson, Parker Anslow, Henry Wirz, Michael Ladd, George Zak and E. Lovell Baker, all members of his department, he directed the major effort of his laboratory to this investigation. We have selected here one of a series of papers from his laboratory published in 1952 presenting an historical summary of work done on the renal excretion of sodium and water and including his own classical Cartesian graph and his formula for quantitating the urinary volume of solute-free water. These concepts and their presentation have profoundly influenced the thinking of investigators, for here again Smith pioneered in opening a new direction for studies of the kidney.

ANALYSIS OF THE FATE OF SODIUM AND WATER in the renal tubules may begin with the classic micropuncture studies of Richards and his co-workers on the amphibia. In 1937 Walker, Hudson, Findley and Richards demonstrated in the frog and *Necturus* that the urine remains isosmotic with the plasma throughout the length of the proximal segment; since in the phlorizinized animal glucose undergoes some concentration in the proximal segment, it was inferred that sodium and water are absorbed there in a parallel or isosmotic manner. Subsequently, Walker, Bott, Oliver and MacDowell, from micropuncture studies in the guinea pig and rat and using creatinine as a standard of reference, concluded that by the end of the proximal segment some 80 per cent of the filtrate would be reabsorbed, but again isosmotically, as in the amphibia. Sodium with its attendent anions supplies some 90 per cent of the osmotic pressure of the glomerular filtrate, and such extensive reabsorption of water by the proximal segment must entail the proportional reabsorption of sodium, other substances contributing little to the osmotic picture. In 1948 Wesson and Anslow adduced evidence from studies of mannitol diuresis in the dog that, in the over-all operation of the tubule, and unquestionably in the proximal segment, the reabsorption of sodium is an active process, analogous to the active reabsorption of glucose; whereas the reabsorption of water appears to be a passive process because a large fraction of the filtered water can be swept into the urine by the osmotic activity of the mannitol with only a slight increment in sodium excretion. They concluded that as sodium and other constituents are absorbed in the proximal segment, water is reabsorbed by passive diffusion and consequently the osmotic U/P ratio remains close to 1.0. Similar conclusions were reached by Mudge, Foulks and Gilman from studies of urea diuresis in the dog [*Figure 1*].

Supplementing the view that the proximal reabsorption of water is a passive process, Wesson, Anslow and Smith proposed that the thin segment of the loop of Henle serves as a region promoting passive osmotic equilibration before the urine enters the distal tubule where the final operations regulating sodium and water conservation are carried out.

Reprinted from Federation Proceedings, *11: 701, 1952.*

Against the older view of Burgess, Harvey and Marshall, that the urine is concentrated to the hypertonic state in the thin segment, may be advanced the arguments, *1*] that its thin epithelium does not on cytological grounds suggest an operation of any such magnitude; *2*] casts, protein or foreign condensations of any kind are rarely observed here, but first appear in the ascending limb of the distal tubule and increase in density in the collecting ducts; *3*] in the human kidney, 7/8 of the nephrons have only a very short thin segment or none at all, and many of these do not descend into the medulla; and, *4*] one may ask rhetorically why should the urine be concentrated in the thin segment, at the expense of considerable osmotic work, before the final operations presumptively attributed to the distal tubule are effected? Therefore what is said below about distal function bears importantly upon our interpretation of function in the proximal segment and thin limb.

Wirz, Hargitay and Kuhn, on the basis of cryoscopic measurements in the frozen kidney, have recently proposed that the urine is actively concentrated, in the osmotic sense, in the extreme tips of the medullary loops, to be diluted again in the ascending limb of the loop of Henle. They conceive that the concentrated urine in the thin segments draws water across the interstitium of the medulla, the vasa recta and the collecting ducts, which must be supposed to be freely permeable to water, thus concentrating the urine in the collecting ducts. We may note that this hypothesis is opposed by all the arguments stated above, and also by the perhaps inadequate teleological argument that such a mechanism requires that all the blood flowing through the vasa recta must momentarily—i.e. for the period of its sojourn in the medulla—be concentrated to the same degree. Since probably no less than 1/5 of the renal blood flow traverses the medullary circulation, this consideration alone would make the operation a very extravagant one. We believe that the concept of isosmotic equilibration in the thin limb is in better agreement with the facts.

It is to the distal segment that we must look for the mechanism for making a dilute urine [*Figure 2*]. This operation in the amphibia cannot consist of the tubular excretion of water, as Brodsky and Rapoport suggest (for the mammal), because the urine as it passes down the distal segment becomes progressively more concentrated with respect to urea, phosphate, dyes and glucose in the phlorizinized animal; dilution must therefore be effected by the abstraction of isosmotically active material from the hitherto isosmotic urine, as originally accepted by Walker, Hudson, Findley and Richards. Direct evidence on distal function is not available in mammals, but indirect evidence indicates that here, too, dilution is effected by the abstraction of osmotically active material (T^{d}_{osm} in figure 2) from the isosmotic urine discharged from the proximal system.

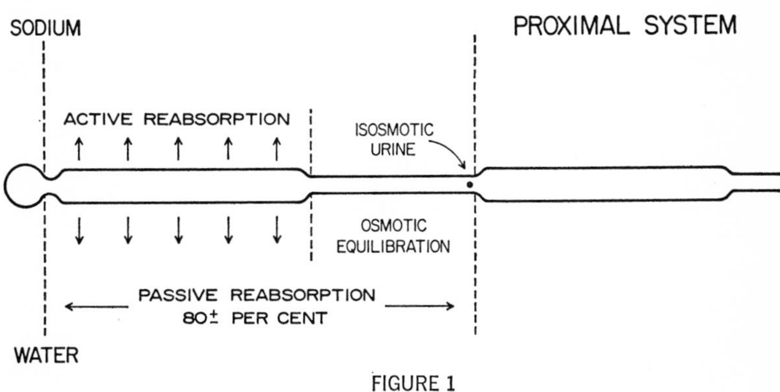

FIGURE 1

It has long been recognized that maximal water diuresis in man represents about ⅛ of the water of the glomerular filtrate. The only substance available in sufficient quantity to afford this quantity of osmotically free water by tubular reabsorption is sodium with its major attendant anions, chloride and bicarbonate. During water diuresis the urine may be so dilute in respect to sodium that we can fairly speak of it as almost sodium free, and the conclusion is unavoidable that this terminal step in the reabsorption of sodium is an active process.

By this active reabsorption of sodium, osmotically unobligated water is for the first time left within the nephron. The urinary clearance of osmotically free water, C_{H_2O}, is directly given by the difference between the total urine flow and the isosmotic clearance,

$$C_{H_2O} = V - \frac{U_{osm}}{P_{osm}} V$$

where U_{osm} and P_{osm} are determined by the cryoscopic method. The solute, expressed as osmols ($T^d{}_{osm}$), abstracted from the urine in order to create this free-water clearance, is given by the product of the free-water clearance times the osmotic pressure of the plasma. If one conceives that only sodium is involved in this operation, i.e., neglecting a possible minor contribution from potassium, the sodium chloride equivalent of this reabsorbed solute is given by dividing T_{osm} by f, the appropriate osmotic activity coefficient of sodium chloride (which we take to be 1.855).

Wesson and Anslow have recently shown that, in *maximally hydrated* dogs, the free-water clearance, C_{H_2O}, is roughly constant, and the osmotic equivalent, $T^d{}_{osm}$, quite constant in any one animal during simple water diuresis and during extreme urea diuresis or natriuresis induced by mercurin plus cysteine. On their evidence we must conceive that so long as the load of sodium is adequate to effect saturation of the distal system, $T^d{}_{osm}$ (or $T^d{}_{Na}$) is constant and maximal ($T^d{}_{mNa}$). This constancy of the free-water clearance during variable osmotic diuresis argues against attribution of water diuresis to failure of water reabsorption in the proximal system.

This problem has been under further examination in man by Zak and Becker in our laboratory, and they find that $T^d{}_{osm}$ is fairly constant as between simple sustained water diuresis and variable mannitol diuresis superimposed on sustained water diuresis. Man, however, differs from the dog in that he presents greater difficulty in respect to attaining copious sodium excretion, and if sodium is not available to the distal tubule in minimal amounts the free-water clearance will be accordingly reduced; consequently, at the present stage of these observations in man it cannot be said that distal electrolyte reabsorption is maximal, even though it is fairly constant in the same individual from test to test. Nor can it be asserted, either for dog or man, that distal sodium reabsorption is removed from endocrine or humoral influence.

In the above view, during water diuresis the urine is composed of isosmotically obligated water (whether by sodium, urea, mannitol, or other solutes is immaterial) plus osmotically free water; the latter is made available by the absorption of electrolyte (presumably mostly sodium) distally. The dependence of gross water diuresis on electrolyte excretion, and the terminal reduction in gross diuresis in subjects who are continuously ingesting water, as reported by Rosenbaum, Nelson and Strauss, may be related to either reduced delivery of sodium to the distal tubule or to variations in urinary water isosmotically obligated by sodium, rather than to changes in distal reabsorptive capacity ($T^{d}_{m_{Na}}$).

We have up to this point been referring to experiments in which sustained water diuresis was maintained by continued hydration of the body. In the absence of such hydration the osmotically free water liberated by the distal reabsorption of sodium is reabsorbed in some place along the distal nephron, reducing the urine flow to oliguric levels. We tentatively suppose that it is reabsorbed *pari passu* with the sodium, possibly by passive diffusion through a facultatively permeable epithelium, leaving the urine again isosmotic with the plasma.

Under the action of the antidiuretic hormone, however, the urine passes above the isosmotic state to a variable degree of hypertonicity, and we now turn to the mechanism whereby an osmotically concentrated urine is elaborated.

The recent studies of Ladd indicate that this hypertonicity is achieved by the reabsorption from the urine, regardless of the volume flow, of a constant quantity of water. In Ladd's experiments on prehydrated subjects, where sodium was the major osmotically active substance in the urine, this quantity amounts to about 2 cc. per 100 cc. of glomerular filtrate.

For convenience of discussion, this concentrating operation has been designated by Wesson and Anslow as $T^{c}_{H_2O}$. There is as yet no direct evidence permitting us to decide whether $T^{c}_{H_2O}$ is functionally related to $T^{d}_{H_2O}$, or whether, indeed, the two processes even occur in the same part of the distal segment. One bit of evidence that they are functionally and anatomically separate is afforded by the clinical observation that concentrating power is frequently lost without loss of the capacity for water diuresis, and conversely during recovery from the ischemuric episode and other renal injuries, recovery of concentrating power is frequently long delayed. Moreover, to assign these two processes to a common locus requires that the tubule must be so constituted that, in the absence of the antidiuretic hormone (i.e., during water diuresis), it is virtually impermeable to water and yet capable of reabsorbing water against osmotic pressure during antidiuresis. While this versatility is conceivable, it seems improbable. The writer has elsewhere presented the speculation that the concentrating operation, $T^c_{H_2O}$, may be located in the collecting ducts, and if so it may operate continuously and independently of the diuresis-antidiuresis mechanism.

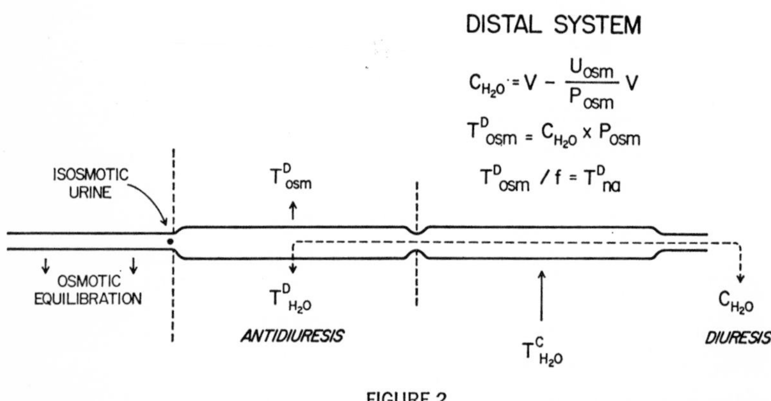

FIGURE 2

Thus, the isosmotic urine entering the distal tubule is subject to two operations. The distal reabsorption of sodium leaves available a quantity of osmotically unobligated water, C_{H_2O}, which is reabsorbed during antidiuresis, but excreted during water diuresis [*Figure 2*]. The magnitude of this free-water clearance as measured during sustained maximal water diuresis indicates that distal sodium reabsorption, T^d_{Na}, is characterized by a maximal rate, and therefore the quantity of sodium delivered to the distal tubule is critical in determining both sodium excretion and the magnitude of water diuresis. The total urine flow, V, at any time represents the sum of the free-water clearance plus the isosmotic clearance of sodium, urea, mannitol and other constitu-

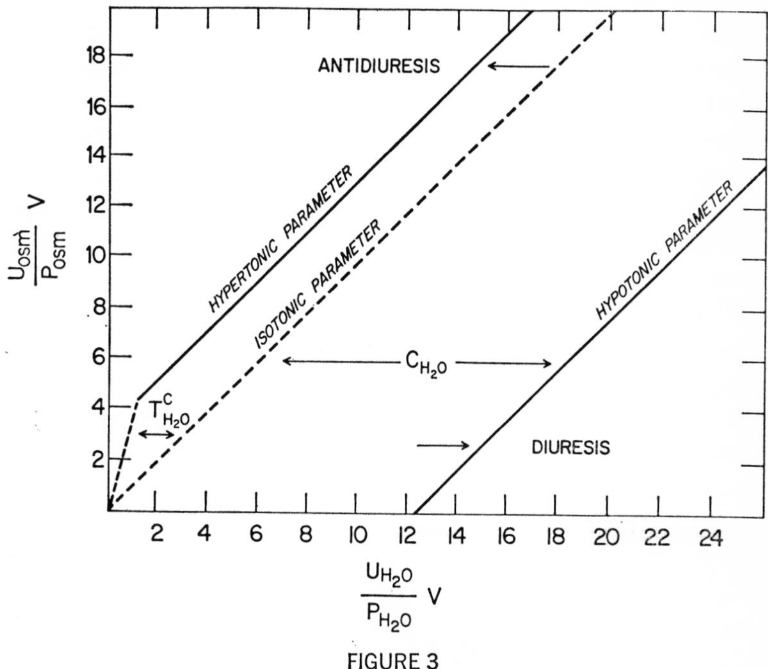

FIGURE 3

ents in the urine, thus generating the hypotonic parameter shown at the right of Figure 3. The only way in which the free-water clearance could come to exceed the osmotic equivalent of distal sodium reabsorption would be in circumstances reducing water reabsorption proximally, so that free-water would be delivered by the proximal system to the distal tubule.

During antidiuresis, on the other hand, this osmotically free water is reabsorbed, and during maximal antidiuresis a fixed quantity of water is reabsorbed from the now isotonic urine to generate the hypertonic parameter shown at the left of Figure 3. Between these extremes of maximal water diuresis and maximal antidiuresis the urine may have any osmotic composition, reflecting the variable secretion of antidiuretic hormone and the variable excretion of osmotically obligated water.

The control of antidiuretic hormone secretion by the osmotic pressure of the plasma, classically elucidated by Verney and his co-workers, needs no discussion here. Attention may, however, be called to the recent evidence presented by Strauss, Davis, Rosenbaum and Rossmeisl and by Leaf and Mamby that critical changes in the volume of the extracellular fluid or, alternatively, in plasma volume or distribution, may mediate true water diuresis independently of changes in osmotic pressure. Similarly in Ladd's prehydrated subjects, the infusion of isotonic saline solution leads to transient but frequently maximal water diuresis in the face of maintained or even increased osmotic pressure of the plasma.

Neither is it necessary to review the extensive literature showing that in the dog changes in extracellular fluid volume cause marked changes in filtration rate, a circumstance which most investigators believe plays a role in the conservation or excretion of sodium by disturbing glomerular-tubular balance. (Cort's recent paper should, however, be mentioned.) In addition to the mechanism of glomerular-tubular balance, however, are changes in the reabsorptive activity of the tubules. That the tubular reabsorption of sodium is influenced by one or more adrenal hormones has been known since 1933 when Loeb and his associates demonstrated that the significant physiological disturbance in adrenal insufficiency is loss of sodium chloride through the kidneys. In 1935 Peters suggested that the kidney retained osmotically active substances, chiefly sodium, when the extracellular fluid volume was depleted. Setting aside necessarily complicated experiments with orthostatic syncope (see Epstein *et al.* for literature), evidence, however tentative, is accumulating that isosmotic expansion or contraction of the body fluids may lead to changes in the tubular reabsorption of sodium, as well as to changes in the tubular reabsorption of water, as noted above. These renal responses appear in an exaggerated form in the prehydrated subjects studied by Ladd. Non-prehydrated subjects excrete isotonic saline solution sluggishly and variably, but if the subject is massively prehydrated 8–13 hours beforehand, the response to isotonic saline solution is now an abundant natriuresis coupled with the water diuresis mentioned above. Changes in the filtration rate are not significantly involved in this phenomenon. During the response to the infusion of saline solution, such prehydrated subjects excreted in peak periods an average of nearly 9 per cent of the filtered load of sodium, a figure comparable with the maximal effects of mercurial diuretics. Since the free-water clearance in such prehydrated subjects is not reduced below its average value of 12.5 per cent of the filtration rate, it is inferred that distal sodium reabsorption is not reduced and that this abundant natriuresis results entirely from reduction in proximal reabsorption. Expansion of the extracellular fluid volume appears to be the most obvious place to look for the stimulus evoking this copious natriuresis. The response of prehydrated subjects to isotonic saline solution is undoubtedly related to the changes in sodium excretion induced in nonprehydrated subjects by the excitation of volume receptors as described by Viar, Oliver, Eisenberg, Lombardo, Willis and Harrison and by the expansion of the extracellular fluid, as described by Strauss, Davis, Rosenbaum and Rossmeisl.

In résumé, it may be emphasized that, supplementing the osmotic pressure of the plasma in controlling water diuresis, is the volume of the extracellular fluid, expansion or contraction of which may lead independently of plasma osmotic pressure to decreased or increased antidiuretic hormone secretion. Of paramount importance in the excretion of sodium is filtration rate and glomerular-tubular balance, and the critical barrier presented to the excretion of sodium by the distal tubule which serves to conserve sodium if the filtration rate is reduced or proximal tubular reabsorption increased. But of equal importance are changes in proximal reabsorption. The tentative interpretation of Ladd's data indicates that in prehydrated subjects proximal reabsorption may be decreased as much as 10 per cent or more by isosmotic expansion of the extracellular fluid, thus greatly overloading the distal tubule despite constancy in the filtration rate. Whether this reduction in proximal reabsorption is mediated through the adrenal cortex is undetermined, nor is it known, as I have noted above, whether or not distal sodium reabsorptive capacity, which at the moment has been measured only under very limited circumstances, is subject to humoral control.

I close with the hopeful note that the problems of sodium and water excretion appear to be approaching a new stage of integration. It is becoming clear that the renal operations involved in sodium and water excretion are integrated not only with the composition of the body fluids but also with their volume. The demonstration of this integration promises substantial progress in the near future for both the experimentalist and the clinician.

6.

The Evolution of the Kidney

Organic evolution always held vital interest for Homer Smith, not only for its own sake but for the light it shed upon his studies in comparative physiology. The functional architecture of the human kidney, he held, is to be explained in terms of "the geologic revolutions that for 600 million years have raised and lowered continents and seas," and of the evolutionary changes that have enabled living forms to survive. We reproduce below a portion of his lecture on the evolution of the kidney, delivered in 1939 at the University of Kansas School of Medicine as one of the Porter Lectures. His concept of the evolution of the kidney has become a classic in the literature on the kidney.

According to the geologist the continents upon which we live are but irregular slabs of granite some 15 to 40 miles thick, floating like isolated islands upon a bed of basalt, the rock which makes up the oceanic floor. Under this bed of basalt, which is only some 700 miles thick, is a zone of semi-fluid magma extending to a total depth of about 1800 miles. Innermost is a core of iron, some 4000 miles in diameter, which is raised far above incandescent heat (6,000°C.) by the enormous pressure existing at the center of the earth. It is now generally agreed by the geologist and the astronomer that the earth was separated from the sun about 2000 million years ago through disruption of the parent body by a passing star, but the daughter planet remained molten and homogeneous for only a short time, quickly acquiring its present stratified structure as it cooled and crystallized.

The continents float above the average level of the earth's crust because their granite is lighter than the basaltic bed upon which they rest; as their exposed masses weather down and the silt is deposited in the sea along their edges, the added weight of this deposit causes the plastic basalt to flow beneath the land masses and to float them higher in the air. It is these slow adjustments to maintain isostatic equilibrium between the continents and the oceanic floor that sometimes cause abrupt movements of the land. But all the earthquakes of historic time are trivial when compared with the disturbances of the past, which have extended not over days or weeks, but millions of years.

As measured, quite accurately it is now believed, by the radio-active clock within its rocks, the earth has had its present cold and semi-solid form for about 1800 million years. During this period it has been cooling and shrinking as a whole, having decreased in diameter something between 200 and 400 miles. Under the stresses resulting from this cooling process, and more particularly in consequence of the alternate fusion and solidification of the basaltic crust, this shrinking has been intermittent rather than uniform, so that at recurrent intervals of roughly 30 million years the continental masses have been wrinkled and folded into great mountain chains. During the intervening peri-

Reprinted from Lectures on the Kidney, *Porter Lectures, Series 9, University Extension Division, University of Kansas, 1943.*

ods of geologic quiescence, the mountains raised by the preceding diastrophic movement have been largely if not entirely worn away to sea level by the slow erosion of wind and rain. Schuchert estimates that the total continental depth eroded in this manner since the opening of the Paleozoic exceeds 75 vertical miles, or more than twenty ranges of mountains like the present European Alps or the American Rockies.

These periodic revolutions, as the geologist calls them, have made us what we are. Because they have changed the form and size of the continents and seas and at times submerged great areas of land beneath the water, because they have diverted oceanic currents, altered the dust and water vapor in the atmosphere, raised barriers to moisture-laden winds and otherwise interfered with the basal forces that control the weather, these revolutions have been accompanied by marked and protracted changes in climate over the entire surface of the earth. In general, periods of mountain building have been accompanied by marked refrigeration so that in some instances glaciers have descended to sea level in equatorial latitudes; while in the quiescent intervals, after erosion had levelled the recently formed mountains to mere hills, warm shallow seas have transgressed widely over the low-lying lands, and even Arctica and Antarctica have enjoyed a climate that was warm and humid.

According to modern experimental biology, the *vis a tergo* of evolution is the production of new varieties in consequence of random mutations in the chromosomes; such of these varieties as are unfitted to survive are pruned away by natural selection, leaving the better fitted mutants to get along as best they can. Mutation is fundamental to evolution, but mutation itself would be of little avail to modify organic pattern did not the *vis a fronte* of natural selection foster the survival of exotic individuals, of the new mutations, by offering them a special environment in which their unique characters are advantageous, by preserving them from genetic extinction through backbreeding with the unmutated forms, and probably in other ways. We may believe that in the shaping of the final evolutionary product as we see it now, mutation and environment have played balanced and equal roles. Though we cannot assign to either mutation or selection any teleological direction, they tend within certain limits to have one result: after a few million years, when many millions of mutations have occurred and most of them have become extinct, we can expect to find among the surviving organisms some that are much better fitted to endure severe environmental changes than was the parent form. It is only here, in the accidental development of increased independence of environment, of increased physiological freedom, in Bernard's sense of the word, that we can speak of evolution as being upwards, rather than just sideways.

The paleontological record reveals that evolution has not been a continuous process, but an intermittent one. In Lull's descriptive terms, it has been a tide of organic specialization moving forward in marked pulsations invariably synchronous with the great upheavals of the earth's crust. It was probably one of these pulsations, synchronous with the Cambrian Revolution, that gave the vertebrates their start. The more important steps in the phylogenetic history of these forms, with special reference to those events that have a close bearing upon the evolution of the kidney, are depicted graphically in Figure 1.

The problem of the origin of the first chordates remains more or less where it was left by the great biologists of the past century–in a sadly unsatisfactory state. A few years ago there was consensus of opinion on at least one point: that the chordates shared with the echinoderms, the acorn worms, Branchiostoma (Amphioxus) and the tunicates, a common marine ancestor, a frail-bodied, ghostly form, similar perhaps to the Dipleurula larva of the echinoderms. The most important features of this hypothetical ancestor were that it possessed a bilateral symmetry comparable to that of Branchiostoma, and like Branchiostoma it kept one end foremost as it swam slowly and feebly through the archaic seas. But the right of this ghostly form, the like of which no one has ever seen, to spawn the great vertebrate phylum has recently been questioned on the ground that the chordates, as they first appear in the fossil record, were depressed, bottom-living, heavily armored and sluggish animals as far removed in appearance from Branchiostoma as one can imagine. This fact is in part responsible for the suggestion of Torsten Gislén which

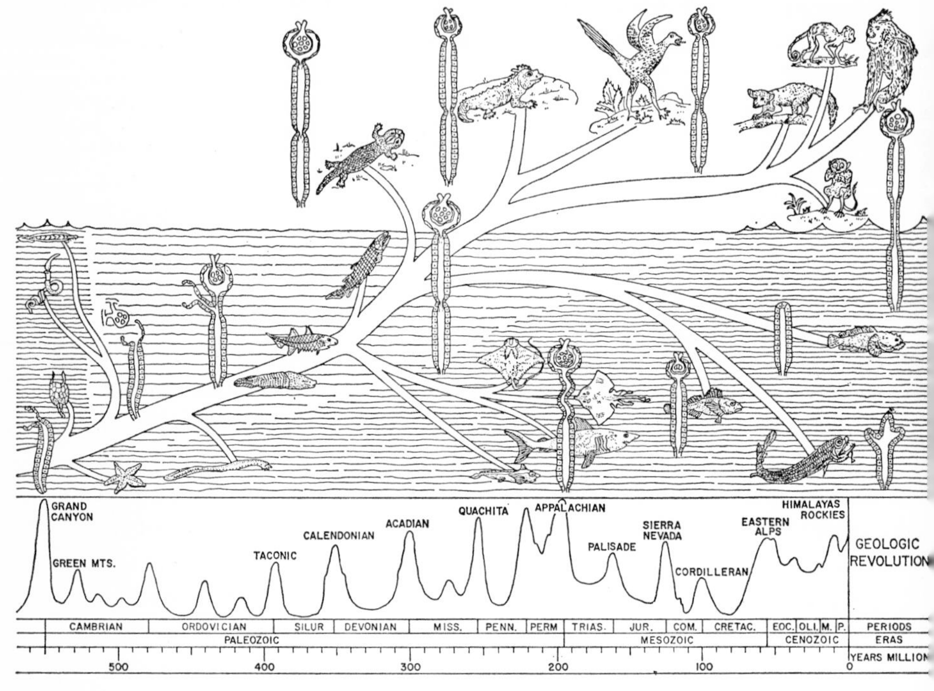

Figure 1 shows in synopsis the evolution of the vertebrates in relation to a salt-water (darkly-shaded) and fresh-water (lightly-shaded) habitat. The irregular curve illustrates mountain-building episodes (geologic revolutions) which have importantly influenced this evolutionary history.

The time scale is such that the Pleistocene era (one million years in length) and Recent Time (about twenty-five thousand years) could not be included, and these are merely suggested by the heavy line at zero time.

The entire period encompassed by documented history is only about six thousand years, or one hundred-thousandth of the interval elapsing since the opening of the Paleozoic era (Cambrian period), when fossilized animals first begin to appear in the sedimentary rocks.

has been seconded by Gregory that the first chordates may have been evolved from a free-swimming paleozoic crinoid, or sea-lily. To this perennial debate we will add one more confusing argument of our own in a later paragraph.

As we cannot say from what forms the first chordates were evolved, neither can we with any certainty name the time of their evolution. Some would assign this evolution to the Ordovician Period, and some to the Cambrian. The opening of the Cambrian was marked by one of the most violent periods of mountain building the earth has ever known. These mountains have long since been washed away, but the sediment to which they were reduced is to be seen in the several vertical miles of red and yellow-banded rocks through which the Colorado River has cut the Grand Canyon, and from which scenic chasm the geologic revolution takes its name. The biologist has repeatedly asserted that the truly unique features of the vertebrates consist, broadly speaking, of bilateral symmetry: of a stiffened and yet flexible internal backbone with an articulated skeleton for the support of muscles so arranged as to produce powerful lateral motions of the body, the backbone, skeleton and muscles being made up of regularly repeated segments; of paired, fin-like expansions of the skin to resist the thrust of these muscles and to maintain an even keel as the animal shoves itself forward in the water; and, of major sense organs located in the anterior end of the body. These features are just such as to endow the organism with considerable swimming power, to enable it to move swiftly through the sea, or, as an alternative, to live in a swiftly flowing river. According to one theory, first propounded by Chamberlain and substantially supported by Barrell, the sluggish ancestors of the chordates had already migrated from the sea into the quiet brackish or fresh-water lagoons of the Cambrian continents when the Grand Canyon revolution overtook them; the tilting of the land accelerated the motion of the rivers, and this accelerated motion fostered the evolution of the dynamic, chordate form. But another theory, offered by Moody, has it that the prochordates appeared in fresh water somewhat later, being literally driven into the rivers and lakes in Ordovician time by the attacks of the giant marine cephalopods that had then risen to supremacy in the seas.

Whichever theory we accept, it is now agreed that it was in the fresh waters of the Paleozoic continents, and not in the sea, that the first chordates, and from them the ostracoderms and early fishes, were evolved. When, in 1930, Professor E. K. Marshall and I reviewed the comparative anatomy of the kidney and on the question of the habitat of the early vertebrates followed the fresh-water thesis as set forth by Chamberlain and Barrel, we were conscious of treading on uncertain ground. But since that time the subject has been carefully reviewed by Romer and Grove, and in the face of this new evidence the fresh water hypothesis can no longer be denied.

Now, the very matrix of life is water, and the evolution of the kidney is essentially the story of the evolution of the regulation of the water content of the body. Marine invertebrates—worms, star-fish, molluscs, etc.—are generally in osmotic equilibrium with the sea, and they therefore face no problem of water regulation. And it may safely be assumed that in the Cambrian or Ordovician prochordate ancestor of the vertebrates the kidney was little, if at all, concerned with the excretion of water, but wholly with the excretion of nitrogenous waste.

Judging from the evidence of comparative anatomy, the marine ancestor of the chordates had in each of the middle segments of the body a pair of open tubules which connected the primitive body cavity, or coelome, with the exterior; these segmental tubules were probably originally gonaducts serving to carry the eggs and sperm out of the coelomic cavity. Possibly before the chordate stage the coelomic membrane had come to play a part in excretion, and the segmental gonaducts which connected it with the exterior, and which were themselves formed by an evagination of the coelomic membrane, perhaps participated in the regulation of the composition of the blood by reabsorbing valuable substances from the coelomic fluid, or by secreting waste products into this fluid as it passed out of the body.

With this rather meagre equipment of a coelomic membrane and a number of segmental ducts the first chordates essayed to enter the fresh waters of the paleozoic continents. In migrating from the sea to brackish estuary and thence up the rivers to the inland lakes these chordates were probably following a protoplasmic impulse to search for peace, but they were destined never to have that impulse satisfied. They encountered trouble, as is obviously revealed by the defensive armor which they soon evolved. The first vertebrates to appear in abundance in the fossil record, the Silurian and Devonian ostracoderms, the arthrodires, antiarchs, and the earliest shark-like forms bearing jaws, the acanthodians, and even the later advanced fishes, were typically encased from snout to tail in apparently impregnable armor which took the form of bony plates, scutes or scales. Any sample of the vertebrate population of Silurian-Devonian times from Pennsylvania to Spitzbergen suggests that some death-dealing enemy, swift, merciless and irresistible, lurked in every corner of the world.

Why all this heavy armor? Romer has pointed out that the only visible enemies of the ostracoderms and early fishes were the eurypterids that shared with them the continental waterways. Admittedly some of these eurypterids were much larger than the ostracoderms and fishes, and possessed strong claws, but they were primarily sluggish mud crawlers and unless they struck with their pointed tails, as does their enfeebled descendant, *Limulus*, or injected poison, as do their offspring, the scorpions, their fearsomeness may have been more apparent than real. The thesis that the armor of the early vertebrates served primarily to protect them from predacious enemies is perhaps open to question. May I offer an alternative suggestion: these vertebrates had an enemy which they could not see, but one which pursued them every minute of the day and night, and one from which there was no escape though they fled from Pennsylvania to Spitzbergen—a physical-chemical danger inherent in their new environment. When the first migrant from the sea took up residence in fresh water, its blood and tissues, bearing the physical-chemical imprint of its marine home, were rich in salts: for we may on straight extrapolation assume that at the opening of either Cambrian or Ordovician time the sea had one-half or better of its present salinity. This saline heritage might be in part erased, but it could not wholly be cast aside without reorganizing every nerve and muscle cell. The evolution of a regulated internal environment, if it had not yet begun, was imperatively imminent. For in the new fresh-water habitat the salts and proteins of the tissue cells drew water by osmotic pressure so that by degrees the organism tended to pass from excessive hydration to edema and *in extremis* to swell to death. We may confidently assert that were the osmotic infiltration of water not arrested, survival in fresh water would be impossible. The first step towards arresting the infiltration of water would naturally be to insulate the body as far as possible by a waterproof covering. Why not believe that the ever-present armor of the fossilized vertebrates of Silurian and Devonian time was a defense against the osmotic invasion of fresh water rather than against the claws and tailspines of the eurypterids?

In the history of evolution we see repeated instances where some adaptation is carried to absurd and disadvantageous overdevelopment, and perhaps an insulation serving primarily to repell fresh water may have been the genesis of spines and tubercles and other armored absurdities as would later serve to ward off strong-jawed, sharp-toothed predators such as had not yet been evolved. It seems that it was from certain of these protuberant spines that the fins were evolved. If we take this path of interpretation, we must conclude that what started out to be merely a waterproof insulation was destined to supply the fishes with fins for swimming and with spines and other armament for battle, and the tetrapods with legs with which to crawl about on land.

But to invest the body in waterproof armor entailed important changes in internal anatomy as well. The multiple segmental openings of the archaic coelomic tubules had to be obliterated, and these tubules had to be arranged to drain into the one posterior member which still pierced the now armored skin. Thus the evolution of the first archinephric duct may have been fostered by the waterproofing of the body. Moreover, with most of the body covered by armor, a few posterior skeletal muscles had to be selected and developed in order to concentrate leverage in a powerful tail; this emphasis on the posterior segmental muscles, together with compression of the middle segments of the body cavity beneath one or a few armor sheets, would tend to obliterate the primitive segmental divisions of the coelome and to foster the development of pericardial and splanchnic cavities as they appear in the higher vertebrates. The evolution of an armored body, the remote, articulated parts of which had to be moved in a coordinated manner, would foster the evolution of a central nervous ganglion or brain, which stood in close functional relationship to the anterior, distance receptors. The development of armor about the head would foster the cranial articulation of mouth parts and the evolution of jaws, which, absent in the ostracoderms, are first discoverable in the mailed acanthodians of Silurian time. But these interesting speculations, and they are nothing else, lie apart from our main theme, namely, that it was in seeking protection against fresh water that the first vertebrates to be preserved in the fossil record, the ostracoderms, came to be depressed, bottom-living armored creatures far removed from the hypothetical dynamic, fast-swimming prototype of classical theory. For even under their best efforts at free swimming the early armored vertebrates found it easier to sink to the bottom and wiggle upon the mud, where indeed most of them remained until the close of the Devonian. If the ostracoderms are viewed as a consequence of evolution in fresh water they offer less difficulty to the dynamic theory, which is recommended on so many grounds.

Yet even thus encased in a waterproof covering, the gills, the mouth, and the intestinal tract still afforded routes by which excessive quantities of water could be absorbed. The ostracoderms and early fishes had to compensate for this excessive influx by increasing the excretion of this substance. Their battle against fresh water was only half won. Evolution frequently works by adapting old things to new uses, and it seems that no better way could be devised to get the surplus of water out of the body than to have the heart pump it out; and the easiest way to do this was to prepare a filtering device by bringing the preexisting arteries into close juxtaposition with the preexisting coelomic tubules, to form the coelomate glomerulus which, as a lobulated tuft of capillaries, still hangs free in the pericardial cavity of some of the lower vertebrates. Later a direct connection was effected between arteries and tubules outside the coelomic cavity, to form the typical glomerulas as found in mesonephros and metanephros of the higher animals. But in many recent fishes and Amphibia, the mesonephric tubules still retain their ancient connection with the body cavity. The essential point is that the renal glomerulus was evolved independently of, and long after, the evolution of the renal tubule. And it will be recalled that in the ontogenetic development of the human embryo the glomerulus is not brought into conjunction and connected with the tubule of the metanephros until some time after this tubule has been formed. It is possible that this interval between the development of the tubule and the glomerulus is an ontogenetic recapitulation of the phylogenetic interval which separated their evolution.

But the very nature of a high-pressure filtration system permits not only water to be pumped out of the body, but also most of the osmotically active constituents of the plasma, which means all the valuable constituents except the proteins–glucose, chloride, phosphate, etc.,–for if these did not pass through the filtering bed, the great osmotic pressure which they exert would effectively prevent the heart from pumping any water through this bed. Hence, with the advent of the glomerulus it was necessary to modify the tubules so that they could reabsorb these valuable constituents from the filtrate. Moreover, there was such an excess of water over salt to be excreted that the urine had to be almost pure water, i.e., it had to have a substantially lower osmotic pressure than the blood. Thus, as a concomitant of the evolution of the glomerulus, there came into existence a tubule capable of reabsorbing large quantities of glucose and similar valuable substances, and capable of elaborating, by the reabsorption of salt, a urine that was hypotonic to the blood.

To whatever extent this new fresh-water kidney was adequate to its time, times changed. The restless earth began to heave again. At the close of the Silurian another diastrophic movement disturbed its crust; no great mountains were raised in North America, but a ridge higher than the Alps was wrinkled up in Northern Europe, of which the low Caledonian mountains of Scotland are all that now remain. Other continental areas were extensively submerged beneath the sea, and what land escaped was plagued by extremes of climate swinging between excess of rain and drought. The fishes of the early and middle Devonian found themselves forced to choose between the invading salt water marshes and the isolated fresh-water pools which periodically contracted into stagnant swamps or hard mud flats. Some of the more powerful elasmobranchs, perhaps now better fitted to compete with the cephalopods and other marine invertebrates, sought sanctuary by turning towards the sea; the fate of these, the first fishes to live in salt water, will be noted in a later paragraph. The more advanced of the fishes, however, in order to survive in the stagnant waters of the continents, took to swallowing air and thus invented lungs and prepared the way for the evolution of the terrestrial vertebrates.

At the close of the Devonian the earth suffered its third major upheaval in vertebrate history; the periodic dry spells of the Devonian were replaced by protracted and widespread desiccation, and many of the air-breathing fishes followed the example of the Silurian elasmobranchs and abandoned fresh water for refuge in the sea, where they founded the Paleozoic-Mesozoic dynasties of marine teleosts. But certain of the fresh-water fishes, the Crossopterygians, learned to use their fins for feet with which to crawl from one pool to another, and thus founded the Carboniferous and Pennsylvanian Amphibia, which needed to return to the water pools only occasionally to drink and to lay their eggs.

For a moment let us consider what must have happened to the bony fishes that took up life in the sea in the Carboniferous. Actually, none of these Mesozoic forms survives today, all the recent marine teleosts having been evolved since the opening of the Cenozoic era; but the physiology of recent forms is adequate to illustrate the difficulties of changing one's habitat from fresh to salt water.

With the migration from fresh to salt water, the osmotic relations between organism and environment are reversed; the body tissues are less concentrated than the sea and, unless the composition of these tissues is completely overhauled, they must tend constantly to suffer osmotic dehydration and ultimate desiccation and collapse. The marine bony fishes face not a perpetual excess of water, like their fresh water ancestors, but a perpetual deficit of it. In theory they could maintain the accustomed proportion of salt and water in the body by excreting a highly concentrated urine; but in practice they cannot do this, for the fish kidney is unable to elaborate a urine which is osmotically more concentrated than the blood. Their lot would be as unhappy as that of the Ancient Mariner were it not that, unlike that thirsty man, they have the happy advantage of possessing gills, and the gill is the only organ in the lower vertebrates capable of doing hypertonic osmotic work. Had the Ancient Mariner possessed such a marvelous organ, he could have lived like a fish by drinking the briny sea; he could have separated the salt from the water by excreting the salt out of his gills in a concentrated form, leaving the water free for his tissues, or for the formation of urine. But with the limitations of the fish kidney, he still would have had cause to deplore his lot, since for every liter of urine formed he would be forced to concentrate a liter of sea water by 66 per cent. It is not surprising that the marine fishes, rather than spend their precious energy in making more concentrated the already concentrated sea, naturally became conservative in the matter of urine formation and excreted no more urine than was required to remove waste products from the body. When the bony fishes migrated from fresh water to the sea, the high-pressure filtering device of the glomerulus was no longer an asset, but a liability. They shut the filtering bed down as far as possible, and with the passing years the glomeruli grew smaller and smaller, fewer and fewer; to examine the glomeruli in a series of marine teleost kidneys reminds one of the old-fashioned Herpecide advertisement: Going–going–gone! Nearly all the marine teleosts show some evidence of glomerular degeneration, and in certain of them (the toadfish, midshipman, goosefish, batfish, sea horse, pipefish, and in certain deep sea fishes) the kidney has become entirely aglomerular. There is no constant rule by which the aglomerular condition is reached; Grafflin has shown that in the "daddy" sculpin the glomeruli cease to function between the young and the adult stage, while Armstrong has shown that in the toadfish and pipefish a glomerulus does not develop even in the embryo. Though evolution is not reversible, the marine teleosts are indirectly converting their kidneys back to the purely tubular form possessed by the prochordate ancestor which left the sea in Cambrian or Ordovician time.

But there is more than one way of solving physiological difficulties, including that faced by the Ancient Mariner and the marine teleosts. Let us return to the elasmobranchs, who had first made the marine migration in the Devonian. These more primitive fishes solved the problem of living in salt water in an entirely different way. The four orders of the subclass Elasmobranchii —the sharks, rays, skates, and chimaeras—separated from the parent stem and from each other in or shortly after the Devonian period; that is to say, the Devonian is the most recent time at which we can assign to all four orders a common ancestry. Yet all four orders possess a common and surprisingly unique adaptation for living in seawater; they have changed the composition of their blood by deliberately bringing themselves, as it were, into a perpetually uremic state; they reabsorb from the glomerular filtrate as it passes down the tubules such urea as is present in this fluid (urea being the chief product of nitrogen combustion) much as the Ordovician-Silurian fishes learned to reabsorb glucose and chloride. They return this otherwise inert waste product to the blood until it reaches concentrations of 2000 to 2500 mgm. per cent. The presence of this urea raises the osmotic pressure of the blood above that of the surrounding sea water and causes water to move from the sea into the body, through the gills; and thus, pure water, free from salt, moves continuously inward at a sufficient rate to afford a vehicle for the urinary excretion of waste products and such excess salt as is present in the food. Where the bony fishes must continuously drink sea water in a steady stream, in the elasmobranchs this fluid serves only to wet the gills.

A unique tubular segment is present in the elasmobranch kidney, just distal to the glomerulus, which is thought to be the site of the active reabsorption of urea from the glomerular filtrate. None of the elasmobranch fishes, in spite of their long residence in the sea, is aglomerular; having always had abundant water available for filtration, they have had no need to abandon their glomeruli.

It is especially interesting that the method of reproduction in this subclass is highly specialized, the majority of the Elasmobranchii being viviparous, the rest producing an egg inclosed in a relatively impermeable egg case. The latter is apparently the more primitive mode of reproduction. Both the viviparous forms and those that have a cleidoic or "closed" egg utilize internal fertilization, for which purpose there exist claspers in the male and accessory reproductive glands in the female. One supposes that this specialized mode of reproduction is concerned with the conservation of urea in the young embryo until such time as its kidneys and its respiratory and integumentary membranes are organized. The Cladoselachii of the Devonian apparently lacked claspers, but these were present in the Carboniferous and Permian hybodonts and pleuracanths and in all the Jurassic sharks. Further paleontological research may, in the above view, be able to reveal to us the exact time at which the uremic habitus, as an adaptation to salt water, was acquired.

Returning now from the fishes to the main evolutionary tree: during the coal ages the low-lying lands were heavily clothed in tropical and subtropical vegetation. There was a high rainfall, the air was humid, the world was a swampy paradise inhabited by spiders, scorpions, centipedes, and snails, and lorded over by Amphibia that lived half in water and half on land. But on the whole, life was as stagnant as the swamps in which it lived. It was too comfortable, and in comfort the living organism comes to rest, its evolution stops or regression begins.

The moist paradise of the coal ages lasted until the Permian; then in the great Appalachian Revolution a majestic range of mountains, three to four miles high, was corrugated in the region that now lies between Newfoundland and Alabama. The Southern Hemisphere passed into a severe glacial period, and in the Northern Hemisphere the warm moist climate of the Carboniferous was replaced by aridity and seasonal chilliness. The cycads, equisetums, clubmosses, and tree ferns of the coal measures were exterminated; all the great families of the marine elasmobranchs were destroyed along with most of the marine and fresh water teleosts; and the stagnant Amphibia changed slowly towards more terrestrial forms. It was the sheer pressure of world-wide Permian desiccation that fostered the evolution of the reptiles, which were driven *in extremis* to living permanently on land. These new reptiles had tough hides and relatively long legs with which to crawl from one water hole to another; the egg, for the first time in vertebrate history, was encased in a waterproof shell and contained within it the allantoic sac to receive the waste products of the embryo; a multitude of adaptations, most of which concern the preservation of the internal environment, had to be effected to liberate the organism from its primeval aquatic environment. One of the most important of these adaptations consisted in a subtle change in the method of protein combustion. Instead of degrading protein nitrogen to urea, as had the fishes and Amphibia, the reptiles overhauled their metabolic machinery and degraded their protein nitrogen to uric acid. Uric acid is a very peculiar substance. It is almost insoluble in water, and yet it readily forms highly supersaturated solutions; the reptiles secrete it in the tubular urine as a concentrated, supersaturated solution; then, as the tubular urine passes to the cloaca, the uric acid precipitates out; leaving most of the water in the urine free to be reabsorbed into the blood, while the uric acid itself is expelled as an almost dry paste. This same uric acid adaptation, like so many other reptilian characters, is found in the birds, for the birds are but warm blooded reptiles with feathers and wings.

When the teleosts risked desiccation in the briny sea, many of them completely discarded their glomeruli as extravagant routes of water loss. In view of the fact that in the arid-living reptiles and the marine birds the need for water conservation is equally extreme, one might expect some of them to be aglomerular too, but no aglomerular reptile or bird has thus far been described. The reptilian-avian kidney is, however, headed in that direction, for the once elaborate glomerular tuft is reduced to a few, in some cases only two, capillary loops, and contains a great amount of inert connective tissue. It is as though these animals, having found the glomeruli largely superfluous but needing to flush the uric acid-rich secretion of the tubules down to the cloaca, had stopped short of the complete obliteration of the glomeruli and retained a vestige of the filtering bed in order to supply the tubules with a feeble, irrigating stream.

At this point you are probably wondering if the title of this discourse is not misrepresenting, since so much of it has been devoted to the lower vetebrates and so little of it to the mammals or to man. I would defend this apparent unfairness by pointing out that all the mammals together constitute but a small fraction of the vertebrates, and man himself but one mammalian species among thousands. The geological age of truly human forms is at most 1,000,000 years, a slight interval indeed out of the 500 to 600 million years which we must apprehend if we are to see the human organism in the proper perspective. But apart from this aspect of the problem, I must confess that at this point in the story of the evolution of the kidney there is a serious hiatus in our knowledge, namely, the circumstances surrounding the evolution of the first mammalian forms.

The mammals have added the only important patent to the kidney since Devonian time: the capacity to excrete urine that is markedly hypertonic, or osmotically more concentrated than the blood. As pointed out in an earlier paragraph, the elaboration of this hypertonic urine is in part effected by the unique, intermediate thin segment which is present in the tubule of all mammalian forms.

We must inquire, how did this capacity to excrete a hypertonic urine come to be evolved? And we may go on to ask, since the mammals were evolved from reptilian forms, why do they not excrete uric acid like the reptiles and the birds? And since the mammals do not generally live in fresh water, since in fact some mammals, such as the kangaroo rat, can live indefinitely upon dry oatmeal, while others, such as the whales and seals, can live indefinitely in the sea without ever taking a drink of fresh water, why have they not lost their glomeruli? Why, on the contrary, have the glomeruli reached their fullest development in the order Mammalia?

Let us review briefly what is known about early mammalian evolution. Through all the Mesozoic the mammals remained in the background and let the reptiles have the stage. During the desiccation of the Permian these thick-skinned animals, their legs ever growing longer, began to crawl on their bellies all over the world and to establish their reputation for grotesquerie. In the Triassic, which was, like the Permian, a period of aridity but one lacking marked seasonal extremes of heat and cold and generally warm enough to permit the luxuriant growth of ferns, tree ferns, and equisetums, reptilian peculiarities began to reach extremes. The more advanced took to walking on their hind legs and strutted about like the lords of the universe. In the Jurassic the climate reverted to subtropical humidity, and the reptilian paradise was but slightly disturbed by the diastrophic movement that raised the Sierra Nevadas and ushered in the Cretaceous. Here reptilian evolution culminated, on the one hand, in the great dinosaurs, the most magnificent creatures and probably the dumbest per kilogram of body weight that the earth has ever seen, and, on the other hand, in the flying reptiles whose jaws were still filled with teeth and whose wings were still tipped with claws. Then, at the end of the Cretaceous, when the Rocky Mountains and the Andes were rising slowly, the curtain is rung down on this Mesozoic scene with a suddenness that is almost dramatic. The dinosaurs disappeared, the birds lost their teeth and shaped their forelimbs into delicate wings, and a host of new actors, in the form of the Cenozoic mammals, rushed upon the stage as though they had long been waiting impatiently behind the scenes.

Where these mammals had been throughout the long and fantastic period of the Mesozoic is still a mystery. The oldest known mammalian fossils date from the late Triassic or early Jurassic periods, and these were already advanced and specialized creatures; no remnants of a stock which could have been ancestral even to the Cretaceous forms have been discovered. However, it must be believed that truly mammalian types were in existence in the early Triassic, and probably even in the Permian, while the reptiles themselves were still in a relatively primitive stage. Certain Triassic reptiles, the cynodonts, resembled the mammals in such features as the posterior jaw elements, the teeth, and the structure of the shoulder girdle, and they stood with their limbs well under the body, and it may be supposed that the cynodont reptiles and the mammals were evolved out of a common Permian stock. It need not be supposed, however, that this common ancestral stock was warm-blooded, nor need it be supposed that it had acquired the reptilian habit of excreting uric acid; rather it may have been a semi-aquatic type that degraded its protein nitrogen to urea, as we may suppose was the case in the Pennsylvanian Amphibia.

Proceeding from this premise, it is to be noted that there were two environmental stresses operating in Permian time: intense aridity and intense frigidity. The Permian was one of the greatest ice ages of all time. Frigidity—the cold nights of the desert and the long, cold, seasonal winters—placed a high premium upon the ability to be continuously active, even as aridity placed a premium upon the ability to travel overland from one water hole to another. A nascent, evolving stock could adapt itself to one of these stresses ahead of the other. Let us suppose that the protomammalian forms got off to warm-bloodedness first, in adaptation to frigidity, rather than to uric acid excretion, in adaptation to aridity. The progressive evolution of warm-bloodedness entailed a marked increase in the circulation of the blood, which in turn entailed a corresponding increase in arterial blood pressure; this increased blood pressure resulted in an increased rate of filtration through the glomeruli, and this entailed an increased need for conserving water by reabsorbing it from the tubules. Thus rapid elevation of body temperature would foster increased reabsorption in the tubules by accentuating the very need for it. It is plausible, therefore, that the accentuated capacity of the mammalian tubule for reabsorbing water was simply a sequel of the evolution of the warm-blooded state, which evolutionary step may have been taken before the habitus of uric acid excretion had become fixed in the general reptilian stock. Once the definitive mammalian kidney had been evolved as an adaptation to frigidity, it served as an adaptation to aridity as well, for the enhancement of water conservation which it effected enabled the mammals to compete, dry spell for dry spell, with the more sluggish reptilian forms. Into whatever dry spot the reptiles could radiate, the mammals could follow them, and when the desert night descended and forced the cold-blooded reptiles into sleep, the warm-blooded mammals remained active and alert. But more important, perhaps, was the change in temperature that marked the Laramide revolution; it may have been the inability of the reptiles to endure this period of refrigeration and desiccation that led to their almost total extinction, while the furry, warm-blooded mammals, equipped to meet both vicissitudes, could carry on.

This interpretation receives support in the fact that in the bird kidney the tubules are of a mixed type, some resembling the reptilian tubule in lacking a thin segment, some resembling the mammalian tubule in possessing such a segment. Functionally the bird kidney is intermediate between the reptiles and the mammals, the bird retaining the uric acid habitus of the former, although it can under certain conditions elaborate a distinctly hypertonic urine. The similarity to the mammalian kidney in the last respect is probably a case of convergent evolution fostered by the common character of warm-bloodedness, for the birds were evolved from reptiles that were far removed from the mammalian stem.

When, at the close of the Cretaceous, the dinosaurs became extinct, the mammals began to populate the earth. In the Paleocene the lemuroids took to living in the trees and became the Eocene tarsioids, who looked forward with both eyes at the same time and depended upon the sense of sight rather than upon smell or hearing. In the Oligocene a tarsioid or lemuroid stock gave rise to the monkeys which in the Miocene in turn spawned the Dryopithecine apes that roamed over Europe, Africa, and Asia. Then the rising Himalayas buckled central Asia into an uninhabitable mountain chain, and such of the Dryopithecine apes as survived were driven to abandon the trees and to seek their living in the southern plains. From Asia a Dryopithecine descendant migrated into Africa, to spawn there in the Pliocene such forms as *Australopithecus africanus*, discovered by Dart, and *Plesianthropus transvaalensis* and *Paranthropus robustus*, recently discovered by Broom, and declared by their discoverers and by Gregory and Hellman to be truly neither ape nor man.

The kidney is not identical in structure and function in all mammalian forms, but the human kidney differs only in details from that organ in the dog, cat, and rabbit. It is not surprising that in function the human kidney has its closest homologue in the kidneys of the great apes, who can claim with man a common ancestor back somewhere in the Miocene.

Examining the pattern of the human kidney, we must not be surprised to find that it is far from a perfect organ. In fact, it is in many respects grossly inefficient. It begins its task by pouring some 125 cc. of water into the tubules each minute, demanding for this extravagant filtration one quarter of all the blood put out by the heart. Out of this stream of water, 99 per cent must be reabsorbed again. This circuitous method of operation is peculiar, to say the least. At one end, the heart is working hard to pump a large quantity of water out of the body; at the other end the tubules are working equally hard to defeat the heart by keeping 99 per cent of this water from escaping. Thus heart and kidney are literally pitched in constant battle against each other—our lives depend on neither one of them ever winning out. Nature frequently opposes two forces against each other in order to maintain a steady state, but the opposition in this instance takes on an aspect of sheer extravagance. Paradoxically, the kidney has to do its greatest work when it excretes the smallest quantity of urine; as the urine flow increases it does less and less work, and if the urine flow were to increase to the colossal figure of 125 per minute—170 liters per day—the kidney, in respect to the excretion of water, would be doing no work at all.

In consequence of the circuitous pattern of the filtration and reabsorption of water, nearly half a pound of glucose and over three pounds of sodium chloride per day, not to mention quantities of phosphate, amino acids and other substances, must be saved from being lost in the urine by being reabsorbed from the tubular stream. There is enough waste motion here to bankrupt any economic system—other than a natural one, for Nature is the only artificer who does not need to count the cost by which she achieves her ends.

The chief waste product which the kidney is called upon to excrete is urea. The glomeruli remove each minute such urea as is contained in 125 cc. of blood, but because of the way the tubules are put together 50 per cent of this urea diffuses back into the blood again, so that in terms of the total renal blood flow (1200 cc. per minute) the over-all efficiency of the excretion is only about 5 per cent. There are certain foreign substances, however (diodrast, hippuran, phenol red, etc.), which have been synthetized only within the past few years, which the kidney excretes with almost 100 per cent efficiency. It is not strange that, in spite of the fact that it has never before encountered them, the kidney should be able to excrete such artificial, synthetic compounds twenty times as efficiently as it excretes the principal nitrogenous waste product naturally formed in the body, and which it has been excreting for millions and millions of years?

The kidney is receiving more attention today than ever before. These scientific problems range from local organic pathology to such subtle matters as the relation of the internal environment and its multiplicity of chemical factors to personality and mental disease. Certainly, mental integrity is a *sine qua non* of the free and independent life. As intermittent rays of light blend into moving images on the cinematographic screen, so the multiform activities within the brain are integrated into images of consciousness and brought into an unstable focus to form that fleeting entity which we call personality, or Self. But let the composition of our internal environment suffer change, let our kidneys fail for even a short time to fulfill their task, and our mental integrity, our personality, is destroyed.

There are those who say that the human kidney was created to keep the blood pure, or more precisely, to keep our internal environment in an ideal balanced state. I would deny this. I grant that the human kidney is a marvelous organ, but I cannot grant that it was purposefully designed to excrete urine, or even to regulate the composition of the blood, or to subserve the physiological welfare of *Homo sapiens* in any sense. Rather I contend that the human kidney manufactures the kind of urine that it does, and it maintains the blood in the composition which that fluid has, because this kidney has a certain functional architecture; and it owes that architecture not to design or foresight or any plan, but to the fact that the earth is an unstable sphere with a fragile crust, to the geologic revolutions that for 600 million years have raised and lowered continents and seas, to the predacious enemies, and heat and cold, and storms and droughts, the unending succession of vicissitudes that have driven the mutant vertebrates from sea into fresh water, into desiccated swamps, out upon the dry land, from one habitation to another, perpetually in search of the free and independent life, perpetually failing for one reason or another to find it.

7.

Plato and Clementine

Smith was much in demand as a speaker. Whenever he accepted an invitation to speak it was characteristic of him to prepare his address with enthusiasm, prodigious effort, and meticulous thought, even when the subject was not of primary scientific interest. His approach was always that of the scholar. His desire to examine personally all original sources generally involved librarians, secretaries, and translators. No paper, whatever its relative importance to him, ever left his desk without being carefully rewritten many times. Even when tinged with humor, the serious, scientific content of his writing was always apparent. The two following pieces, "Plato and Clementine" and De Urina, *are excellent examples of this subtle combination of scholarly content and humor. In "Plato and Clementine," an address given at the University of California in 1946, he gently and good-naturedly spoofs the statistical method; and in* De Urina, *delivered at Kaiser Foundation Hospitals of Northern California in 1957, he presents the history of the study of urine and its contribution to medicine, science, and philosophy.*

I HAVE BEEN THINKING MUCH OF LATE about the word "normal"—the physiologically normal, the anatomically normal—a word which we use a dozen times a day. Webster defines the normal as that which conforms with natural law, but by this definition only the supernatural is abnormal. This distinction is not very useful to a physiologist, so I have been trying to discover what *I* mean by normal. I am afraid that for all my thinking I have come out by the same door where in I went, but while I was wandering through this labyrinth of thought I have come upon some collateral matters that have perhaps left the experience something better than an absolute loss. I invite you to join me in retracing my labyrinth for whatever the adventure may be worth.

Our use of the word "normal" in biology and its derivative sciences stems, I think, from the Greek philosopher Plato, whose name I would put high in the list of the intellectual enemies of mankind, among those personages who should be starred with black daggers in the book of history for falsely directing, and thus retarding, the development of human thought. Historians have long since charged Plato with economic and political bias in the development of his philosophy; they have traced to his Idealism some of the major elements in late Roman and Medieval times which strangled intellectual inquiry and fostered the spiritual development and mental stagnation of the Dark Ages; they have pointed to the Renaissance and the succeeding centuries when modern science was born and developed as a period during which Platonism was driven out of one field after another. They assume that today we are reasonably free of its philosophic aberrations. In this last I think they are in error. Determinism applies as much to the shaping of human thought as to the shaping of mountains, and we may have to wait until a new intellectual age when the mountains which we now know are worn away before we shall be wholly free of those distortions in our thoughts which are traceable to this Athenian aristocrat.

Determinism applies also to the making of men, and Plato was a product of his environment, of local circumstances, and of his innate constitution. "I thank God," he said, "that I was born a

Reprinted from the Bulletin of the New York Academy of Medicine, *23: 352, 1947.*

Greek and not a barbarian, freeman and not slave, man and not woman; but above all, that I was born in the Age of Socrates." Here are the keynotes to his philosophy, the philosophy of an aristocrat, a snob, a bigot, and of a man with limited perspective.

Long before his time the land of Greece had suffered the troublous transition from a primitive tribal culture, characterized by inherited family privileges, to a loose conglomeration of city states grown rich with vulgar commerce and ever seeking new and more profitable adventures. Trade had produced great personal wealth, and this wealth had sought safety in reinvestment in the land until private property had become the foundation of social distinction, of the new oligarchy of rich and poor, aristocrats and commoners, freemen and slaves. It was in this turmoil between the old and the new that Socrates was hailed to trial by the democrats and condemned to death on the charge that he had been aiding and abetting the aristocratic Thirty.

Plato, born an aristocrat, hated the democrats before Socrates' death, and after this tragedy he was fired with bitterness and driven into philosophy as the only politically safe way in which to pay off the vulgar horde. He thereafter devoted himself to the discovery of that special kind of "truth" or "justice"–the two were essentially synonymous in an age when the only standard of reference was politics–which would protect aristocratic interests. Truth for Plato was identified with tradition, with inherited lands and privileges, with stability and unchangeableness, with divine decree that transcended the individual; truth was the antithesis of individuality as well as of change, of all the hated democratic forces that worked like ferments in the mob of sailors, shipowners, traders, moneylenders, wheat speculators, adventurers, slaves, to keep them in a perpetual state of turbulence and revolution. Democracy not only placed the individual on a pedestal but it defended the very rightness of change as a natural and just phenomenon. Plato despised democracy because in fact and in principle it threatened the security of his aristocratic privileges, and in the end he rhetorically annihilated it, and all possibility of its existence, by philosophic decree. He argued that since change is the denial of the unchangeable, the absolute, and since only the unchanging and absolute can be either knowable or true, that which changes is untrue, a half-truth, an illusion of the senses.

The *physiologi*, Thales, Anaxagoras, Heraclitus, Democritus, had asserted that what truly exists is matter, which contains within itself all the laws necessary to its existence and operation, and all else is but flux and movement of atoms. These persons Plato classed with the damnable democrats, the defenders of flux, under the most scathing term he could think of—*materialists,* who ignorantly took as real the objects of the world as they appeared to be, and falsely presumed to find in change and process something that is both knowable and significant. Thus developed his philosophy: since what is true must always be true, truth is absolute and eternal; the unchanging and unchangeable is the only reality, and all that deviates from it is the product of error.

Thus he built his philosophy of the Ideal with the aid of the Pythagorean theory that only numbers are real, and with the aid of the Pythagorean term Idea, or the essence of things. To cite the oft-quoted example, a particular circle is drawn by hand and proves to be slightly eccentric, so it is erased and another circle is drawn, and another, and still another, no one of them ever perfect, no one of them indestructible, no one of them to last forever. But the archetype of the circle, call it perfect circularity if you will, was there before the hand attempted the first imperfect circle and will survive after the last imperfect circle has been erased. It alone is real. And so it is that all particular objects of whatever kind approach in greater or lesser degree some Ideal or universal. The Ideal circle is not inherent in the substantive circle which we draw, but in the mind; but not in my mind or yours, or of any particular man, for particular men come and go. Since the Ideal circle endures everywhere and forever, it must be inherent in some universal, unchanging mind, which can only be the mind of God.

The world, which to our naive view appears to be made of substantive things, is, according to Plato's argument, but a shadow-show of half-truths. Its particular circles, its particular men and cities and laws, indeed its particular apples and catfish and billygoats come and go, all of them but imperfect images of the perfect and eternal Ideas of the divine mind. The Ideal billygoat (or its mathematical counterpart) existed in the divine mind before the first actual billygoat was, or smelled, and will continue to exist and smell when the last actual billygoat, imperfect in form and odor, has ceased to be. If the democrats, the defenders of the individual, of change, of conflict, of revolution, thought for one moment that they too might be an Ideal in the mind of Zeus, an ultimate to which they approximated however imperfectly, they stood convicted of a vulgar and unphilosophic error—nothing that suffered change or conflict or revolution could exist in the divine mind, and therefore it could not be true.

It has been said of Aristotle, Plato's pupil, that he loved his master, but that he loved truth more. He forthrightly denied Plato's doctrine of the Ideal. He believed that reality consisted of particular things, and not of universals; he accepted that change and process were as much a part of nature as fixity, and indeed he doubted the existence of the absolute. The world of philosophy has ever since been divided between Plato and Aristotle, and indeed Coleridge said that men are born either Platonists or Aristotelians. From the days of the Academy philosophers have continued to wrestle with the opposition between the Platonic universal, representing what we may call the philosophic norm, and the Aristotelian thing as is. The Christian church inherited Platonism largely through Neo-Platonism, and biology inherited Platonism largely through the Christian church.

Platonic Idealism intrudes itself into our thinking whenever we use the term "normal," since the word implies both perfection and predetermined plan. It also implies some measure of stability, for a standard of reference ceases to have meaning if it is never twice the same. It implies a pattern or paradigm which exists apart from things themselves, since we sense that perfection is not to be found in any one individual but can only be approximated to by abstraction from a relatively large group.

Biology has both historic and factual warrant for conceiving the normal as uniquely stable. It was recognized long before Aristotle that in each species of animals and plants one can perceive a type which is reproduced generation after generation. Indeed, our grandfathers adhered so strongly to this doctrine that they believed that God had created all animal and vegetable species according to type in the year 4004 B.C., after which Adam had named them, and that they had remained unvaryingly true to type ever since. Post-Darwinian biologists recognize that Bishop Usher was wrong in his calculation and that our grandfathers were wrong in their faith, that specific types had actually come into existence hundreds of thousands, some of them hundreds of millions of years ago. Yet the extension of geologic ages serves only to emphasize that this stability of type is one of the most emphatic facts in nature–it is change in type that is so infrequent as to seem miraculous. Certainly we are tempted to believe that nature has a template upon which she patterns every starfish, every oyster, every man, and it is in large measure this stability which imbues us, as it imbued Plato, with a strong sense of the absolute in our use of the word "normal."

Yet we perceive that within each species individuals are not all identical, but deviate above and below a mean in every character. We point to the influences of environment on development, or to the chromosomal mechanism of reproduction, and infer that during reproduction or development this or that little accident occurred, and consequently one little starfish is a little longer in the legs than another. The "normal" starfish would be one escaping all such accidents, it would perhaps represent the Ideal template.

It required the *Origin of Species* to liberate biology from the absolute, the unchanging, which was the essence of Platonic-Christian theology. The thesis of the *Origin* was biological variation, for it was on the observed data of biological variation that Darwin laid the foundations of evolution, and Mendel the foundation of genetics. Biological variation is the antithesis of both the Platonic Ideal and the stable Norm, since a variable absolute is by definition a contradiction of terms–nonsense. Yet we still quite generally fail to recognize this fact. Striving for specious simplicity, we tend to exclude variation from our thinking, either by ignoring its existence or by mathematically compressing it into a rigid, artificial mold. We tabulate the anatomical and physiological dimensions of our fellow mortals and, after averaging them, we correct them to what we call "ideal man," never blushing that we know nothing about "ideal man" except that he has a body surface of 1.73 square meters and an ideal basal metabolic rate of some 40 calories per square meter per hour. We measure his cardiac output, his respiration, many functions of his glands and kidneys, and even of his psyche, and in our tables we presumptiously apply a correction factor to women to bring them up to the male's ideal measurements, without asking ourselves, Whence comes this creature of statistical perfection, this paradigm, this prototype, to whom we approximate real men (and women) by an easy mathematical correction?

It is clear that the attributes of "ideal man" are but a collection of mathematical averages of various features which are subject to biological variation. An average value is not only a most useful one, but almost necessary to our thinking. It presents us a single concept, easily pictured and easily remembered, which we can convey to others or otherwise shape into a useful ideological tool. We could scarcely form any clear conception as to the duration of human life from observing a hundred thousand individuals, unless by taking the average; or form any idea of their adult height, weight, or other vital statistics unless we reduce the pertinent data to convenient categories and thus learn what averages and ranges are to be expected. It has been said that the whole of statistics depends upon the use of such averages.

There is, of course, the other application of averages that is equally important. Ten authorities estimate the magnitude of some measurable matter, or one authority makes ten estimates, and many or all of the results differ slightly from each other. If we have no reason to attach greater weight to one result than to another, experience shows us that the average of all the estimates is more likely to be right than any other value. In this usage, the average of mensuration, the mean represents a thing actually existing, and the more carefully the mean is derived the closer our concept comes to the reality; whereas in the first usage, the average of biological variation, the mean represents something that is nonexistent, a mere product of our imagination, and the more carefully it is derived the more removed it is from reality, in that there is less probability of its being identified with any one individual. And for us as Aristotelians, it is the individual that counts.

If we measure a large number of individuals in a given population, we find that the variations in this or that feature tend to distribute themselves above and below the mean, between certain minimal and maximal limits, in a characteristic manner. We conventionally divide the variable into equal categories and count the number of individuals in each category. When the frequency in each category is plotted against the size of the category, we obtain what is called a frequency-distribution curve which, in the "normal" form, is a symmetrical structure of some beauty [*Figure 1*]. This frequency-distribution curve reveals at a glance the dispersion of the variable under consideration and affords us a description of the entire population, and thus takes cognizance of biological variation as a fact.

Because of the way our textbooks are written, this frequency-distribution curve is often associated in the student's mind with errors of measurement. The terms "probable error" and "standard error," and the use of the standard deviation, σ, as

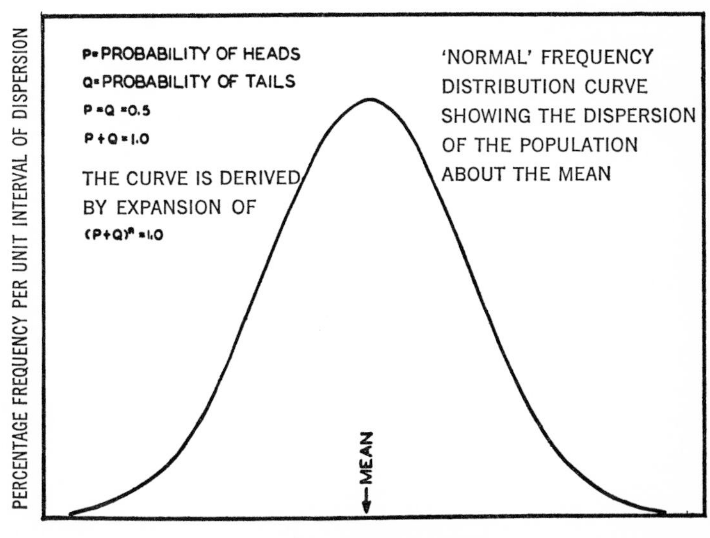

FIGURE 1

an index of the magnitude of error, constantly drive home this application. If any of us were to set a student to measuring the height of one of his colleagues and his error extended over the range of 4 feet 9 inches to 6 feet 3 inches, we would at once stop all measurement. The term "error" early became attached to the curve in connection with the development of the theory of error in measurement, and here it has stuck, to the misfortune of the student of biology, who is thereby befuddled as to the curve's more important meaning. He fails to see it for what it is, a graphical epitome of nature, a cabalistic symbol of her compounded mysteries.

The curve presented in this figure is the so-called "normal" frequency-distribution curve derived from the p:q formula applicable to the tossing of pennies for heads or tails. I need not labor you with the elementary facts that a penny has only two faces, heads or tails; that it is practically impossible for it to come to rest on its edge after descending on a hard surface, and that, assuming symmetry, the chance of its coming up heads, or p, is precisely equal to the chance of its coming up tails, or q,–i.e., $p = q$. This equation merely says that we know of no natural or supernatural force that will influence pennies in midair in the way of favoring heads or tails; and that we can discover nothing of that kind for the simple reason that the equation always works when we test it exhaustively. For all we know, there may be all sorts of gods and demons struggling amongst themselves to get heads or tails, but if we toss the penny often enough, we end up with the fiends evenly matched. Or perhaps because the mass of a penny is so great, these supernatural beings, currently allowed to operate only through the Heisenberg principle of uncertainty, are unable to turn it in its fall. Anyway, we learn from experience that $p = q$, and, of course, $p + q = 1$, denoting that heads plus tails equals all the probabilities there are, unless a penny rolls off the table and gets lost, when $p + q = 0$. Were we tossing pennies so constructed that if a particular penny fell heads, one or more other pennies would as a consequence have to fall heads, pure chance would no longer operate, and the frequency distribution curve could have almost any and every shape.

From these two equations it is simply a matter of algebra to

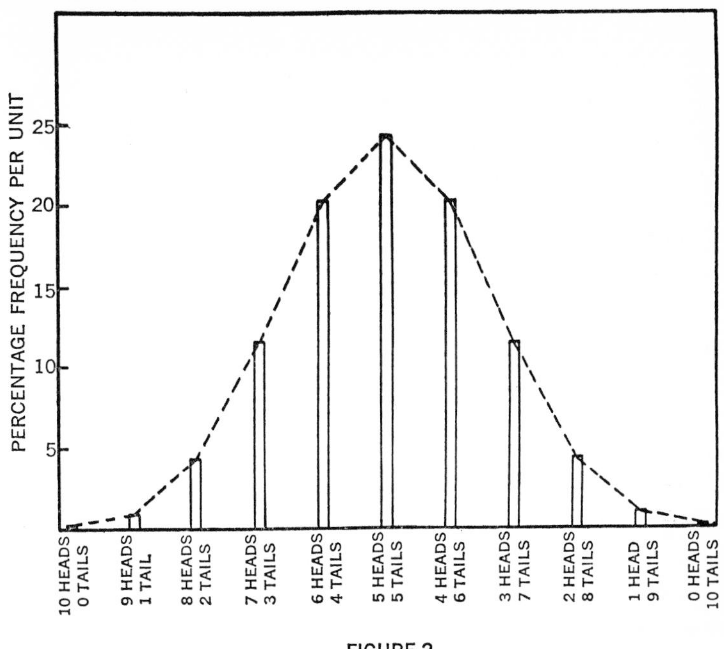

FIGURE 2

derive the unsmoothed frequency distribution curve [*Figure 2*] showing the chances of getting any combination of heads or tails when ten pennies are thrown simultaneously and in such a manner that they will not influence each other's destiny. The symmetry of the curve stems from the fact that no one event (i.e., heads in a particular penny) influences or is influenced by any other event (i.e., heads or tails in any other penny). Hence the curve is also called the curve of independent variation, i.e., each penny comes up heads or tails independently of every other penny. The destiny of every penny is a matter of "pure chance." Why the theory-of-probability experts call the "pure-chance" curve the "normal" curve is obscure, unless it is to absolve penny tossing of any implication of demonic influence.

In the normal or theoretic curve [*Figure 3*], the mean, the mode, and the median coincide, and the range theoretically extends from zero to infinity. In practice, frequency distribution curves rarely achieve the perfect symmetry of the normal curve, and the range always extends between some minimal and some maximal finite value. The curve may, however, be narrow or wide. The normal curve has its own internal measuring rod. This is the distance from the mean to the point of inflection of the ascending or descending limbs, which affords a convenient measure of the median range, or the degree of dispersion, of the variable under consideration. This distance is well known to you under the name of σ. The structure of the curve is such that 1 σ to either side of the mean will include 68.2 per cent of the population, $\pm 2\sigma$, 95.4 per cent, and $\pm 3\sigma$, 99.7 per cent.

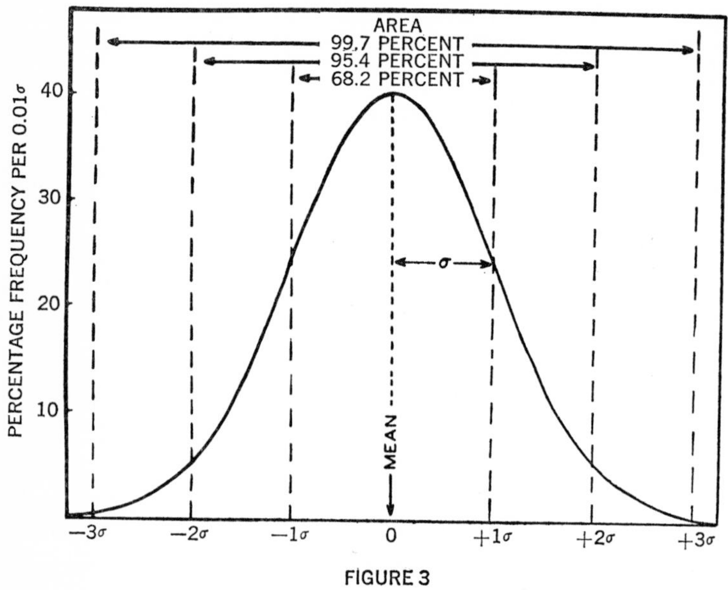

FIGURE 3

Where is the normal in relation to this curve? We cannot identify the normal with the mean, for the mean is a mere mathematical abstraction not possessed in any sense by any individual in the population. Nor can we identify the mode as normal merely because the population density is greatest at that point, nor yet the median merely because this point stands in the middle counting from left to right. We may arbitrarily assign the term "normal" to a band encompassing a substantial fraction of the population above and below the mean, but shall we draw this band at $\pm 1\sigma$ from the mean to include 68.2 per cent of the population, at $\pm 2\sigma$ to include 95.4 per cent, or at $\pm 3\sigma$ to include

99.7 per cent? Clearly nothing about the curve itself will aid us in making this decision. All we can say is that at $\pm 1\sigma$, $\pm 2\sigma$, $\pm 3\sigma$ from the mean, the chances are 1 in 3, or 1 in 20, or 1 in 300, that a given individual behaves consistently with the presumptively homogeneous population from which our curve in the first instance is derived. In erecting the curve we assume that all the individuals whom we tally therein are "normal," in the same sense that we assume that all 10 of our pennies are normal. If the term "normal" is used at all in reference to the normal frequency-distribution curve, it must include the entire range from the lowest to the highest value; the entire population must be considered normal. This definition is admittedly not very useful.

But, you say, this curve is as much a mathematical abstraction as the mean itself; it differs from the mean only by having two dimensions, magnitude and frequency, instead of the single dimension, magnitude. And where is the *thing* in itself, the individual, which Thales, Anaxagoras, Heraclitus, Democritus, and Aristotle accepted as the proper subject of philosophic and scientific study? With this criticism I agree. As Aristotelians we must base our thinking upon actual and material things with three dimensions. For that reason I beg permission to include in this discussion one who, conceived as flesh and blood, will stand in vivid and realistic contrast to such abstractions as the population, the mean, median, and standard deviation, one who as much by her actual dimensions as by her admirable qualities and pleasing personality will impress us with the importance of the individual. I refer, of course, to our old friend Clementine, whom we all recall from early, happy days.

There are some who, because of the almost pernicious accident of rhyme between her name and the size of her shoes, will remember her first on this account. But there are others, I am sure, whose minds are less inclined towards sardonic trivialities, who will recall that it was in the beautiful state of California,

> In a cavern, in a canyon,
> Excavating for a mine
> Dwelt a miner, forty-niner
> And his daughter, Clementine.

As Aristotelians we have agreed that it is the substantive things of life, the specific objects with mass and size and color, particular persons whom we know, that supply the proper data for scientific inquiry and philosophy. But biological variation is also a fact, and without the background of a frequency-distribution curve, a single individual is only an unrelated episode, an unintegrated experience. Perspective requires that in our search for the meaning of "normal" the individual must be assessed in proper relation to the total population of which he or she is a member. Only thus can we render our judgments in impersonal terms, and not in the manner in which we judge, let us say, a favorite melody, that which is entwined with our memory of Clementine, or any other. And thus must one who is conceived by those who remember her as normal in nearly all, if not all respects, be viewed lest we fall into that deceptive enchantment which distance, time, or personal predilection cast upon our unwary faculties. If there seems to be something heartless in my coldly analytic attitude, in my insistence that Clementine, who in our memories approaches the ideal, be judged by comparison with mortals, it is not because I lack affection or loyalty, but because these are not the instruments by which we will achieve our goal.

The all-important data, the so-called vital statistics, are things that we rarely gather about our friends. From some perversity in human nature we accumulate fewer vital statistics about our friends than about our enemies. I am in the unfortunate position of not having at my command all the vital statistics that I would we possessed about Clementine. For such facts as I do possess I am indebted to Mr. Percy Montrose, who in 1884 reduced them to immortal verse. Mr. Montrose, I regret to say, has apparently been lost to history, a diligent search having failed to disclose his origin or his end. But the charm of his meter and rhyme, if I may venture so bold a metaphor, are of a parity with the charm of the young lady whose sorry fate has stirred thousands of men to throaty and tearful song.

Although Mr. Montrose has given us many facts, I have been forced to supplement his all-too-brief biography by careful inquiry among mutual friends. Allowing for reasonable error, but error which I am sure will not vitiate our final judgment, I think that most of the lacunae in the documented history can be filled.

Light she was, and like a fairy,

is of course in part poetic extravagance on the part of her inspired biographer, and yet, perhaps not so much of an extravagance at that. I do not know Clementine's age at the time of reference, and like so many statistical data the time of reference to one detail may not be simultaneous with purportedly related data on other matters; but assuming that the impression here epitomized in a classic simile is to be taken seriously, and weighing carefully the considered assessments of my advisors, I deduce with some confidence that her weight was approximately 117 pounds at or about the age of twenty-one.

Is this—or was this—weight normal? As I have said, we must not allow either the enchantment of time or the persuasion of predilection to sway our opinion in such a matter. The only unprejudiced approach is to refer this datum on weight to the normal frequency-distribution curve [*Figure 4*] showing the weights of females in her age group.

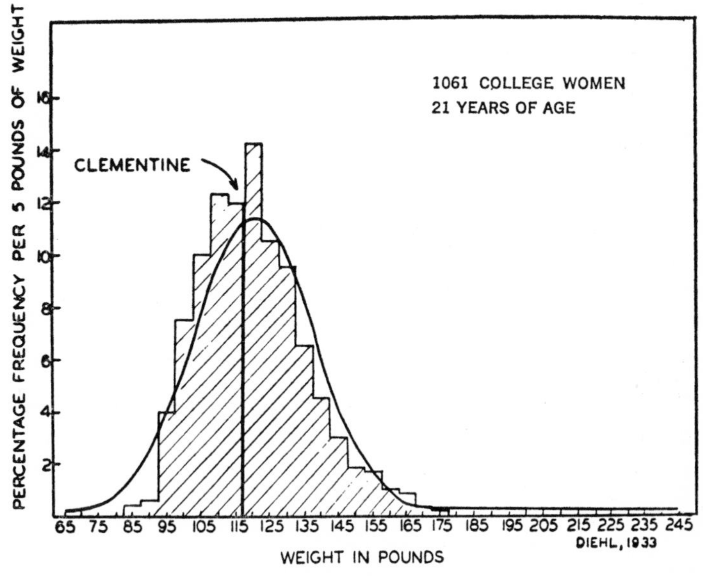

FIGURE 4

One thousand and sixty-one American college women twenty-one years of age should certainly afford us a sound sample of the normal. The range in weight is from 65 to 245 pounds, a broad spread for the normal however you look at it. The mean is 120.7 pounds, but not a single woman weighed exactly that amount. The high frequency of women weighing between 95 and 122 pounds is balanced by a relatively few women of large weight, or moment, as the mathematician says, where the curve is skewed to the right. Nevertheless, the frequency distribution corresponds closely to the normal curve, indicating that the factor or factors which make for inequality of weight in American college women largely enjoy independent variation and operate by pure chance, at least in this sense: the circumstance that one college woman is light or heavy does not influence the probable weights of her classmates. Or does it? May not the circumstance that one college woman is slender lead other college women to dietary restrictions, and thus squeeze the histogram to the left and out of the boundaries of the normal curve? We will later raise the question whether the circumstances of going to college may influence the weights of all the women who do so.

Clementine, who, in a manner of speaking, has been in every college in the United States, weighed less than the mean by 0.216σ, indicating that 83 per cent of the population can be expected to deviate from the mean more than she does. We have taken as our normal standard of reference "the weights of college women 21 years of age." By that definition Clementine is normal in that she is consistent with the standard in respect to weight.

The question arises, however, whether it is adequate in judging normality to use only one criterion of reference, weight; so let us try a second criterion, namely, height [*Figure 5*]. Secondary sources which I need not detail, but which when collated with other data are wholly convincing, lead me to set Clementine's height as close to 66 inches. Thus she was above the average height by 1σ, indicating that 32 per cent of the population can be expected to deviate from the average height more than she does. She is still consistent with our standard of normality. The only other thing we can deduce from this additional datum is

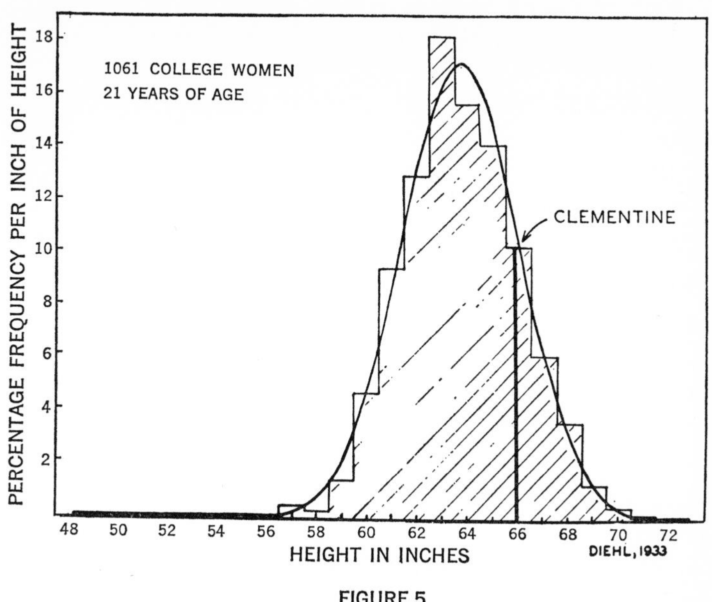

FIGURE 5

that she was slender, or tall for her weight. Statistics have a teasing way of proving what one already knows!

But is it abnormal to be slender? This is a matter of the correlation of two variables. Do they simultaneously enjoy independent variation, or do they tend to wax and wane together? The answer in this case is that they do not enjoy simultaneous independent variation but tend to vary in proportion to each other. Thus we are spared extreme skinniness in very tall women, and complete rotundity in very short women. The statistician, that ingenious person who is guiding us through this labyrinth, has integrated the two variables by calculating what he calls "body-build," which is equal to weight x 1000/h. According to this quotient, which affords quantitative, mathematical precision to what the eye can only qualitiatively assess, Clementine is still consistent with being a college woman. In this case, multiplying one reasonable certainty by another has only led to a third reasonable certainty; but this manipulation of figures calls to mind that it is yet to be proved, certain physicists to the contrary, that a mathematician can get anything out of an equation that he has not put into it, other than the leisure which is made available by any labor-saving device.

Let us try a third criterion—foot size [*Figure 6*]. It is something of a surprise that though most women's colleges measure something, and many of them measure almost everything that is measurable about women, no one of them seems to have taken any interest in the size of feet. So for our standard of reference we must turn to the sizes of shoes bought by women in the general population. The modern prejudice in favor of wearing shoes may be discounted as merely modish or even abnormal, and

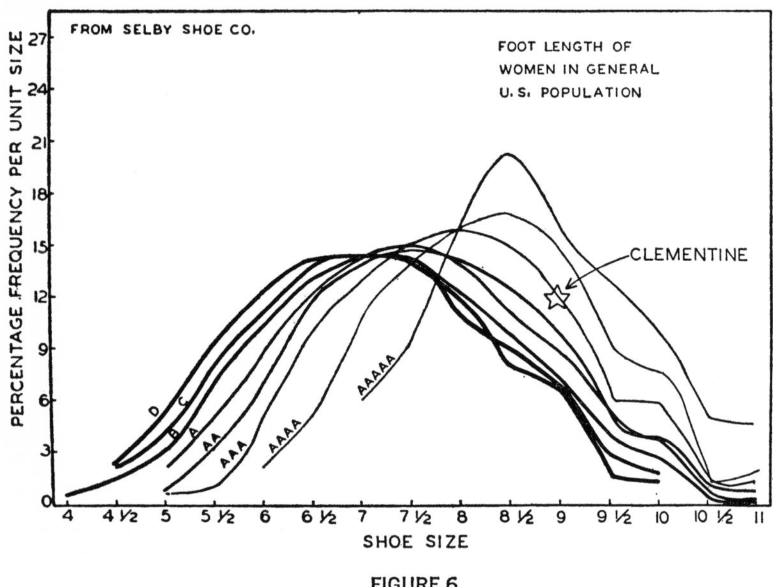

FIGURE 6

it is probable that shoes were rarely worn in the remote gold-mining camps of California in the early '50's. However, Clementine was adverse to walking barefooted over the rocky trails, for, as Mr. Montrose tells us,

> Herring boxes, without topses
> Sandals were for Clementine.

An authority on herring boxes of that period advises me that they were of course variable in size, but generally of a width of some three inches. This datum, combined with her body build, leads me to infer that she wore a AAA shoe. The matter is, however, of slight importance. If the width of Clementine's foot did not exceed a AAAAA, she is still consistent with what we have chosen as our normal standard of reference.

It will be recalled that we initially took as our standard of normality 1061 American college women. But can we be confident of the reliability of any population of women as a normal standard of reference? Should we not examine them against a broader background before accepting them as a sample of the absolute? One method that suggests itself is to compare them with college men of the same age [*Figure* 7]. The range in

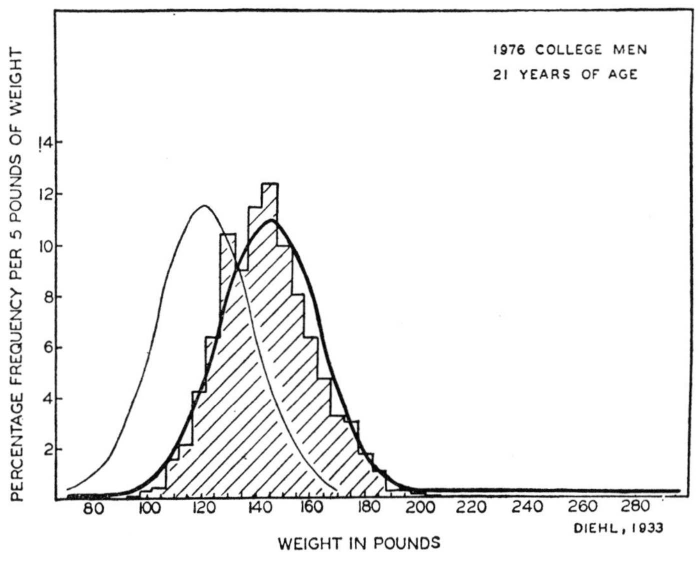

FIGURE 7

weight is substantially greater than among women, 68 to 298 pounds as compared with 65 to 245 pounds. Moreover, the frequency-distribution curve for weight is somewhat wider for men than for women, i.e., the variation or dispersion about the mean is greater. The degree of variation about the mean is expressed by σ, and appropriate comparison of σ for the two curves shows that women are significantly more uniform than men; they conform more closely to a hypothetical stable ideal, as they doubtless have always thought. But does this greater stability in weight make them more normal than males? There is an aphorism from the library of Assurbanipal, king of ancient Nineveh, which asks, "Does a woman conceive when a virgin, or grow fat without eating?" Voluntary dietary restriction is certainly not normal.

There are, of course, other factors operating, as is evident when we compare men with women with respect to height [*Figure 8*]. Here again women are more stable, they show less variation about the mean. To understand how this may come about, let us compare height and weight. In both sexes the

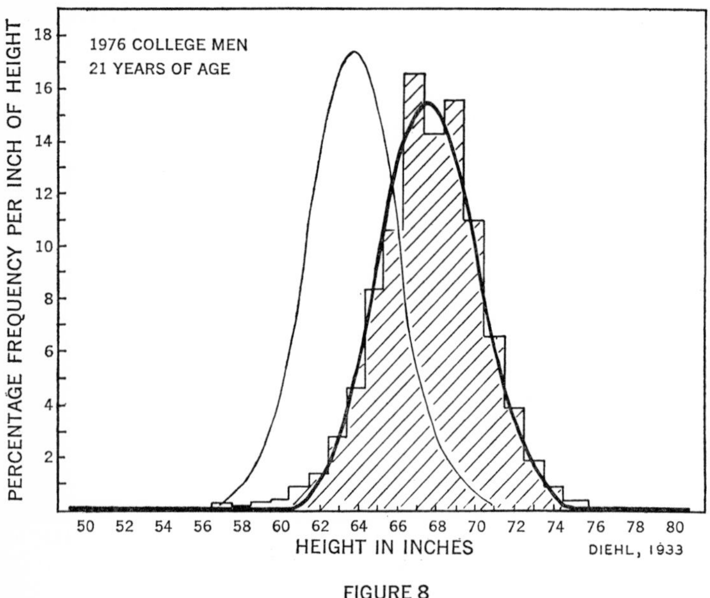

FIGURE 8

variation in height is much less than in weight; height is a much more stable feature of the human body than weight. If the body were shaped roughly like an egg, its mass would increase as the cube of its height, a circumstance which itself would make for greater variation in weight than in height, even among ideal eggs. But neither men nor women can be conceived as behaving like ideal eggs; in both sexes weight is largely a matter of soft tissue which can be added or subtracted by indulgence or hardship. Height is largely a matter of long bones and the vertebral column, the dimensions of which are less susceptible to fluctuations in dietary fortune, but are largely determined by the pituitary gland. Are women more normal than men because they agree about pituitary secretion among themselves, but disagree with men?

The question has arisen whether going to college affects the parameters under consideration. It does, in advance of matriculation. Both men and women who enter most colleges are taller and heavier than the noncollegiate general population. College women at the age of 16 average five pounds heavier and over one

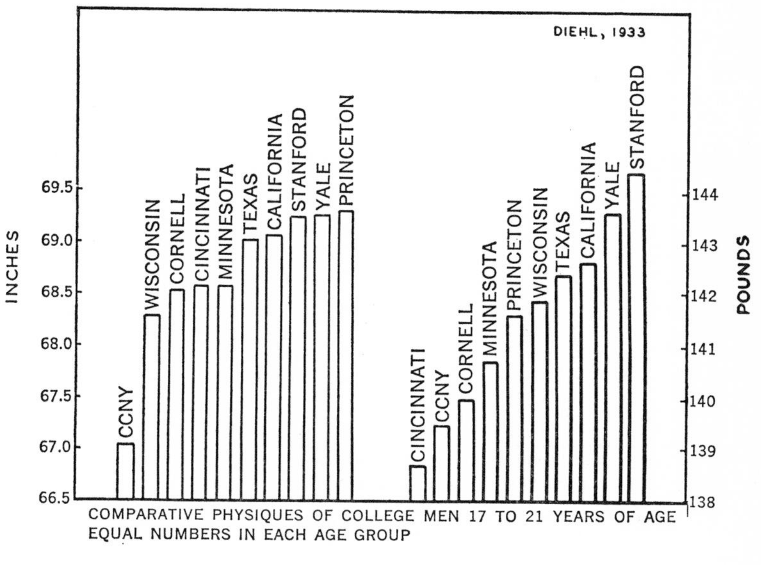

FIGURE 9

inch taller than their noncollegiate sisters, though at the age of 21 they are four pounds lighter. Unlike women at large, college women between 16 and 21 do not increase in either weight or height. It has been suggested that restriction of diet may retard their growth, but I have not observed that anyone has considered a possible causal relationship to the college diet itself, or, even less remotely, the effects of the intellectual life. Similarly, college men are taller and heavier than the general population. Apparently, in the college group acceleration in development has occurred prior to the age of 16, so that by the age of 17 or 18 years they have more nearly approached full growth [*Figure 9*].

But the situation is not the same in all colleges; among men, Stanford and California are exceeded in height only by Yale and Princeton, while in respect to weight only Yale is a competitor. C.C.N.Y. comes out short in both respects [*Figure 10*]. Among women, Stanford comes out first in height, but in weight is beaten by an ounce by Smith. Our criterion of "normal" depends on what college we pick. Is this predilection of a few colleges for mass and length normal?

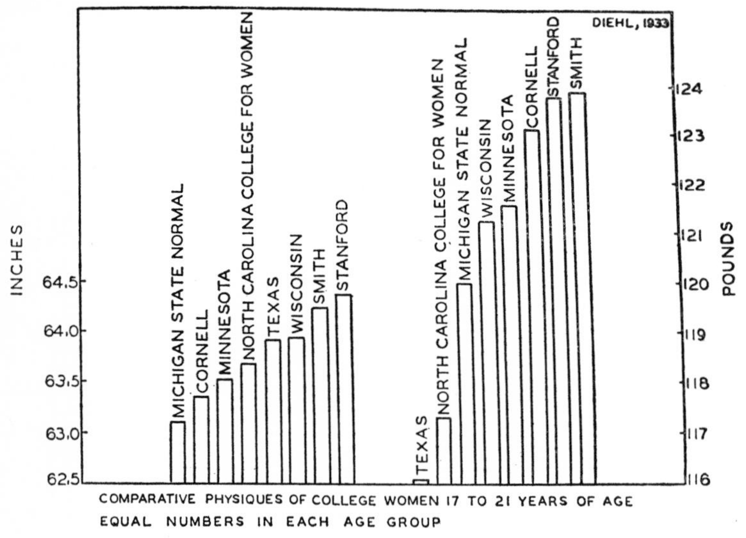

FIGURE 10

These general differences awaken us to a new difficulty, that of finding a stable population. Numerous studies have revealed that over the past century and even in the past few decades there has been an acceleration of growth and maturation. In several regions menarche occurs two years earlier than a century ago, and in three American Universities the mean menarchial age has dropped by one year in the last thirty years. The average height of English soldiers has increased about 4 inches in the past century, that of American college men by about 2 inches in the last half century, that of women only slightly less [*Figure 11*]. For several generations children have quite generally exceeded their parents (of like sex) in stature and earliness of puberty, and berth length in American sleeping cars has been repeatedly lengthened, from 71 inches (center to center of partitions) in 1859 to 77.5 inches actual mattress length in many cars now being made. Diet may have played a part in this acceleration and extension of growth, but some investigators relate the phenomenon to a period of reduction in the temperature of the earth, and believe that the growth and development peak may have been reached with rising temperature in the 1930's, and that future decades are likely to witness a racial recession.

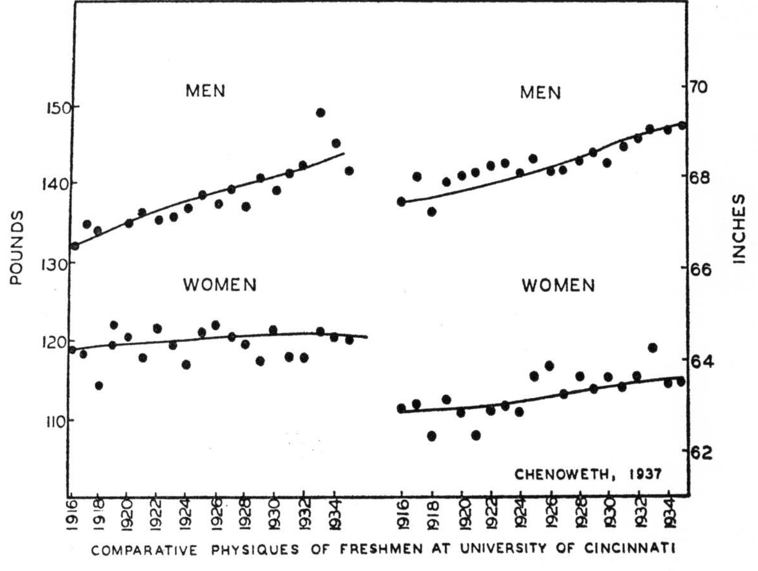

FIGURE 11

We have asked ourselves to what extent can our ideal, Clementine, be conceived as approaching the normal in respect to any one of several mensurable variables. We may measure Clementine, but we have not as yet measured the normal. If the word is to have any meaning, it will have to be in reference to some selected population. In the face of the above facts it is clear that we cannot lay our hands upon a stable population. On what grounds, then, can we call anything human "normal," unless we call *everything* human "normal"?

Perhaps we have been searching in the wrong direction. Perhaps the mere dimensions of things do not comprise their essence. Perhaps we should seek in the dynamic, rather than the static, to discover the normal. One of our colleagues, a neuroanatomist, has in effect already made this search in terms of function. Rejecting, as we have, the average as a mere mathematical computation, a specious name representing no reality, he defines the normal as "that which functions in accordance with its inherent design." He suggests a simple example: if we come across a broken wheel, it is possible to infer not only the inherent function of the object, but in addition what is wrong or abnormal about it. ". . . the essence of [its] design is circularity including the presence of an axis . . . [and] the function potentially associated with circularity in a discrete object is revolution." To those who may object that we learn the relationship between circularity and rolling by experience, and therefore by the law of averages, he replies with assurance that we can recognize a broken wheel the first time we ever see one, even though we have had no other experience with wheels. In this nascent experience the thing is not a novel object of unaccustomed design and function; we are under no disability whatever to recognize either that it is a wheel, with at least the implication of rotation, or that the local departure from design which prevents the fulfillment of the wheel's natural function is to be accounted for by the circumstance that the wheel has been broken. Were this not true, he says, the first wheel could never have been either recognized or invented.

The origin of the wheel is wholly obscure. Whether it was discovered by a perspicacious inventor who shared with our author this inborn insight into the relationship between design and function, or by a comparatively stupid dunce who fell upon the idea by slipping on a round stone or log, i.e., by the law of averages, I do not know. But I do not think that to define normal as the relationship between design and function is going to get us far. If it is normal for an intact wheel to roll in accordance with its design, is it not equally normal for a broken one to fail to roll, in accordance with *its* design? And why must a wheel roll, anyway? Only a boy who wants to play hoops, only a lazy man unwilling to carry his load or to walk from place to place, or who finds in the relationship of circularity to rotation a tempting teleological argument, would insist that a wheel must roll. Is a wheel not functioning properly when it lies flat upon the ground? Many a chipmunk thinks so. Our definition of "normal" must not be subordinate to human usefulness. We appear to be in a blind alley. Indeed I think we are slipping backwards, for let us see to what conclusions the author's own anthropocentric argument leads him:

"We intend to assert," he says, "a direct, but largely unremarked, implication of biology, viz., that the organic design of the human being is the one complete design of its kind existing within the entire organic kingdom on this planet. The detailed arguments on which the statement rests are too lengthy for present reproduction but it is felt that almost any biologist must agree with them upon reflection. They are based not only upon structural considerations but on functional ones as well; no other creature behaviorally manifests the integration of intellectual, affective, and sensori-motor response which characterizes man or, if any do, then by no means to the same degree of completeness. Thus the human design represents the complete and fundamental organic pattern from which other species depart by one degree or another, and the basic paradic [= normal] of the organic kingdom is the anthroparadic. . . . On the basis of completeness the anthroparadic must be the ultimate paradic of the whole organic kingdom."

Oh, Clementine. . . ! How little did you suspect that you were the "paradic," the paradigm, the norm for the whole organic kingdom! But do not be alarmed by this apotheosis. . . . These arguments are not new despite the fact that the paper I have quoted was published in the year of diminishing grace 1945. Christian theologists, beginning with Augustine, elevated man to the cosmic dais. They modestly recognized, however, that man had a few minor imperfections, and so under the doctrine of the Perfection of the Original Creation (prior to Adam's sin, of course, on which occasion the serpent tempted Eve, who was weak and perhaps abnormal, and Eve tempted her husband, and because of Adam's sin Creation was despoiled) they pointed to Adam, and not to Adam's progeny, as the paradigm of Creation. I would that we could do the same. I would that we had Adam—I mean no disrepect—on our dissecting table so that we could study all his "paradic" parameters, the width and breadth of his skull, the weight of his brain and heart and kidneys. I would that we could even make a few observations on his cardiac output and his renal clearances. . . . No Clementine, you are, if I may say it without being misunderstood, no Eve; and in any case, even the doctrine of Original Perfection and the legend of Adam and Eve have been heavily discounted since the publication of Mr. Darwin's book, since man has been revealed to be something less than a fallen angel and inadequate to serve as a model for the whole of organic creation. . . .

Have we, then, in our search for the normal, become lost in an endless labyrinth? Let us return to where we started, the stability of type that pervades the entire organic kingdom. It has been this stability of type, coupled with the Platonic Ideal, that has fostered our illusion that the word "normal" has any meaning. But is this stability of type real; does nature have a common template upon which she patterns every starfish, every oyster, every man? We know more about men than about oysters and starfish, and for man we can confidently answer, No. The high improbability that any two men are exactly alike in their chromosomal pattern (except in the case of identical twins) is one of the best established facts of biology. Every man differs from every other man not only in his finger prints but doubtless in a thousand other characters. If no two men are exactly alike in their chromosomal pattern, then where is the normal man?

The concept of the normal is an illusion of our own making. It is not easy to abandon one's illusions. Those who walk among the sick ask themselves many times a day, is this normal or abnormal? The physician who would prevent rather than cure disease must carry the question into that no-man's land where disease is nascent and difficultly discoverable. Where does the normal end and disease begin? We are engaged in an issue between life and death, and we cannot define our enemy. What is disease? Is it not normal for some men to be infected with nonpathogenic pneumococci—do we not call it abnormal only when the organism is pathogenic? But do we gain anything thereby? What does it aid us to define pneumonia as abnormal when we are not embarrassed to think that a pneumococcus is a normal organism that follows a normal course of reproduction in somebody's alveoli, to the victim's inevitable distress and until he dies—unless treated with sulfanilamide—all in accordance with laws apparently as unchanging as Plato's universals, the whole a normal sequence of events? Is it not normal for a diabetic to exhibit glycosuria, for a cretin to be just what a cretin

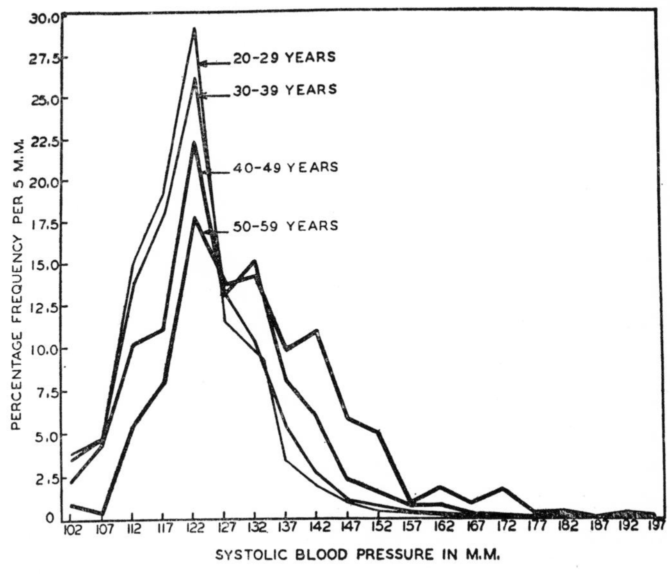

FIGURE 12

is, for a malignant tumor to do just what a malignant tumor does, for a schizophrenic to behave like a schizophrenic?

Let us take one more example of a physiological variable where we habitually use the word normal—blood pressure [*Figure 12*]. Where will we set the limits of normal blood pressure? To do this in an arbitrary manner would be not only intellectually dishonest, but dangerous, for these blood-pressure, frequency-distribution curves are charged with pain, disability and death. . . .

Is it not true that we are concerned not with the preservation of tradition or of aristocratic rights, or with the apotheosis of an

Ideal blood pressure, but with these brute facts—pain, disability, and death? And are there not many ostensibly normal circumstances that lead to pain, disability, and death? Senescence is normal—I doubt that any biologist will deny it—and childbirth is normal, and between birth and senescence it is impossible to define disease except in these terms—pain, disability, and death.

Our task is to ameliorate pain, to relieve disability, and to postpone death by reading the future in the present constellation of events, in the hope of modifying future events. Whether we choose to call any particular constellation of events normal or abnormal is not of the slightest significance. That we have in some measure been successful in our task of avoiding pain, disability, and death is partly attributable to our great theory of disease, stemming largely from Cohnheim, namely, that singular, particular causes underlie disease. If a man has pneumonia, it is because a specific noxious agent has invaded his body and made headway against his defenses. And so with the deficiency diseases, resulting from the absence from the body of particular, necessary elements; and here, too, one can place malignancy. Particular body cells, perhaps only one cell in the beginning, have escaped from control and by accelerated development and overgrowth destroyed vital organs. And here, too, one can place many inheritable diseases, as well as established predispositions to disease—modern genetics permits us to believe that in all such cases a particular fault in one or a few chromosomes may be responsible.

Under this particularistic theory it has been relatively easy to slip into the error of dividing everything into the normal and abnormal. But as opposed to or supplementing a theory which looks always for simple causes (and is confirmed by always finding them complex), is it not conceivable that there can be disease which may not be so particularistic in its genesis, nor yet necessarily inheritable? Suppose we examine the frequency distribution of a well-shuffled pack of fifty-two cards. There are only four chances in 635,013,559,600 of being dealt thirteen cards of one suit, and yet when such a hand falls upon the table it falls in accordance with all the rules that govern the fall of cards in a common or modal hand. It is as much a normal hand as any other, even though a very rare one. Suppose those fifty-two cards were so many chromosomal determinants of somatic characters, none of which is very obvious or very important in itself; but suppose that in rare combinations, like thirteen cards of one suit, they spelled jeopardy for the unlucky player. The organism is in perpetual conflict with its environment, and what is one man's environment may be another man's ruin. It has been said that God must love the common man, because he made so many. May we not suspect that there are more individuals at the mode of biological variation because they are better fitted to survive in a specified environment than are the individuals at either extreme of the range? The man who gets too many of any one suit in his genetic makeup may be destined for an early death because of his inability to cope with the stress of his environment. Yet by all the rules, he has had a normal deal. His obscure pathology need not be inherited by his children, nor could one point to a particularistic cause such as pneumococcus, a vitamin deficiency, a tumor or a default in some particular gland, as the primary cause of his distress. Can we name such diseases? Perhaps senescence is such a disease, a matter of too many, or too few clubs. Perhaps there are others. Perhaps we have looked so hard for particularistic causes under Cohnheim's influence that we have found them where they do not exist. Perhaps by classifying everything as normal or abnormal under Plato's influence we have overlooked other possibilities. Perhaps the pathologist should take the theory of probability into his laboratory and apply it to ostensibly normal people.

And there's that word again. The Platonic Ideal lives on in our Aristotelian house of science, a formless, limitless, insubstantial ghost not to be captured by any trap set by the anatomist, physiologist, or statistician. There is no such thing as an ostensibly normal person—only persons who show no ostensible danger of pain, disability, or death. The word "normal" is useful in only one sense—as a tag for ignorance.

It is a paradox that when probability came into philosophy, freedom was expelled. Causality took over our lives and our innermost thinking, and even disease and death were constrained to run a deterministic course. Environment, circumstance, and constitution—these three became our Fates. No better example could be adduced than the following tragedy, reference to which I have hitherto avoided. As Mr. Montrose recounts of Clementine, in the manner of those who depend for their sustenance on Nature's bounty and who must discharge their obligations to Nature's creatures promptly and regularly,

> Drove she ducklings to the water
> Every morning just at nine.

Here, in environment and circumstance, was the fatal pattern laid. Though I cannot exclude the possibility that constitution in the matter of her foot and footwear accelerated the mischance, when there is sufficient repetition probability becomes dead certainty, and one morning Clementine

> Hit her foot against a splinter
> Fell into the foaming brine.

I am sorry that at this point I must interject a harsh note of criticism of our biographer for committing a solecism as indefensible as it is shocking. Fully recognizing the demands of meter and rhyme in poetic form, and appreciating the difficulties of discovering another noun adequate in respect to both context and euphony, I fail to understand how Mr. Percy Montrose could have penned that iambic tetrameter. That the cool rivulets of condensed cloud trickling between mossy stones high on the Sierra Nevada, the springs which well forth from canyon wall or glacier's lip, the gurgling brooks and torrential streams which tumble and toss down the deep-hewn, shadowed gorges of California's mountains—that any one of these crystal cataracts should be called *brine* is an offence against truth and taste from which I cannot recover.

I would also like to place on record my conviction that the sixth and seventh verses, commonly appended at the end of the musical score as though to conserve space, are in truth removed from the manuscript proper for a better reason. Careful study of internal evidences convinces me that these verses, the one relating the death from sorrow of Clementine's father, and the one starting "In my dreams she still doth haunt me," are in fact spurious, apocryphal forgeries by a later hand attempting to imitate Mr. Montrose's rhythm, but rendered indelicate by too many trips to the beer keg. And I may also note that, according to my authentic record, in the last bar of the chorus the melody does not follow the frequently heard (if not inharmonious) course from C to E, but repeats high C precisely in the manner of the verse.

But these details are unimportant. My point is that, not in the normal or abnormal, but in environment, circumstance and constitution is concealed our potential fate, and each of these is complexly manifold and complexly changing. Against the potentialities of fate we must oppose calculated action.

Ruby lips above the water,
Blowing bubbles soft and fine,
A-las, for me! I was no swimmer,
So I lost my Clementine.

We must abandon our dream of the absolute, the unchanging, which began when Pythagoras created the world of eternal numbers, and Plato of eternal Ideas. It is required of us that we find that which is significant not in the absolute, but in diversity and change and transmutation.

In a churchyard, near the canyon,
Where the myrtle doth entwine,
There grows roses and other posies,
Fertilized by Clementine.

Our search for the Ideal, the paradigm, the pattern of perfection, has led us only to disillusionment because that which we seek is but the product of our dreams. The normal is gone because it never was.

O my darling, O my darling,
O my darling Clementine,
You are lost and gone forever,
Dreffil sorry, Clementine.

If we cherish the Ideal the more because we cannot attain it, because nature has never attained it, this poignant craving but serves to fire us with greater zeal and fidelity to our proper companion in philosophy, the substantive, despite her imperfections and the fact that she is never twice the same. Some modern but unknown philosopher has captured the nuance of the Platonic-Aristotelian transformation in a quatrain which perhaps you know, and love:

How I missed her, how I missed her,
How I missed my Clementine,
'Till I kissed her little sister,
And forgot dear Clementine.

8.

De Urina

IN HER VOLUME OF SHORT STORIES entitled *Seven Gothic Tales,* the Danish writer Isak Dinesen puts into the mouth of an Arab sailing along the coast of Africa by starlight the speculation, "What is man, when you come to think upon him, but a minutely set, ingenious machine for turning, with infinite artfulness, the red wine of Shiraz into urine?" When you come to think upon him, man is many things depending on your point of view, and he has shown some ingenuity in the exploration of the infinite artfulness of himself. It will come as no surprise when I assert that urine has contributed as much to this exploration as has any other single feature of his body.

It was probably not until he abandoned the forest for the cave that man began to urinate into a pot and had the opportunity not only to discover that wine and water do, in fact, come to much the same end, but to suspect that this mysterious liquid might have some values beyond wetting the earth. Only those upon whom the Cromwellian period imposed the strictures of Puritanism hid the urinal under the bed; throughout most of history, and for most living peoples, urine had been and remains a respectable and sometimes valuable commodity.

In keeping with his primitive philosophy, man's earliest efforts to utilize what would otherwise go to waste were doubtless in witchcraft and magic; among the aboriginal peoples urine, like blood, hair, nails, and tears, is imbued with soul-substance, the impersonal personality that pervades all primitive philosophy. Some rub it on the body to make them bullet-proof; some use it as a lethal agent in sorcery; some believe that animals can be impregnated with a human being by drinking human urine; some hold that rain is the urine of a deity; while in the island of Kisser a young man urinates on the urine of his heart's elect, hoping thereby to make her love him.

OF MORE interest to us is the use of urine in medicine, for there is scarcely a disease which has not been treated with it, either by external application or by internal administration. The therapeutic use of urine is attested in the Egyptian papyri, and many such applications in Roman times are recounted by Pliny, Galen, and

Reprinted from Kaiser Foundation Medical Bulletin, *6: 1, 1958.*

Sextus Placitus and persist today all over the world. These practices were not mere repetitions of morbid appetite but usually the logical application of the prescientific suppositions of the age. No less a man than Robert Boyle, the great seventeenth-century pioneer in chemistry, is quoted as saying that the virtues of human urine, as a medicine, would require for their enumeration an entire book (truly an understatement), and he is asserted to have written a volume on the subject himself under the anonymous letter B. The most intriguing prescription is perhaps one for the preparation of a quintessence of urine to be distilled when the sun and Jupiter are in the constellation "Piscibus." There is one certain fact, and that is that the thousands of recorded prescriptions have apparently cured as many diseases with miraculous rapidity.

A little more scientific, perhaps, is the use of urine for hygienic or cosmetic purposes. In France the wealthy ladies of Boyle's day took urine baths to beautify the skin while persons in rural communities today use urine to soften the hands. It was commonly employed as a mouthwash and prophylactic against dental caries in Roman times, a practice that persists among many primitive peoples. "Rectified urine," a strongly ammoniacal solution, as well as *sal ammoniac* (ammonium chloride) were recommended in the eighteenth century by Pierre Fauchard, the "father of dentistry," as a dentifrice and tooth-ache remedy (*Bull. Hist. Dentistry*). The use of fresh or fermented urine as a dentifrice persists in many areas at the present time, and the addition of ammonium compounds and urea to some modern dentifrices echoes this age-old relation of urine to the teeth.

Peter Freuchen, in his autobiographical work, *Arctic Adventure*, recounts going to a dance with an Eskimo girl. "Arnarak was her name," he says, "and she was lovely." To permit her to put on her party dress he went with her to her father's house, where he was received as a guest of honor. "The girl dressed," he says, "and then discovered that she had to reset her long, beautiful hair. She loosened it and it gave me a shock to see it flow straight and black over the floor as she combed it. The sun falling upon it through the window gave it a blue-black look of a raven's wing. I was in an agony of love, and my sailor's heart nearly burst with pride that I should be the one taking her to the dance.

"All might have gone well had she not been so eager to make an impression upon a white man. To prove to me what a remarkably clean girl she was, she hauled out from under the ledge a big pail of human urine used for tanning hides and washing. Carefully she lowered her beautiful hair into the pail and thoroughly shampooed it, while my love cooled and my admiration sank as low as the tide in the English Channel."

It is asserted that until the introduction of yeast urine was used by European bakers as a leaven, and within relatively recent times it is said to have been used to macerate tobacco leaves in the cigar industry, and to flavor cheese. I have been told that in the Arctic region pots of human urine are used to draw salt-hungry caribou near to human habitations, and I can certify that in California some farmers place pots of urine around fruit trees for a contrary reason–in order to keep away maurauding deer.

ONE correspondent advises me that urine found a novel use in World War II. He related that men on overseas missions for the Office of Special Services were supplied with emergency ration kits, and that among the packages were cans of asparagus with instructions to fill the can with urine after eating the contents, and to use the urine for fish-bait. Two chaps ventured out to a coral reef and urinated in the shallows after eating the asparagus, and the result was so successful that they fled ashore for fear of being attacked by the large and numerous fish which were attracted. I have been unable to obtain confirmation of this episode from Washington or the Library of Congress, and one expert on survival kits believes it to be apochryphal. From my own experience in World War II, however, I would suspect otherwise, because no other good idea ever went to waste. I have also heard that the characteristic odor imparted to the urine by asparagus is present in some persons but not in others, but I have seen no reference in any work on human genetics to this matter. Perhaps the odorogenic factor represents a recessive and infrequent genetic character, which may explain why asparagus in survival kits did not survive the war. Apochryphal or not, this legend has led to the addition of odoriferous compounds related to asparagus to lobster bait, with, so I am told, some success.

You have doubtless read of the studies of Dr. and Mrs. Hubert Frings of Pennsylvania State University, who have recorded the alarm cry of the starling and found that when this cry is broadcast at a flock of roosting birds it causes them to fly away in fear. For many days or weeks the bird may circle but will not land on the particular trees, or on that face of a building, from which they took startled flight. The thesis has not been proved, but it is a reasonable hypothesis that in the first moments of agitation they defecate and the droppings carry some persistent and odoriferous warning. If this explanation is accepted, it remains to be determined whether the telltale factor comes from the urinary or the gastrointestinal tract.

OF GREATER medical interest is the use of urine in diagnosis and prognosis. Fragmentary records show that the Sumerian and Babylonian physicians gave attention to its color, consistency, and frothiness, and to the presence of clouds, sediments, casts, and blood. Possibly as old as the Mesopotamian records are those of Hindu medicine, preserved in the writings of Charaka and Susruta (800–600 B.C.), where morbid conditions involving the urine are divided into twenty varieties. The Hindus recognized prostatic hypertrophy and its sequel of urinary suppression, and they identified the disease diabetes mellitus by the name of "honey urine": it had been observed that trains of black ants were attracted to the sweet urine, and thus these insects came to be recognized as a means of diagnosis—probably the oldest diagnostic test in the history of our science.

The Egyptians mention the urine as having an unpleasant odor, and refer to various diseases of the urinary bladder. They also noted involuntary urination in relation to spinal injuries, but none of the papyri mentions the diagnostic use of urine. In the Hippocratic texts, however, the characteristics of urine in disease are mentioned 182 times, and these characteristics are used both for diagnosis and prognosis. Galen praises Hippocratic medicine for the acuteness of its observations on urine, but adds nothing new to the notions of the Greeks.

With Paulus Aegineta of the seventh century the visual examination of urine became more systematic and detailed, and in that century Theophilus mentioned the application of heat as a diagnostic test, referring to the cloudiness caused by heating albuminous urine. In the eleventh century Avicenna pointed out the difference between urine passed in the morning and that passed at night, and remarked on the influence of age, food, and drugs on its color; and Constantine Africanus, one of the founders of the school of Salerno, wrote that the "urine is better than the pulse to discover the disease from which the patient suffers." Early in the twelfth century Alsaharavius cautioned the physician not to allow himself to be imposed upon by the color of the urine, which may be affected by the patient's having taken saffron, cassia, or other drugs. "Such tricks," he says, "are often practiced upon water doctors." The expression, "water doctors," implies that by this date the visual examination of the urine had become the specialty which, as uroscopy or water-casting, was soon to spread over the whole of Europe.

UROSCOPY was the art (if we may call it such) of making a diagnosis and prescribing therapy solely on the evidences afforded by looking at the urine, for which purpose the fluid was studied carefully in a specially shaped flask and by an almost ritualistic procedure. Toward the close of the twelfth century the Salernitan physician, Gilles de Corbeil, wrote a long poem on uroscopy entitled *De Urinis* which served to popularize the practice, and for several centuries uroscopy came close to excluding all other types of medical observation. By the fourteenth century another Salernitan physician, Bernard Gordon, was able to declare that "the science of judging the urine is so easy that all can learn what they wish to know." The uroscopists were largely ignorant of both anatomy and therapeutics, and their activity ultimately expanded into that form of divination known as uromancy; yet it was a day when, apart from taking the patient's pulse and listening to his history, there was little that the physician could do in the way of diagnosis or therapy, and the uroscopist, or water-caster, water juggler, water judge, or as he was later called, the piss-prophet (Oxford English Dictionary, VOL. VII, p. 905) with his elaborate gown and headdress, his mysterious urine glass and solemn mien, must have had a strong appeal for the sick and in many instances probably imparted to them some measure of psychosomatic benefit. Uroscopy was the degeneration of empirical observation into pure quackery, but for several centuries its charlatans traveled the country by horseback with only a urine glass slung on the arm, preying on the credulity and ignorance of the people. The uroscopist served as the subject of almost every illustrious artist of the day, and it is said that one painter even protrayed Jesus in this role.

Shakespeare cautiously refers to the practice in *King Henry IV* (Act 1, Sc. 2), and also in *Two Gentlemen of Verona* (Act II, Sc. 1), but other poets with less reserve turned their attention to the presumed reciprocal relation between the volume of urine and the volume of tears in grief. This poetry, however, is rarely read today because Rabelais is not the only writer who has been expurgated. When the Lord Chancellor, Sir Thomas More, was imprisoned in the Tower by Henry VIII because he disapproved of Henry's divorce from Catherine and his marriage to Anne Boleyn, it is said that he cast his own urine by way of divining his fate. He obtained a favorable prognosis, but when the King learned that Sir Thomas had said to a fellow-prisoner that no Parliament could make the King supreme head of the church, he nevertheless lost his head.

IT WAS not in the arts of diagnosis and of divination, however, that urine was to play its most important role, but in the practical arts that supplied the foundations for the science of chemistry. Urine is a weak detergent by virtue of its urea content, and this detergent property is greatly enhanced when it is allowed to undergo bacterial fermentation in consequence of which most or all of the urea is decomposed into ammonium carbonate, a moderately alkaline salt. Such fermented urine has probably been used since time immemorial as a soap, and by aboriginal peoples it is used in the tanning and softening of hides, for extracting dyes from various plants, and for mordanting other dyes in woolen fabrics. Ancient literature bears no testimony along this line until the Roman period when urine became the agent of choice for removing the fat and dirt from wool, and for softening and bleaching the woolen fibers before dyeing. The Roman epigrammatist Martial inveighs against the nauseous smells emanating from the fullers' vats and relates that for this reason the police banished the guild to the far side of the Tiber. The Romans also used urine to remove ink stains, and prepared from it a flux for soldering gold. In the ancient Roman port of Ostia there still stand in the market place marble seats so arranged that the urine could be collected in one pool from people coming from all parts of the world. So important was urine in Roman economy that, according to Suetonius, the emperor placed a tax upon such as was collected in the public reservoirs. The use of fermented urine in fulling and crofting persisted until recent times, and by long tradition a genuine Highland homespun or Harris tweed is expected to carry the odor of the fermentation vat.

The word "urine" is, of course, derived from the Latin *urina* through the twelfth century Old French *urine*, the English usage appearing in the fourteenth century and remaining in hushed but polite circulation today (*Oxford English Dictionary*. VOL. XI: U, p. 461). Also from the Old French *pissier* comes the English "piss," in use as a noun and verb before the time of Chaucer and Wycliff. It has many derivatives, as, for example, the noun pismire (*Oxford English Dictionary*. VOL. VII, p. 905) for the ant, so called because of the odor of the ant hill. Whence Wycliff's translation in 1388 of Proverbs 6: 6, "O! thou slowe man, go to the pismire." In English the word piss, however, has not been in polite use since the spread of Puritanism, though all travellers are familiar with the corner *pissoir* of France, at least as a place for posting placards.

THE PISS POT, often elaborately decorated with flowers or verses, and sometimes even made of silver or gold, remained in universal use until the invention of the latrine about the time of Elizabeth I. Frequently the pot was emptied out of the window by the chamber maid: as Dryden, translating Juvenal's *Satires*, wrote,

'Tis want of sense to sup abroad too late
Unless thou first hast settled thy estate;
As many fates attend thy steps to meet
As there are waking windows in the street:
Bless the good gods and think thy chances rare
To have a piss pot only for thy share.

The Scots generously allotted to the unwary passersby a "Lord have mercy on you!" which contracted to the almost unintelligible "gardy loo!" or by another tradition, was derived from the French expression "gare de l'eau"—beware of the water!

However, long before the first law was passed to protect pedestrians (in Paris in 1372, in Edinburgh almost a century later) the chamber pot was emptied with more profit on the garden where it supplied potassium and nitrogen to the soil. The use of urine as fertilizer has sometimes been accompanied by a quasi-religious belief in plant nutrition. One group in Germany that adheres to the "organic gardening" concept holds that in order to begin a proper compost one must go to a high mountain when the moon is in a certain position, prepare the compost of plant residues, bring up a virgin (it is not clear whether the virgin has to be beautiful or not), and have her urinate on the compost. This is said to be the ideal way to start a new compost which can then be utilized to start many others.

IT WAS in alchemy that the uses of urine first began to acquire a truly scientific cast. Earlier alchemical interest had centered on the salts of ammonia: ammonium chloride and ammonium sulfate, collectively called "volatile salts" to distinguish them from nonvolatile salts such as sodium chloride. Pliny in his *Natural History* refers to *Hammoniacus sal,* but how the Romans prepared *sal ammoniac* is unknown, though the name is said to have been derived from the fact that this salt was first made in the vicinity of the Egyptian Temple of Jupiter Ammon. Later alchemists prepared volatile salt for medicinal use by the dry distillation of fermented urine, and this salt was used in many alchemical operations. In the fifteenth century Basil Valentine showed that a pungent, volatile gas, free ammonia, was liberated from *sal ammoniac* by the action of alkalis; in 1777 the Swedish chemist Scheele showed that ammonia contained nitrogen, and in 1785 Berthollet demonstrated that it is composed of nitrogen and hydrogen.

An even more exciting substrate for alchemy was the element phosphorus. This word, in Latin meaning the morning star and in Greek a bringer of light, was early applied to any substance that glowed in the dark, and it was only after the seventeenth century that it was restricted to the element *phosphorus mirabilis* or *igneus,* a waxy crystalline solid with a disagreeable odor which possessed the remarkable property of burning, when exposed to air, with a bright flame and great heat, for which reason it had to be prepared in the absence of air and stored under water.

Pure phosphorus was first obtained by the alchemist Brandt of Hamburg in 1669, who started with microcosmic salt (ammonium sodium hydrogen orthophosphate), so named by the alchemists because it was obtained from the decomposing urine of man, the "Microcosm"—an ancient Babylonian antithesis opposed to the great world or "Macrocosm" in which man lives. Though abundant in the earth and in all animals and plants, phosphorus is never found free in nature, and Brandt was able to sell the secret of its preparation to a man named Krafft who in 1677 exhibited some elementary phosphorus in England, where it attracted the attention of chemists. In 1678 Kunckel, and in 1680 Boyle worked out Brandt's secret of evaporating urine and dry-distilling the residue, collecting the distillate under water (*Encyclopaedia Britannica,* Eleventh Edition, VOL. XXI, p. 478).

Boyle communicated the method to a Mr. Hawkwitz, a druggist of London, who for more than twenty years prepared phosphorus from urine and sold it to all the natural philosophers of Europe for a fancy price. Urine remained the sole source of this exciting element until Scheele in 1775 developed a method of preparing it from bones. In 1801, however, Fourcroy was still able to recommend that urine might be an economical source of phosphorus in houses where a great number of persons lived and where urine could be collected by means of troughs.

IT WAS in the seventeenth century that chemistry began to develop as a quantitative science. Alchemy had been a mixture of empiric observation with astrology, mysticism, and religious philosophy, and it had operated invariably in a cloak of secrecy and expressed itself in esoteric symbolism. Now the chemists, disregarding the stars and all transcendental implications, worked more or less openly and confined themselves to the composition and transmutation of what seemed to be the fundamental substances of nature. Urine was to supply much of the basic knowledge of the composition and transmutation of the substance of living animals.

The quantitative study of urine properly begins in the seventeenth century, when van Helmont accurately determined in 1655 the specific gravity of urine by weighing it in a glass vessel with a narrow neck and known to hold a certain weight of rainwater; he thus noted the dilute nature of the fluid excreted after the ingestion of water and the concentrated nature of that excreted after absention from water and in fever, observations that took much of the force out of the examination of random samples by uroscopists. Bellini showed that changes in taste, color, and limpidity could be reproduced by careful evaporation and redilution with water, thus taking much of the mystery out of its variable composition; while the physiologist Haller quantitatively related the changes in concentration to variations in the intake of water or fluid meals.

The alchemists had long used urine or one or another of its

derivative salts in their search for the philosopher's stone, but the chemists were to put it to an alchemy of another sort. Before the end of the eighteenth century they had prepared from it a variety of inorganic salts: sodium chloride, potassium chloride, ammonium chloride, ammonium phosphate, sodium phosphate, sodium acid phosphate, magnesium phosphate, sodium sulfate, calcium sulfate, calcium acid phosphate, triple phosphate of soda and ammonia (microcosmic salt), magnesium ammonium phosphate, and sodium dihydrogen phosphate—a notable list when one considers that few earthy substances had as yet yielded to analysis or chemical transformation.

It was generally known that the urine of man typically turned syrup of violets red, indicating the presence of an acid, whereas that of herbivorous animals turned this indicator blue or green, indicating an alkaline reaction; and now as the phosphate salts came under examination, attention was turned to variations in the acidity of the urine, preparing the way for modern studies of acid-base balance.

Though phosphate is important in the usefulness of urine as fertilizer, the nitrogen of its urea, ammonia, and other compounds is of no less significance in this respect, and urine as a source of nitrogen supplies us with an heroic example of what man in his ingenuity, when hard pressed, can achieve. I refer to the sad plight of Selma, Alabama, during the Civil War. To prepare saltpetre for the manufacture of gunpowder, the Confederates had to resort to all sorts of devices such as leaching the earth from old smokehouses, barns, and caves, and making artificial beds of all kinds of nitrogenous refuse, having agents for this purpose in every town and city. The agent at Selma was particularly energetic and enthusiastic, and advertised in the newspaper as follows:

> The Ladies of Selma are respectfully requested to preserve the chamber lye collected about the premises for the purpose of making nitre. A barrel will be sent around daily to collect it.
>
> JOHN HARROLSON
> *Agent Nitre Mining Bureau*

This came to the attention of a poet in the Confederate Army who responded lyrically as follows:

HE ADVERTISED FOR CHAMBER LYE

John Harrolson! John Harrolson! You are a wretched creature.
You've added to this bloody war a new and awful feature.
You'd have us think while every man is bound to be a fighter,
The ladies, bless the dears, should save their P for nitre.

John Harrolson! John Harrolson! Where did you get the notion
To send your barrel 'round the town to gether up the lotion?
We thought the girls had work enough making shirts and kissing,
But you have put the pretty dears to patriotic pissing.

John Harrolson! John Harrolson! Do pray invent a neater
And somewhat more modest mode of making your saltpetre;
For 'tis an awful idea, John, gunpowdery and cranky,
That when a lady lifts her shift she's killing off a Yankee.

This poem was printed on toilet paper and circulated all over the Confederacy, and a copy was smuggled across the line to fall into the hand of an anonymous Yankee poet who replied,

THE YANKEE'S VIEW OF IT

John Harrolson! John Harrolson! We've read in song and story
How women's tears through all the years have moistened fields of glory,
But never was it told before amid such scenes of slaughter
Your Southern beauties dried their tears and went to making water.

No wonder that your boys are brave, who couldn't be a fighter
If every time he fired his gun, he used his sweetheart's nitre;
And vice-versa, what would make a Yankee soldier sadder
Than dodging bullets fired from a pretty woman's bladder?

They say there was a subtle smell that lingered in that powder,
And as the smoke grew thicker and the din of battle louder,
That there was found to this compound one serious objection,
No soldier boy could sniff it without having an erection.

To return to the ways of peace, Thomas Willis rediscovered the sweet taste of urine in diabetes mellitus and recorded the fact in his great work on the brain (published in 1664 and, incidentally, illustrated by Sir Christopher Wren); a century passed before William Cruickshank, Dr. Johnson's personal physician, showed in 1778 that the sugar in diabetic urine was not milk sugar, and in 1815 Chevreul suggested that this sugar was grape sugar, an identification proved by Bouchardat and Peligot in 1838. After Claude Bernard's studies on glucosuria and liver glycogen in 1878, it became clear that glucose was the major fuel of the body, and it remained only for von Mering and Minkowski's work on glucosuria in depancreatized dogs to initiate the modern era of carbohydrate metabolism.

Creatinine was discovered in human urine, allantoin in the fetal urine of the cow, and hippuric acid in the urine of horses and other herbivora, and Fourcroy and Vauquelin proposed the hydrolysis of the hippuric acid in the urine of cattle as a profitable source of benzoic acid. The amino acids leucine and tyrosine were early isolated from urinary sediments, and cystine, along with the first known purine bodies, xanthine and uric acid, were discovered in urinary calculi, or bezoar stones.

The word "bezoar" is a generic one denoting a variety of concretions found in the gastrointestinal or urinary tracts of mammals. First brought to Europe by the Arabs, bezoars became a universal antidote against disease, those of Oriental origin being most highly valued, and it was to warn innocent persons against fake Oriental bezoars that Du Laurens, physician to Henry IV of France, coined the familiar phrase, "Beware of imitations." Since European color dealers dispensed their pigments in the urinary bladders of oxen and other animals, and the butchers, in preparing these bladders, came upon large numbers of bezoars, the chemists had a good supply for their examination. Sydenham first recognized the coincidence of urinary "gravel" in man with the painful swelling and concretions in the joints of persons suffering from gout, but Fourcroy was the first to give a reasoned account of the deposition of uric acid in the urinary tract and joints of the gouty victims, and also the first to distinguish calcium oxalate and other types of urinary concretions from those formed by uric acid.

MOST important, however, was the discovery of urea and its subsequent synthesis by Friedrich Wöhler in 1828. Viewed in full perspective, there are few more important events in the history of biology, because here was the beginning of the rise of synthetic biochemistry and the decline of vitalism.

I am impelled to enlarge on this subject by the suspicion that there may still be some persons who have never considered the consequences for their immortal souls of Wöhler's synthesis of urea from ammonium cyanate.

It was in the seventeenth century, which saw the end of so much that was old, the beginning of much that was new, that modern physical science was born. That century opened with Galileo in the Chair of Mathematics at Padua from 1592 to 1610, and with Harvey matriculating as a medical student at that same University in 1598. It was in 1600 that Giordano Bruno was burned in Rome because of his lack of ecclesiastic reverence, his skepticism of dogma, and his adherence to the Copernican theory; but it was only nine years later that Kepler formulated two of the cardinal principles of modern astronomy, the laws of elliptical orbits and of equal arcs, and that he first ascribed the oceanic tides to the gravitational attraction of the moon.

It was in 1628 that there was born, near Bologna, Marcello Malpighi, who was to turn Galileo's telescope wrong-end-to and, with the resulting microscope magnifying some thirty-fold, explore the fine structures of animals and plants. Nor let us forget that it was in 1633 that Galileo, at the age of seventy, was humbled by the inquisitors of Pope Urban VIII, who sought to bring the Copernican theory, the telescope, and the freedom of the intellect itself, into disrepute. But the damage had been done, not by the mountains on the moon or the phases of Venus, but behind the inquisitors' backs and in an area which, out of their ignorance, they disdained. When, five years before Galileo was condemned, William Harvey published his *Studies on the Motions of the Heart and Blood*, the sharp wedge of naturalism, which the church so feared might endanger its metaphysic of cosmogony, was driven into the metaphysic of man himself. By reducing the motions of the heart and blood to Galilean mechanics, by so much Harvey reduced man to the category of mundane things, contrary to the basic premise of neo-Jewish-Christain speculation. Harvey was the founder of modern physiology, and it will be physiology and not astronomy or physics that will bring the speculations of theology to an end.

What Harvey started by his naturalistic description of the circulation of the blood was sped on its way by René Descartes, the great mathematician of France, who systematized modern algebra and fused algebra with geometry into analytical geometry. Where Harvey had sought only to exorcise the mystic spirits of Galen out of the heart and to strike a balanced account between the blood in the arteries and the veins, Descartes sought to drive these mystic forces out of the earth, sun, and stars. For these mystic forces he substituted Galileo's motion: the quantity of motion in the universe can neither increase nor decrease, and the only circumstance to be considered is the transfer of motion from one particle to another and the change of its direction. And thus Descartes came upon two laws that served Newton later: the one, that a body unaffected by extraneous causes perseveres in the same state of motion or rest; and the other, that elementary motion is always in a straight line. He insisted that all laws must be universal, and that scientific progress is to be achieved not by the mere multiplication of facts but rather by searching out the basic laws of nature.

Descartes did not rest with his effort to reduce gravity, heat, and magnetism to the motion of particles, but he turned his argument upon organic life, especially of animals and man. Though his anatomy and physiology were crude and worthless, two of his speculations found their mark. His primary motive, to drive immaterial spirits out of the animal body as they were fast being driven out of physics and astronomy, represented a distinct advance beyond medieval thought, and we still cherish his conviction that a living animal should be regarded as a machine which works in accordance with physical laws. And so it is today that we associate the philosophy of "mechanism," which pervades all biology, with his name. I would define mechanism, as we use the word today, as the belief that all activities of the living organism are to be explained in terms of its component molecular parts.

But to Descartes it seemed that, however adequate a mechanistic explanation might be for plants and animals, it would not suffice for man because man was a thinking, rational being; and to meet this need he retained Aristotle's "rational soul," coupling it to the mechanical body through the pineal gland which was conveniently located close to the brain and for which there was no other demonstrated function. Here, in the pineal gland, the soul meets matter; here, receiving passively the data of the senses, it cogitates upon them; and here, through its volition, it bends the body to its will. And thus it is that we speak of Cartesian dualism because, in Descartes' scheme, body and soul, or as we more commonly say, body and mind, were split asunder by the supposition that the soul (or mind) exists independently of the body.

Cartesian dualism is a very comforting philosophy and one now widely held in the West despite the fact that it has no verifiable foundation at the very point where some foundation is most needed—namely, evidence for the independent existence of what is called soul or mind. Paradoxically, most arguments for Cartesian dualism have taken the form of an attack upon Cartesian mechanism: if one can prove that the body is *not* a self-sufficient mechanism, dualism in some form or other becomes, by so much, more plausible, if not inevitable.

Challenges to Cartesian mechanism have assumed a variety of forms, but they may be lumped together under the term vitalism. The use of immaterial, spiritistic or vital forces to explain natural phenomena is a device as old as man himself, but vitalism in the scientific sense is a relatively recent invention. Its roots go back to the seventeenth century, and essentially to Georg Ernst Stahl, the author of the chemical doctrine of phlogiston, who held that the phenomena of life are attributable to a "sensitive soul" which works directly on chemical processes; an immortal, spiritual, and immaterial principle coming from afar and, at death, returning to whence it came. But vitalism also had its origin in a reaction against the efforts of Descartes and other mechanists to explain physiological phenomena in grossly mechanical terms, and their failure to do so. There were many who held that a mystic power, a *force hypermécanique*, neither physical nor chemical in its nature, was active in living organisms, and here alone, and that this vital force was a necessary condition for vital phenomena.

Then Galilean-Cartesian mechanism, which had been so productive in astronomy, physics, and chemistry, began to spread. Between 1772 and 1777 Lavoisier discovered oxygen and, in collaboration with the astronomer Laplace, demonstrated the nature of combustion and in a rough way laid the foundations for the First Law of Thermodynamics: that throughout the multiple transformations of nature energy is neither created nor destroyed. Then the science of biochemistry, derivative of physiology, began to extend Cartesian mechanism to the molecular phenomena of life, against the opposition of the vitalists who held that man, the conscious and self-conscious creature, and all other living things in the so-called "organic kingdom," were imbued with a mystic, vital force that transcended air and fire and water and the stuffs of inorganic earth.

Until urea drew the attention of the chemists. This compound had been separated from urine in an impure form by Von Rouelle in 1773, and a few years later the French chemist Fourcroy and his colleague, Vauquelin, developed a quantitative method for its determination and showed that it was present in the urine of all animals which they studied. Fourcroy was the first to call it *urée*, and he speaks of it as "a most exalted animal matter . . . compounded by vital action."

Here, in Fourcroy's expression, "a most exalted animal matter . . . compounded by vital action," is epitomized the viewpoint of the year 1800, and the great division between the "organic" and "inorganic" world. Alchemy and chemistry had long operated on mercury, potash, sal ammoniac, sulfur, quicklime, and of course on all the important metals such as gold, silver, tin, copper, and iron; but these substances were contained in rocks and earth devoid of life, whereas urea, like other compounds of animal or vegetable origin, was elaborated in the living organism by this mysterious "vital force."

Urea was the first such organic compound to be separated in a relatively pure state and to have its elementary composition determined in terms of the ammonia and carbon dioxide of which it is composed. Because its innermost secrets were known, it was the prize jewel of organic chemistry, still muddling along as that science was in impure syrups, extractives, albuminoids, proteids, and essences. Then, in 1828, the 28 year old Wöhler from Heidelberg, who had been diverted by Berzelius from the lucrative practice of medicine into a poorly paid position as a teacher of organic chemistry in a newly established technical school in Berlin, prepared urea from a solution of inorganic ammonium cyanate by the simple expedient of letting the solution stand for a few days in the sunlight, and the "vital force," the mystic alchemy of life so precious to man and his self-consciousness, was reduced to the dull category of molecular reaction, and the distinction between the inorganic and the organic kingdoms was relegated to the realm of rhetoric, except in our institutions of higher learning where the separation serves now to divide the chemical curriculum into a lesser and a larger part. Before the end of the nineteenth century chemists had synthesized organic compounds by the tens of thousands, outdoing nature herself in versatility. More scientific papers have probably been published on urea, however, than on any other organic compound.

AND urea supplied another important key to the mystery of life. Lavoisier had shown that the burning of the candle and of the mouse amount to much the same thing: fuel plus oxygen end up in carbon dioxide and ashes. Where urinary glucose was to supply the key to the metabolism of carbohydrate, urea was to supply the key to the metabolism of protein, and derivatively, to the metabolism of fat. The mysteries of the warmth of the body, its muscular movements, its growth, and all its related activities, had been pushed, so to speak, over the threshold of description.

Within a decade of Wöhler's synthesis of urea, animals and plants had been shown to be composed of cells that reproduce by cellular division; and within two decades Pasteur had refuted the doctrine of the spontaneous generation of life and given a naturalistic explanation for the conversion of grape juice into wine, and for the causation of disease. By 1868 Huxley was able to speak of protoplasm as the physical basis of life, and to emphasize that if the phenomena exhibited by water are its properties, so, too, the phenomena presented by protoplasm are *its* properties, and an understanding of both is to be sought in "molecular physics," as he called it.

By the middle of the century vitalism, in most areas of biology, was in full retreat. The effort to explain physiological phenomena by reference to the same laws as operate in the domain of inorganic nature was first expounded fully by the German physiologist Carl Ludwig in his *Text-book of Human Physiology* (1852–1856), and shortly the whole of biology, or almost the whole of it, was transformed into what Sir Michael Foster in 1885 called "molecular physiology," by which he meant Cartesian mechanism at the molecular level.

AS WE look over the biological sciences today we find that vitalism is no longer popular; it is in disfavor in both botany and zoology; it has no toe hold in the whole domain of organic chemistry, in metabolism, enzymology, muscular contraction, digestion, kidney function, nervous conduction, reflex action, or in the more elemental operations of the brain. Vitalism finds no place in our theories of the causation of disease, or in our theories of inorganic and organic evolution. Nor even in embryology, which has been the most fertile ground for vitalistic speculation from the time of Aristotle on. The achievements of molecular physiology in the last few decades are so numerous and so profound in significance that we ourselves are sometimes startled by the rapidity of its progress. Only in one area does vitalism retain a quasi-respectable position, and that is in the area which perplexed Descartes, namely, the problem of consciousness. Cartesian dualism, which sees consciousness as a function of something called mind, and mind as existing apart from matter, still has its scientific proponents here and there, but their number is diminishing in each decade. A search of some two dozen recent textbooks of physiology fails to find a single one which contains the word "mind" in the index. Few of these textbooks contain the word "consciousness" in the index, either, but the parting of the ways has come: no textbook of physiology published after this decade will be worthy of the name unless it contains an adequate treatment of the physiological basis of consciousness at the neuronal level.

Why this change of opinion, as between the seventeenth and twentieth century, in respect to the nature of man? And of consciousness? Chiefly because the development of molecular physiology, on the one hand, and of evolutionary theory, on the other, have rendered the dualistic hypothesis wholly untenable. Most biologists are forced by the evidence to accept man as a creature of earth, and consciousness as a phenomenon of protoplasm dependent on the elaborate organization of the nervous system. Elsewhere I have argued that consciousness has been evolved in the animal kingdom as an adaptive device which binds one instant to another and thus permits the predatory animal to pursue, capture, and consume its prey, and to retreat in safety from other predatory animals before it itself is eaten. The vertebrate brain is a most wonderful mechanism for wresting freedom out of necessity, and the vertebrate brain attains its greatest efficiency in man. But the evolution of the vertebrate brain parallels the evolution of the neuromuscular system, and the evolution of the neuromuscular system in all its complexities has been made possible by the evolution of an internal environment of constant composition. I need not emphasize that this internal environment is in effect synthesized by the kidneys, that every drop of this environment is resynthesized by the kidneys some sixteen times a day. Historically and physiologically, consciousness and urine formation are inseparable.

The year 1801 saw the publication of Fourcroy's *General System of Chemical Knowledge*, a work which in the English translation of 1804 ran to eleven large volumes. This was the first work of its kind, and almost one entire volume was devoted to the composition of urine. Where hitherto chemists had seen in this fluid an "attenuated oil, the ultimate products of the efforts of life and of the motion of the organs," Fourcroy speaks of it as neither a unity nor an end in itself; several different substances are evacuated at the same time, each presenting a particular advantage to the organism in its discharge. Thus he adumbrates the role of the urine in the regulation of what, six decades later, Claude Bernard so aptly called our "internal environment." Man is indeed one of the most intricate mechanisms ever to exist on earth, to turn the good red wine of Shiraz into urine, and to turn necessity into freedom. It is a fair epitome to say that in great measure man is what he is because his urine is what it is. Now that the story can be told of how man has evolved into his high estate, the elaboration of what Fourcroy would have called a "perfected urine" is seen to be the very foundation of his evolution. Fourcroy in 1801 dismissed the philosopher's stone as a figment of alchemical imagination, but in his last volume he wrote:

> The urine of man is one of the animal matters that have been the most examined by chemists, and of which the examination has at the same time furnished the most singular discoveries to chemistry, and the most useful application to physiology, as well as the art of healing. This liquid, which commonly inspires men only with contempt and disgust, which is generally ranked amongst vile and repulsive matters, has become, in the hands of the chemists, a source of important discoveries, and is an object in the history of which we find the most singular disparity between the ideas which are generally formed of it in the world, and the valuable notion which the study of it affords to the physiologist, the physician, and the philosopher.

9.

The Biology of Consciousness

This lecture, delivered in 1957 at the Downstate Medical Center of the State University of New York, well illustrates Smith's method of inquiry into any subject that interested him. Starting with a painstaking collection of facts in historical perspective, he critically selected the contributions of the best minds and indicated those aspects that had been examined and established by the scientific method. Utilizing all available information, and adding his own interpretation and his own conviction, he customarily avoided dogmatism by pointing out with great care what could reasonably be accepted as proven and what required further confirmation.

In 1637 an obscure and somewhat peculiar Frenchman, living at the time in Holland, rested his pen on the last page of a manuscript destined to become one of the great landmarks of philosophy.

Peculiar in many ways: born in 1596 into the demi-noblesse of Touraine, enjoying exceptional social privileges and a good education by the best of Jesuit scholars, he early abandoned the companionship of men, except for a very few friends, in favor of the companionship of his own thoughts. Small in stature, faint of voice, and with a big head and projecting brow, prominent nose, eyes wide apart, black hair coming down almost to his eyebrows, and dressing usually in black, he must have presented what we would call a pedantic appearance. As a youth he possessed feeble health and acquired a life-long habit of remaining in bed throughout the morning in order to give himself over to reflection—his was unquestionably the most profitable lifetime on record, so large a part of which was spent in bed.

His systematic education was limited to nine years at the celebrated Jesuit College of La Flèche, where between the ages of ten and nineteen he acquired a mastery of Latin and enthusiasm for mathematics. He spent the next four years in Paris where mathematics and music held his interest, and at the age of twenty-two he decided to travel in order to read for himself "in the great book of the world" because, as he said later, his greatest satisfaction came "not from attending to the proofs of others but from discovering them by my own efforts." In those days travelling was most conveniently furthered by soldiering, and so he joined the army of Prince Maurice of Nassau, and a little later the Bavarian Military Service; and during nights of meditation as a soldier, at the age of twenty-three he came upon what he called "the foundations of a marvellous science," a new science in which lines and curves were given mathematical dimensions characterized by "constants" and "variables," and on the foundations of which he was later to fuse geometry and algebra into analytical geometry. A year more and he speaks of a "marvellous discovery," apparently his first glimpse of the nature and possibilities of a new *method* for discovering truth, or that which is so certain that it is beyond all possibility of doubt, a method which was to be elaborated in his *Discourse on the Method of Rightly Conducting the Reason and of Seeking for Truth in the Sciences.* For an interval in this period he returned to Paris, but no society except his own possessed many charms for him; and when in 1629 a graceless friend disturbed him in bed at eleven o'clock in the morning, he fled in annoyance to Holland where he could lie in bed as long as he wished, and walk the streets a stranger among strangers. Here he spent most of twenty years, living in thirteen different towns and at twenty-four different addresses known only to a few confidants among the priesthood, speculating on astronomy, optics, anatomy, and medicine, and writing letters and essays which gained for him such fame that he was ultimately enticed to become advisor on philosophy and politics to the twenty-year-old Queen Christina of Stockholm, and to his death. René Descartes died in 1650, at the age of fifty-four, of inflammation of the lungs aggravated, so it has been said, by getting out of bed at five o'clock in the morning in Sweden's January weather in order to give the young Queen her daily instruction in philosophy.

Though not the first to be written, the first of Descartes' essays to be published was his *Discourse*, which appeared in 1637, and which is at once an intellectual autobiography and a system of philosophy. The basis of this philosophy was simply this: there is a truth which is worthy of being called such; and the guiding rule by which a man may find it is to give no assent to any proposition unless its credibility is so clear and distinct that it cannot be doubted. "I did not imitate the sceptics," Descartes wrote, "who doubt only for doubting's sake, and pretend to be always undecided; on the contrary, my whole intention was to arrive at a certainty, and to dig away the drift and the sand until I reached the rock or clay beneath." Thomas Henry Huxley called this rule "the first commandment of science." It consecrated doubt, which in the seventeenth century was a grievous sin, and enthroned it in that high place among man's primary duties where it has ever since been honored.

But he who searches after truth finds life full of delusions.

Authority may err; testimony may be false or mistaken; unguided reason leads us to endless fallacies; memory is as tricky as hope; the very senses sometimes misinform us; dreams are real as long as they last, and what we call the reality of waking may be only another long and restless dream. It is conceivable that some powerful and malicious demon may have deluded me into believing that which is not. Of what, then, can I be certain? Only that I possess the power of awareness, and hence the capacity to think. I may be deceived in everything else, but I cannot doubt that I am doubting. Hence Descartes started from what he thought to be a self-evident and irreducible axiom: *Cogito ergo sum*—"I think, therefore I am."

Philosophers are agreed that the Cartesian argument is less an irreducible axiom than a logically faulty aphorism, nor does it afford the firm bedrock of truth which he sought. At best, it gives certitude only to the conscious experience, and fails when consciousness seeks to go beyond itself, to postulate that which is external to the immediate conscious experience. It is incapable of certifying the judgments by which we can pass from immediate experience to that which is not immediate, and thus affords no instrument for the acquisition of knowledge, and in the end it proves unreliable for the conscious experience itself because the *cogito* rests upon the notion of "self," which is a tentative and fallible interpretation of sense and not an irreducible statement regarding real existence. In *Cogito ergo sum* consciousness only contemplates itself without learning anything about itself.

In extending his philosophy Descartes argued from the verb *cogito* that thinking belongs to a thinking substance, a *res cogitans*, which not only has other thoughts but remains the same from day to day. Avoiding the material implication of *res*, we paraphrase Descartes and speak of "mind" as that which directly apprehends its own thoughts. Against mind he set a second thing, *res extensa*, or matter, which is characterized by the property of extension (of occupying space), whereas mind does not have extension (i.e., does not occupy space). Matter is passive, mind is active. Because it occupies space, matter is divisible *ad infinitum* (since nothing is so small that God cannot further subdivide it); while mind is indivisible. Matter is constrained, dependent; mind is unconstrained, independent in respect to both belief and action. Thus the definitions of matter and mind consist of negations applicable to the other.

Since matter cannot think, and thought cannot have the property of extension, they can meet only in some greater unity whose thoughts are the thoughts of men, and whose other thoughts are things in themselves. Why Descartes identified this greater unity as God and how he sought to prove the existence of God by independent arguments need not concern us here. We need only note that where Spinoza (1632–1677) and Malebranche (1638–1675), independently proceeding along different paths from Descartes, accepted that it is God who really thinks in the apparent thoughts of man, Hobbes (1588–1679) and Hume (1711–1776) asserted that man, in thinking, has created God.

THE CARTESIAN dualism of matter and mind is still the nominal philosophy with most uncritical persons in the western world, and also the reasoned position of a few critical philosophers and scientists; but it is not for his dualism that I discuss Descartes, but rather for another of his contributions to philosophy which, for us as scientists, is of far greater importance, namely his doctrine of mechanism.

Descartes lived in the early and highly productive phase of the seventeenth century revolution in science. It had been around 1590 that Galileo had developed his principles of dynamics at the University of Pisa; by 1611 the founder of modern physics had constructed a telescope magnifying distant objects about thirty-fold and by means of it had discovered Jupiter's satellites, the mountains on the moon, the rotation of the sun, and the phases of Venus—existence of the last, Copernicus had said, would prove his heliocentric theory. Kepler had previously reduced the motions of the planets to elliptical orbits which had the sun as one of their foci, but he had these planets moved in their courses by spirits or genii, and he cautiously left the question of the earth's mobility undiscussed. By the time Descartes left La Flèche, however, the Copernican theory had come to be accepted by most savants in France. The essence of Galileo's work on the motion of physical bodies was the invariability between cause and effect, the immediate consequence of which was to reduce the swinging pendulum and falling body from mystical metaphysics to mathematical mechanics; while his *Sidereus Nuncius* (1610) reduced the Milky Way and great nebulae to congeries of stars, the planets to Galilean moving bodies, the moon to a mountainous satellite, and the earth to seeming insignificance.

Descartes now sought to drive all occult forces out of both earth and heaven by replacing them with Galilean motion. Nature, he said, is essentially dead matter with no will, no self-determination, no force of its own; it possesses only motion, and the quantity of motion in the universe can neither increase nor decrease; the only circumstance to be considered is the transfer of motion from one particle to another, or a change in its direction (foreshadowing the First Law of Thermodynamics). Motion itself is subject to geometric description by lines and curves, and thus he came upon two laws which had scarcely been apprehended by Kepler and Galileo, but which served Newton later: the one, that a body unaffected by extraneous causes perseveres in the same state of motion or rest; and the other, that elementary motion is always in a straight line. Matter is uniform in character and has infinite extension: it fills the infinite universe, and true empty space, as distinct from material extension, is a fictitious abstraction. All motion is therefore relative, one body with respect to another, and there is no fixed point in space and nothing is really at rest (thus adumbrating a theory of relativity of space and motion). Since one particle cannot move without simultaneous movement of all other particles, motion takes the form of whirlpools or vortices which vary in size and velocity and continuously interlace dynamically with each other to interchange their motion. Long before Newton advanced the corpuscular theory, he propounded the rectilinear (though instantaneous) propagation of light, implicitly, at least, by vibration. He first used the prism to analyse white light; he made the first slit spectroscope; and he is credited with the discovery of the law of sines of refraction and in this connection gave the first accurate, naturalistic explanation of the rainbow. He developed principles for the improvement of spectacles, magnifying glasses, telescopes, and microscopes. He probably invented the iris diaphragm, the drawtube, the parabolic mirror and hyperbolic condenser, and spelled out the theoretical aspects of useful aperture, magnifying power, focal length and spherical aberration. From his anatomical studies, in which he had repeatedly dissected the eyes of animals, he formulated the principles of physiological optics with respect to lens contraction, convergence of the eyes, movement of the head, and the apparent size of objects.

The Cartesian cosmogony based on vortices proved to be short-lived (though an ethereal vortex theory of matter was later propounded by Lord Kelvin), but for sheer simplicity, creative imagination and grandeur, it has never been surpassed. Other men in later times had better empirical foundations on which to build.

Descartes did not lean heavily on the experimental method, but neither was he a rationalist in the Scholastic-Aristotelian sense, one for whom the logical syllogism alone can unlock the secrets of the world. Though he held that physics must be guaranteed by metaphysics—that what is fundamental in nature ought to be known before attempting to comprehend its specific features—he conceived that natural philosophy is strictly deductive. However, he recognized the value of observation and experiment and deplored the fact that he had neither the money nor the time to carry them further; but he was not greatly concerned with the works of others—"Here are my books," he is reported to have told a visitor as he pointed to the animals which he was dissecting. Certainly his optics, where he made his most lasting contribution to physics, was arrived at by the use of lenses, and he also investigated many other kinds of phenomena: the weight of air, the laws of sound, and the properties of oils, spirits, common waters and salts. In meteorology he dealt with the properties and formation of fog, clouds, rain, hail, snow, and frost; and he again anticipated Newton in the formulation of the kinetic theory of heat. In physiology he held advanced views on the nature of muscular contraction and the function of sensory and motor nerves; he recognized the brain as the chief organ of consciousness, and held that "trace effects" are left in this organ in the wake of sensory and motor activity.

In short, Descartes stood at the parting of the ways between Scholastic rationalism and scientific empiricism. He was held to the former, perhaps, only by the chains which he had forged for himself in attempting to demonstrate two things—"that material bodies do exist and that they are in nature really and completely different from minds." Lafleur has described scientific empiricism as God's loyal opposition; Descartes was trying to vote both ways at once.

If one were disposed to say, with Descartes, that Descartes himself had a "mind," it would have to be admitted that his mind worked in a thoroughly Cartesian manner, for it persevered in a straight line. He insisted that scientific progress is to be achieved not by the mere multiplication of facts, but rather by searching out the basic laws of nature, and that nature's laws must be universal. Consequently, he was not content to rest with his effort to reduce gravity, heat, magnetism and all inanimate "forces" to the motion of particles, but turned his argument on organic life, particularly of animals and man. As Harvey's work on the heart had supplied the circulation with motive power and served to dispel the mystic spirits of Galenic tradition out of the arteries and veins, and as Galileo had dispelled them from earthly and celestial mechanics, so Descartes now sought to drive all occult forces of whatever kind out of the animal body. All animals, he said, are automata, machines.

It was a period when the mechanical genius of the Continent was fabricating the most extraordinary figurines whose clockwork produced complicated motions simulating those of animals, impressive to the initiated and uninitiated alike. Such automata were to be seen in many shops and amused the guests in many sophisticated salons. A man necessarily uses the analogies of his age when he wishes to make a point, but Descartes, in speaking of animals as machines, was not so naive as to look for springs or wheels in the carcasses which he dissected. The vortices out of which he would have compounded the physical universe, the principle of conservation of motion, the mathematics which he infused into analytical geometry and cosmic mechanics, were anything but naive. He had early taken an interest in medicine, perhaps from a medical grandfather, and at least throughout his residence in Holland he carried on the dissection of animals which he obtained from the slaughter house. He performed many experiments on living animals and was particularly attentive to embryology (or "embryogeny," as he called it) because he saw here one of the most intriguing problems, that of reproduction. He based his hope for the future of this and other medical sciences on the further development of the microscope, which would reveal, he thought, the details of structure in animal organs as the telescope had revealed the details of the sky. Yet his anatomy remained crude, his knowledge of chemistry necessarily nil; and about the only physiology available to him, other than his own observations, was Harvey's work on the circulation. Nevertheless before van Helmont began to write about "ferments" he held that digestion is not to be explained as the operation of a special digestive "faculty" but by the chemical properties of a glandular secretion. Half a century before Willis coined the word reflex he recognized this automatism for what it is; and a century and a half before Cabanis he held that the same principles which operate in the reflex are sufficient to explain cerebral activity.

The full historical significance of these ideas can only be appreciated when viewed against the cultural climate of Descartes' time. Despite the physical and intellectual discoveries of the early seventeenth century, the general atmosphere remained medieval. For the populace generally, astronomy was still enamored of astrology; alchemy was more concerned with the philosopher's stone than with the philosopher's "substance"; and physics was frequently a form of magic. At a more sophisticated level, Aristotelianism as transformed by Scholasticism still sought its explanations in teleological ends or final causes, in purposeful "faculties" for doing this or for being that, and metaphysical "form" and "essence" stood on a parity with "substance" and "causality."

Now Descartes sweeps away not only all occultism but much of Scholastic Aristotelianism, to replace them by self-determining "process" characterized only by diversity of composition and by the arithmetical, geometrical, and kinematic concourse of parts. He has no atoms and molecules, but his vortices serve him just as well. The plant, the animal, and all the material part of man are, he says, differentiated from inanimate matter in no essential respect except in exhibiting "greater complexity in the disposition and function of (their) parts and greater heterogenity among (their) constituent corpuscles," a statement which, to the Schoolmen, was twice heretical because it was both anti-Christian and anti-Aristotelian.

The nerves, he said, transmit sensations to the brain, and from the brain to the organs of motion; the beating of the heart, the digestion of food, the respiration of those who sleep, and many of our actions when we are awake, walking, talking, singing, are performed without conscious intention, and sometimes even contrary to the latter. Then what proof is there that animals are other than intricate machines that eat without pleasure, cry without pain, desire nothing and know nothing, and only simulate consciousness in what is really a series of unconscious activities? If consciousness and selfhood be allowed to animals, where can the line be drawn between animals and man? Or between plants and animals? How much simpler it is to set man apart from the rest of nature—man is the only one who can say "I think," and therefore he alone possesses consciousness.

Far from being naive in saying that plants and animals are machines, Descartes here initiated the first great revolution to occur in natural philosophy since Aristotle, a revolution less dramatic but for all human affairs far exceeding in its immediate importance that effected by Copernicus. He is commonly called the founder of modern philosophy because he was the first to emphasize that all knowledge must be constantly held subject to critical re-examination, and otherwise laid down the lines on which modern philosophy was to build. With this encomium I certainly have no quarrel, but I find it paradoxical that his greatest positive contribution to philosophy, the doctrine of mechanism, should remain unnamed and unrecognized for its full importance by those who write on the history of philosophy.

OF COURSE I speak as one who is admittedly prejudiced in favor of the doctrine and who discounts all contrary hypotheses which have hitherto been advanced. Challenges to Cartesian mechanism have taken numerous forms, but most of them may be subsumed under the term "vitalism." The use of immaterial spiritistic or vital forces to explain natural phenomena is a device so primitive that it must be as old as human history; the atomistic, pre-Socratic philosophers are notable for being the first men on record who were suspicious of this easy answer. Between Plato's Idealism and Aristotle's "final causes," however, the work of the atomists was undone. Vitalism in the more primitive sense was reintroduced into philosophy from alchemy in the sixteenth century by Paracelsus (1493–1541) in the form of *archei*, to which Paracelsus' disciple, van Helmont (1577–1644), added the *blas humanum*, *blas meteoron*, and other kinds of *blas*, as well as a "sensitive and motive soul" which was unique to man and which resided in the pylorus. Van Helmont's "soul" was mortal, but it served as the instrument of the immortal spirit which used it to direct the major and minor *blas*, ferments, etc., to vital ends. Then in the early eighteenth century Georg Ernst Stahl (1660–1734), who discovered the nonexistent phlogiston, dispensed with the intermediary agents of Paracelsus and van Helmont and held that the phenomena of life are attributable to a "sensitive soul" which works directly on chemical processes, an immortal, immaterial principle coming from afar, and at death returning whence it came. Vitalism in one form or another found support in the reaction against the efforts of Descartes, Borelli, and other mechanists to explain physiological phenomena in grossly mechanical terms, and their initial failure to do so. There were many who held that a mystical power, neither physical nor chemical in nature, was active in living organisms, and here alone, and that this vital force was a necessary condition for vital phenomena.

Then Galilean-Cartesian mechanism, which had been so productive in astronomy, physics, and chemistry, began to spread. Between 1772 and 1777 Lavoisier demonstrated the true nature of combustion, and the first half of the nineteenth century saw the law of conservation of energy applied to the living organism by Mayer, Helmholtz, and other early students of metabolism. In 1828 Wöhler synthesized the organic compound, urea, and shortly thereafter chemists began to synthesize organic compounds by the hundreds. By 1839 it had been established that all animals and plants are composed of cells that reproduce by cell division; and within two decades Pasteur had refuted the doctrine of the spontaneous generation of life and given a naturalistic explanation for the conversion of grape juice into wine, and for the causation of disease. The antivitalistic movement in physiology gained impetus from the work of Johannes Müller, Helmholtz, du Bois-Reymond, and Claude Bernard, but the first effort to explain a complicated physiological process by reference to the same laws as operate in the domain of inorganic nature was made by the German physiologist, Carl Ludwig, in his theory of urine formation published in 1842, and the principle was expounded more fully by Ludwig in his *Lehrbuch der Physiologie des Menschen* published between 1852 and 1856. By midcentury Karl Vogt (*Physiologische Briefe*, 1845–46), Jacob Moleschott (*Kreislauf des Lebens*, 1852) and Friedrich Karl Büchner (*Kraft und Stoff*, 1855) had sought to construct a metaphysic compatible with the rapidly changing picture of the world. The severest blows of all to vitalism came with the applications of the Malthusian principle of natural selection to organic evolution by Charles Darwin (*Origin of Species*, 1859), and the application of the evolutionary principle to man himself by Thomas Henry Huxley (*Man's Place in Nature*, 1863). At the opening of this century, the whole of biology, or almost the whole of it, had been transformed into what Sir Michael Foster in 1885 presciently called "molecular physiology," which to me means Cartesian mechanism at the molecular level.

As we look over the biological sciences today we find that vitalism is no longer popular; it is in disfavor in botany and zoology; it has no toe hold in the whole domain of organic chemistry, in metabolism, enzymology, muscular contraction, digestion, kidney function, nervous conduction, reflex action, or in the more elementary operations of the brain. Vitalism finds no place in our theories of the causation of disease, physical or mental, or in our theories of inorganic and organic evolution. Nor even in embryology, which has been the most fertile ground for vitalistic speculation from the time of Aristotle on. With confidence I can assert that Cartesian mechanism, the "molecular physiology" of Sir Michael Foster, is the dominant, almost exclusive philosophy among biologists today. In the last two centuries it has added thirty years to the life expectancy of man and immeasurably increased his health and happiness. Though all these facts together cannot prove the metaphysical validity of molecular mechanism, I may confidently assert that it is the most effective working hypothesis of animate nature that man has ever possessed. I would define mechanism, as we use the word today, as designating the belief that all the activities of the living organism are ultimately to be explained in terms of its component molecular parts. This was Descartes' greatest contribution to philosophy, next to his principle of doubt. Abandon Cartesian mechanism, and you will close up every scientific biological laboratory in the world at once. You will turn back the clock by three full centuries.

IN APPLYING the principle of mechanism, however, Descartes divided nature into two parts. Aristotle had attributed to plants a vegetative soul, and to animals, a vegetative and a sensitive soul; to man he had also attributed a rational soul, since man alone can think. Descartes swept away the Aristotelian vegetative soul and sensitive soul and left animals as but curiously contrived machines which may even utter a note of joy or pain, but with no consciousness or feeling. In the strictest sense they are automata, even if infinitely more complicated in the number and dispositions of their parts than the most elegant contrivances of the clock makers of Amsterdam, Bern and Paris. "The greatest of all prejudices we have retained from our infancy," he said, "is that of believing that the beasts think." To man, however, he left the Aristotelian rational soul, the *res cogitans* or thinking substance, as he called it, or "mind" as contemporary parlance has it, which, except for a series of negatives set antithetically against matter, can only be defined as that which feels and thinks. Since man's material body is an unfeeling, unthinking machine like the body of any animal, Descartes coupled the mind to the body through the pineal gland, which was conveniently located close to the brain and for which there was no other demonstrated function. Here in the pineal gland, the mind meets matter; here, receiving the sensory messages transmitted by the nerves, it cogitates upon them; and here, through its volition, it moves the bodily mechanism to its will.

In retrospect I can understand why Descartes left the rational soul in man. Man was so obviously a rational creature, so obviously capable of modes of behavior which seemed infinitely removed from any parallel to be observed in animals, that the gap was unbridgeable in his time. Half a century had to pass before the apparently transcendental quality of man's rationality could come under the sceptical scalpel of Locke's *Essay on the Human Understanding* (1690), a full century before Hume in his *Treatise on Human Nature* (1739) could deny the reality of mind as something existing apart from individual sensations, two centuries (to 1859 specifically) before the uniqueness of man's behavior could suffer serious challenge in the lysis of a general theory of biological evolution. Descartes' *res cogitans* was a wholly forgivable if not an almost unavoidable error.

My principal reason for spending so much time on Descartes is that, as Aristotle said, "he sees things best who sees them from the beginning." After Descartes, all speculative philosophy is in a sense merely a prolonged commentary on his work. Philosophy branched out along almost as many roads as there were philosophers, and indeed to obtain accredited membership in the guild about all a man had to do was to construct a new System of Philosophy. Though most of us have no impelling desire to join the guild as professionals—as Newton remarked, "Philosophy is such an impertinently litigious lady, that a man has as good be engaged in law suits, as to have to do with her"—every thinking person must, to a certain extent, and however ineptly, take some philosophical position on the do-it-yourself principle, and the historical approach invites us to start with Cartesian dualism.

Personally, I reject it. I reject it on five counts. First, it lacks confirmatory, objective evidence in support of the cardinal premise that something called mind exists independently of matter—matter as defined either by Descartes or by contemporary physics. Second, the interaction of mind and matter presents an internal contradiction by Descartes' own definitions. Third, it has failed to effect the integration or clarification of existing observations on consciousness. Fourth, so far as I can recall, it has failed to be productive of a single new extension of knowledge, which is one of the criteria of a useful hypothesis. And fifth, its history over three centuries is littered with seemingly irreconcilable contradictions of its basic premise with respect to mind—all neuranatomy, neurophysiology, neurochemistry, psychology, and psychiatry have developed as definitive and more or less exact sciences not by its aid but in spite of it, and all, in a multitude of ways, controvert it.

Despite its great diversification, post-Cartesian philosophy follows two general paths, one leading by the way of Berkeley (1685–1753) and Hume (1711–1776) to Kant (1724–1804) and idealism, the other by way of Hobbes (1588–1679) and Lamettrie (1709–1751) to materialism in one form or another.

Berkeleian idealism elevated the Cartesian entity of mind to a transcendental category; matter was held to be a creation of or manifestation of mind. In Berkeleian idealism the world is saved from anarchy only because individual minds are somehow subsumed within and patterned by a universal mind, which Berkeley and idealists generally identify as the mind of God. Logicians from Hume on have argued, cogently enough, that we cannot absolutely prove the reality of matter as something independent of our knowledge of it, but I cannot accept that this negative proposition justifies equating what we call "matter" with what has (fallaciously, I will argue) been called mind. You can prove nothing by a negative. For this reason, and for others, I reject idealism. It was, so I recall, as a rejection of idealism that Margaret Fuller is alleged to have said, "I accept the Universe." I react as did Thomas Carlyle, who remarked, "By God! she'd better."

IN OPPOSITION to dualism and idealism, philosophic materialism denotes broadly any doctrine that denies that something called "mind" exists independently of a material substratum. Materialism has taken a variety of forms, but the tedium of enumeration can be avoided by proceeding immediately to an extreme variant which we will designate as conscious automatism.

Descartes' animals were not conscious automata, they were unconscious automata without any capacity to feel or think. I have suggested that his premise of a rational soul for man was historically unavoidable, but his denial of feeling, of all consciousness, to animals is more difficult to understand. He had vivisected many animals, and he certainly had ample opportunity to observe them asleep or awake, caring for their young, playing with each other or with their masters, and in most of these activities exhibiting the sheer joy of living. It seems that when he introvertedly turned away from the world of men he also cut himself off from the robin's song. The inference is unavoidable that he never lived on intimate terms with a pet dog or cat. Here, in conceiving that animals are unconscious automata, was where he made his great mistake—not that the mistakes of a great man need be any greater than those of lesser men, but they have far greater consequences. Except for denying consciousness to animals, he might have speeded the development of many aspects of biological science and of philosophy by at least a century.

It was largely a consequence of his position on this question that his philosophy of mechanism came to be stated in the other extreme: man and animals alike became conscious automata. Apparently the first to state the doctrine of conscious automatism explicitly was Shadworth Hodgson, who in 1870 denied the causal efficacy of consciousness on philosophic grounds. William James paraphrased Hodgson's position by likening consciousness to the colors on the surface of a mosaic in which the molecular events of the nervous system are the stones; the colors cannot cause any new relations or sequences among the stones because they are but passively attached.

The most notable exposition of conscious automatism, however, is that by Thomas Henry Huxley. Lest in calling Huxley's essay to your attention I may seem to deprecate him, I hasten to say that I look upon him as one of the greatest scientists of a great century, and though he never qualified for a philosopher's union card, I think that time will show that his agnosticism—the withholding of opinion on the unknown until credible evidence is made available—is, or should be, one of the cardinal principles of philosophy. In the light of the rest of Huxley's work, his position on consciousness is all the more difficult to understand.

Huxley was a careful student and ardent admirer of Descartes, and his essay on this philosopher, written in 1870, brings us not only Descartes but a great measure of Huxley himself. Huxley saw the logical fallacies in *Cogito ergo sum*, and also the fallacies in Berkeleian idealism; and, through Hume and Kant, he saw the fallacy of all talk about absolute truth. And in this essay on Descartes he threw both dualism and idealism out of court. "I believe," he said, "that we shall, sooner or later, arrive at a mechanical equivalent of consciousness, just as we have arrived at a mechanical equivalent of heat." He accepted as legitimate materialism "the extension of the conceptions and the methods of physical science to the highest as well as the lower phenomena of vitality"; and he said that he would go along with the materialists so long as they admit that man "is a machine capable of adjusting itself within certain limits."

Then abruptly, four years later at the British Association meeting in Belfast (1874), in his lecture "On the Hypothesis that Animals are Automata and its History" he throws consciousness as a biologically efficacious fact out of court. He starts this lecture, after speaking of Harvey's work, with a discussion of Cartesian mechanism. In defence of going so far back into history, he notes that there is "no more effectual method of clearing up one's own mind on any subject than by talking it over, so to speak, with men of real power and grasp, who considered it from a totally different point of view. The parallax of time helps us to the true position of a conception, as the parallax of space helps us to that of a star." One of Huxley's many admirable characters was the great radius of his philosophic orbit.

Huxley rejected the view that brutes are lacking in consciousness. "The doctrine of continuity," he said, "is too well established for it to be permissible to me to suppose that any complex natural phenomenon comes into existence suddenly, and without being preceded by simpler modifications; and very strong arguments would be needed to prove that such complex phenomena as those of consciousness, first made their appearance in man." Assuming, however, that "molecular changes in the brain are the causes of all the states of consciousness," he asks, "Is there any evidence that these states of consciousness may, conversely, cause those molecular changes [in the brain] which give rise to muscular motion?" And from the behavior of the pithed frog he answers No: "The consciousness of brutes would appear to be related to the mechanism of their body simply as a collateral product of its working, and to be as completely without any power of modifying that working as the steam whistle which accompanies the work of a locomotive engine is without influence upon its machinery." Or in another simile, "The soul stands related to the body as the bell of a clock to the works, and consciousness answers to the sound which the bell gives out when it is struck." ". . . the voluntary acts of brutes [the acts which they desire to perform] are as purely mechanical as the rest of their actions, and are simply accompanied by the state of consciousness called volition . . . Their volitions do not enter into the chain of causation of their actions at all."

Thus having converted the brutes into conscious automata in which feeling (pain, hunger, fear, anger, comfort, joy—the sheer joy of living) may be likened to the meaningless noise of molecular machinery, he had no logical alternative but to relegate the consciousness of man to this same limbo of meaninglessness. Here he argues in part from the reflex actions of man after the spinal cord has been transected, but, more importantly, from the case history reported in a French medical journal in 1874 by Dr. E. Mesnet of l'Hospital Saint-Antoine of a sergeant who had suffered a brain injury in the battle of Bazeilles, and who subsequently alternated between periods of conscious awareness of his acts and periods of highly effective but apparently unconscious automatism. The medical record of this unfortunate individual need not detain us because it presents the not uncommon instance, more familiar to us now, of automatism which may follow epilepsy or traumatic or other injuries of the cerebral hemispheres. After reciting for some ten pages how this man could perform the most complicated activities without presenting any evidence that he was aware of the meaning or consequence of these activities, Huxley concludes, "It seems to me that in men, as in brutes, there is no proof that any state of consciousness is the cause of change in motion of the matter of the organism . . . our mental conditions are simply the symbols in consciousness of the changes which take place automatically in the organism; . . . the feeling we call volition is not the cause of a voluntary act, but the *symbol of that state of the brain* which is the immediate cause of the act."

Fortunately, no one took Huxley's lecture very seriously. Like Huxley himself, men went happily on their way enjoying their great illusion, their "symbol of volition," and their subordinate symbols of sight and sound, taste, smell, touch, pain, hunger, fear, anger, comfort—but nonetheless occasionally reflecting on and trying to foresee the potential consequence of their acts.

One difficulty which weighed heavily with Huxley was that of proving whether Dr. Mesnet's patient was conscious or unconscious: ". . . it is absolutely impossible," he said, ". . . to prove the presence or absence of consciousness in anything but one's own brain, though, by analogy, we are justified in assuming its existence in other men." I hesitate to use the word "prove" in any connection, but I believe that we can go beyond Huxley's reasoning by analogy to reasoning by empirical evidence as to whether consciousness is present or not if we can establish an objective criterion for, or definition of, the conscious state. And I have tried, for whatever the effect may be worth, to formulate such an objective criterion.

Consciousness has been defined as "awareness of environment and of self," but this is circular because "awareness" and "consciousness" mean much the same thing, and the word "self," as here used, is purely subjective in content. By this definition I cannot possibly ascertain whether at this moment you are conscious now or not.

To clear away any possible misconceptions, let me emphasize that I use the word consciousness as a definite noun designating a certain special, and very specialized, activity of the nervous system. For me the word has no transcendental implications. As observed subjectively in myself, consciousness is not an all-or-none phenomenon but varies in intensity, complexity and pattern in the waking state; it waxes and wanes, and for our present purposes we may say that it ceases to exist, utterly disappears, in the dreamless state. When I am dreaming it presents distorted and fragmentary patterns, and (to argue for a moment by inference) its intensity and pattern are subject to many chemical influences such as fever, anoxia, anesthesia, electrical excitation of the brain, and various hallucinogenic drugs. To argue from the neurophysiologist's correlations, its presence or absence in experimental animals and man is generally characterized by certain typical features in the electroencephalogram. The capacity for consciousness is not necessarily modified by removal of large portions of the cerebral cortex, but it has recently been found that sustained arousal from the sleeping state seems to depend on the integrity of structures in the central core of the brain stem, particularly the ascending reticular formation.

This brief paragraph perhaps summarizes all that need be said here about the physiology of consciousness, and I return to the problem of seeking an objective criterion or definition (apart from the electroencephalogram). This can be achieved, I believe, by viewing consciousness, as we view all other activities of the organism, as a product of biological evolution and molecular mechanism. With Huxley, I hold (though not solely for the reason he stated) that the capacity for consciousness did not come into existence suddenly, and that it is not unique to man. On the contrary, I believe that it has been progressively developed in the animal kingdom, more elaborately in some branches than in others, in special relation to the mobility of the organism, to the necessities of going from here to there.

The history of the evolution of the animal kingdom is the history of natural selection operating on a multitude of natural variations, and evolutionary survival represents an essentially balanced account between reproduction and destruction. All animals are dependent on either plants or other animals for food, and from its beginnings the evolution of the animal kingdom has in the main presented a pageant of predator and prey—eat or be eaten! In the Cambrian period, which opened some 550 million years ago, there may have been many soft-bodied animals which are not preserved in the fossil record, but most of those which are preserved possessed destructive mouth parts, prehensile limbs and muscular appendages by which they could pursue their prey, and they were themselves protected from their enemies by chitinous or calcareous exoskeletons. The predatory habit (with obvious exceptions for scavengering, vegetarianism, and parasitism) early became what we may call the typical habitus of the animal kingdom.

It is as a product of natural selection operating on this characteristic manner of living—eat or be eaten—that I see the evolution of consciousness. The mobile, predatory habitus required that the successful animal solve the Cartesian problem of the moving body—its own movements and those of other bodies—not just in two or possibly three dimensions of space, but in four: accurate timing was a *sine qua non*, and accurate timing required the integration of events in the recent past with those of the present moment, thus permitting extrapolation into the future.

The nerve impulses in the sensory and motor fibers, and most of the activities in the spinal reflex, are isolated events of very short duration, generally no longer than a few thousandths of a second. When multiplied by repetitive excitation they serve effectively to bring the skeletal muscles into and out of action, but sensory excitation lasting twenty or fifty milliseconds is not long enough in this world to permit one to go after one's dinner, to capture it, and to retreat again to safety. Moreover, the dinner will generally be moving and is to be caught not at the position where it is first perceived but at some point in its trajectory where it will be some seconds, or even minutes, hence. We can sum up the problem of useful animal mobility by calling it the problem of take-and-put, or of going-from-here-to-there. Given the isolated nature and short duration of neural events in the peripheral nerves and spinal cord, the problems of take-and-put and of going-from-here-to-there could only be solved by fusion of rapid neural events into a continuous or persistent image in which elapsed time appears as dimension.

This fusion is the neurophysiologic essence, as I see it, of the evolution of consciousness. The unique feature of consciousness is its time-binding quality, its persistence beyond milliseconds into seconds or even minutes, carrying a residue of sensory activity from one moment to the next, giving the semblance of continuity to what are, in fact, extremely brief and isolated events in the rest of the nervous system. As Descartes resorted to a contemporary and familiar analogy when he likened animals to machines, I must resort to a contemporary and familiar (if rude) analogy and liken consciousness, or the neurophysiologic mechanism thereof, to a television tube with a so-called long decay-time, such that it continues to glow for a substantial period after it has been excited, and thus affords a continuous rather than a flickering image. Within the parameters of this image the conscious animal can relate past experiences to anticipated future and react accordingly, and with respect to one or another of various possibilities which may be presented simultaneously. Insofar as selectivity enters into this reaction we may speak of "choice" without giving this much-abused word any metaphysical implications; and insofar as any of the alternative modes of action promote the organism's welfare, we may designate the resulting activity as "self-serving."

From the perspective of evolution, then, we may venture tentatively to define consciousness as awareness of environment and of self revealed objectively by self-serving neuromuscular activity which exhibits choice between alternative actions and relates past experience to anticipated future. Whether the time-binding activity extends over a period of seconds or of years is immaterial to the cogency of the definition.

It would be misleading to attempt to argue the biological nature of consciousness from the consciousness of man. He plays the game of take-and-put in a very elaborate form with abstractions, symbols, checkers, chessmen, letters, words, logical and mathematical relations, theories and hypotheses, with all the armamentarium of his culture. And he goes from here to there only after weighing many factors against each other. But these are derivative or secondary exercises which serve more to conceal than to reveal the problem, because "the human thinking machine is the most complicated mechanism on earth."

It would be equally misleading to impute to lower animals, such as the invertebrates, any substantial measure of consciousness as it is observed in man. "Awareness of environment," yes, because the crab and octopus, the butterfly and bee, possess sensory devices imparting to them information about their world (though very different information from that which we obtain), and they engage in integrated time-binding, self-serving action involving extrapolation from the past and present to the immediate future. "Awareness of self," possibly in some lowly measure, but certainly not in the anthropomorphic sense. Even in man the "self" is an impermanent pattern of neural activity which develops slowly after birth and in maturity forms and dissolves in successive instants and never reforms the same.

Accepting the definition, however, it follows that the capacity for consciousness requires the anatomical substratum of a nervous system of some sort, with sensory, integrative, and motor components. One need not look for consciousness in the Protista even though they swim or crawl and show simple positive or negative tropisms; or in degenerate parasitic forms; or the quiescent pupae of insects, or in eggs or sperm or immature embryos. There is no requirement for awareness of the environment or of self in the individual organism until it develops to the point where it possesses the physical freedom to go from here to there and the neuromuscular system necessary for it to take advantage of that physical freedom. Hence, one need not look for consciousness in the entire nonmotorized plant kingdom. Evolution occasionally leaves useless things in its wake, but it does not create them *de novo*.

METAPHYSICS has been defined as man's search for the answer to two questions:

1] What is the world of things we know?

2] How do we know it?

The answer to the first question, What is the world of things we know? I happily leave to the physicist. In 1952 the number of so-called "fundamental particles" was 22; as of this month I find that the number has increased to 28—a fantastic array of entities capable of independent existence, some for only millionths of a second, some for millions of years; and one of them, the neutrino, now experimentally verified, is a masterpiece of anti-Cartesianism. It has zero charge, zero mass at rest, and zero magnetic moment; and hence I suppose we must say that it has zero Cartesian extension so long as it does not move. Yet even the neutrino conforms with the mechanistic pattern of physical particles and the principle of conservation of motion, as recently modified. The neutrino would, one thinks, have pleased Descartes as he lay in bed cogitating on the fact that nothing could be so small that God cannot further subdivide it.

The answer to the second question, How do we know the things which comprise the world? has been obtained, insofar as we have obtained it, through physiology and its allied sciences, which have traced the sequence of molecular events from the peripheral sense organs into the infinite complexities of the central nervous system. How neural events in the central nervous system are translated into subjective awareness remains to be determined. The problem seems to be one for the physiologist to solve, and not the physicist. And the physiologist (though no more than the physicist) is disinclined to seek answers prematurely; he is content for the moment to file the question in his drawer labelled "unknown."

To repeat what I have said elsewhere, this much seems clear: my consciousness resides not in any particular atoms or molecules, because the atoms and molecules that are part of me today, tomorrow will be gone from me to be replaced by others—there is scarcely one that is "mine" for more than a few weeks at most—but rather in their unique and transient patterns of activity as structured in the complexly interconnected nerve cells of my brain, which consists of only a dozen-odd sorts of atoms out of the 92 naturally occuring species in the periodic table.

The bold facts are, however, that for matter to know itself in *me* some ten billion neurons in this brain, and many, many times that number of functional connections, are required to give me the past, the present, and the all too inaccurately divined future that contrive this moment. Five hundred million years of vertebrate evolution have been required to produce this brain; and given the best of fortune, it can know itself in self-awareness for at most three- or four-score years.

Descartes looked forward to the day when the microscope, to the development of which he had contributed so much, would reveal the minute mechanisms of animals and plants. I think that he would be more than pleased to hear a discourse on the mechanism of the brain and its relation to his (falsely so-called) *res cogitans* or thinking substance; and I think that he would remain unruffled in the face of my assertion that his *res cogitans*, unlike the neutrino and contrary to his original notion, has the property of extension, i.e., of occupying space—in my instance competent students of anatomy agree that it almost completely fills my cranial cavity and weighs about 1300 grams.

And now we return to Huxley's problem, can consciousness enter causally into the sequence of neuromuscular activity, or is it merely an epiphenomenon having no causal relation to this activity? I am wholly inclined to agree with Huxley that someday we shall measure the mechanical equivalent of consciousness as an aspect of neural activity, and in this view I must dismiss the description of consciousness as an epiphenomenon. Rather, my consciousness enters into the determination of my activities, my going from here to there, just as do many other physiological processes, the energy equivalents of which are accurately known; and I believe that someday we shall arrive at an understanding of the energy (mechanical) equivalent of these cortical and subcortical activities no less explicit than our present understanding of the energy equivalent of activity in the peripheral nerve.

In the expression "reflex action," the word reflex is an adjectival noun denoting that the action is mediated *by way of the anatomical pathways of the reflex arc*, and not that something called a "reflex" is the "agent" which initiates the action. When, at the conscious level, I assert that I do something out of my "volition," am I saying other than that my action now includes the three parameters of consciousness: (1) awareness of my environment and my "self"; (2) the possibility of choice between alternative actions; and (3) that it relates past experience to anticipated future?

You very kindly *asked* me to address you on this occasion, so I *extrapolated* from the past into the future as I could foresee it and *thought* out what I wanted to say; I now *anticipate* that you are growing tired of the discussion; I *choose* not to tire you unduly; and, as a *self-serving* action, I bring my peroration to an end . . . If you please, by my volition.

10.

"Consciousness at the Keyboard"

It was inevitable that a mind so curious about the world would take an interest in music. Smith derived deep satisfaction from writing and playing his own compositions. One of his most admired writings is the study, here reprinted, of the pianist's hands in motion. No one but a physiologist could have performed this analysis of bone and sinew at the keyboard; and no physiologist but a musician, possibly, would have tried.

A MAN IS MOMENTARILY, however belatedly, conscious of his immediate voluntary actions, but the conscious record is sometimes so faint and transient that it is as readily forgotten as a dream and he finds himself behaving like an automaton. He may spend a busy day at the office engaged in seemingly intelligent conversation with his secretary and a dozen associates, answer the telephone, read his mail and write letters, and then drive five miles through congested traffic and stop for innumerable red lights on his way to dinner, without remembering one-tenth of his voluntary and (at the time) fully conscious actions; and by the time he has had dinner he may have completely forgotten where he parked his car, if indeed he can recall whether he drove the car uptown. These consciously directed but unconsciously mediated actions are called "automatisms." (Such automatisms must be clearly distinguished from instincts, which are genetically predetermined, specific, stereotyped, and invariable patterns of behavior characteristic of a given species, the acquisition of which does not depend on learning, as does the acquisition of all automatisms. Man has relatively feeble instincts as compared with the lower animals, and these are dominant in his behavior only in the first months and years of life.)

In the most complicated patterns of voluntary activity consciousness may play a very limited role. A good example for discussion is the piano, because the most intricately and perfectly co-ordinated of all voluntary movements in the animal kingdom are those of the human hand and fingers, and perhaps in no other human activity do memory, complex integration, and muscular co-ordination surpass the achievements of the skilled pianist. In the early stages of learning, the novice strikes each note only after conscious deliberation. In effect he says to himself, "Now I will strike this note, now I will strike that one–" until, as he acquires competence, he finds himself anticipating the future. "After I strike this note then I will strike that one . . ." and so on until he gains command both of his fingers and of the score, and the conscious contribution can be reduced to, "Now I will play this movement generally *piano* and *largo*, because I think that is the way that the composer meant it to be played." A musician who has to concentrate on the mechanical details of his music is not expert. With competence he gives thought only to his interpretation. At the orchestral cue, his fingers spell out the harmony and rhythm so faultlessly that he has scarcely a sense of playing the smashing chords and complicated arpeggios, remembering each note for only a fraction of a second (though let him strike a wrong one and he will remember it!) as he gives attention to the smooth interchange of melody between the orchestra and his instrument, and to the thousand and one matters affecting interpretation. In retrospect he is perhaps more keenly aware of the quality of his performance, which is just as complicated a matter as the mechanics of the performance itself, than of the innumerable mechanical details.

Sir James Paget, a noted nineteenth-century British surgeon, once timed a friend, Mlle. Janotha, while she played a *presto* by Mendelssohn, "one of the fastest pieces of music known to her." (This was presumably the '*Perpetuum mobile*,' OP. 119.) She played 5995 notes in four minutes and three seconds, or more than twenty-four notes per second. Recognizing that each note required at least two voluntary movements–flexion and extension–as well as lateral movements in either direction, Sir James estimated that not less than 72 distinct motor actions were required per second, each accurately timed and exercised with judgment. (This calculation takes no account of the movements of the hand, forearm, arm, and foot.)

The Mendelssohn *presto* does not, however, present the most complex kinds of difficulties that are to be encountered in piano music, difficulties that separately and collectively serve to retard the over-all speed set by the limitations of either the keyboard or the fingers. As demonstrated to the writer by Dr. David Saperton, a five-note "blind trill," or tremolo, with each hand playing alternate notes, can be played at a rate close to 80 notes per second. This is not necessarily the greatest speed, though it is one compatible with musical rendition. At this level, speed may be limited by the action of the piano, since the reisitance offered by the key, the depth to which the key must be depressed, the length of the lever from tip to fulcrum and fulcrum to hammer, the speed of rebound of key and hammer, and other mechanical features, all contribute to the limitations imposed by the keyboard itself. A greater speed can possibly be achieved with certain types of electronic organs where mere contact between the finger and the key may suffice to produce a tone, and it is conceivable that, per finger, rapid chromatic passages on the violin may exceed in speed the fastest possible action on the piano.

A rapidly executed trill is, however, only one of the innumerable movements that a musician must execute, which include the wide spacing of keys to be struck in succession by a single finger, and hence wide lateral displacements of both the finger and the hand or arm, as well as forward or backward displacements of the finger or hand in passing from the white to the black keys and back. Each of these motions requires time and offers an additional impediment to speed; and consequently the introduction of harmony and melody, the compounding of thematic passages, of two or more voices, and of connected phrases, all serve to slow the music.

Fingering reaches what is perhaps its greatest complexity in the works of Leopold Godowsky (1870–1938). For example, in this composer's "Badinage," Chopin's "Black Key" Etude (OP. 10, NO. 5) is alternated with his "Butterfly" Etude (OP. 25, NO. 9) in the right and left hand, respectively, with preservation of the original melodies; both hands are working furiously throughout and operating against all the resistance factors enumerated above. As recorded by Dr. Saperton for Command Performance Records (NO. 1202), this work, containing 1680 independent finger movements, requires 80 seconds, or involves an average of 21 notes per second. The execution of this work is not made easier by the constant use of two notes against three (polyrhythms), sometimes with two in the left hand and three in the right, and sometimes the reverse. There is no doubt that Godowsky's "Badinage" is far more difficult to play than the Mendelssohn *presto*, as is attested by the fact that the former, like much of Godowsky's music, is rarely heard in public performance, and to the writer's knowledge his most difficult compositions have not been recorded by anyone except Dr. Saperton.

In this same category is Godowsky's arrangement of Strauss's "Artists' Life" waltz which, in the original, has a different theme for each movement. Godowsky often fuses two or three of these themes into a simultaneous pattern while maintaining a three-four rhythmic motif in the bass, and when in one place a vertical or harmonic factor is added, there are five factors in simultaneous execution, played with such individual emphasis that the separate themes can be distinguished. Here the achievement not only involves finger speed and complex motions of the hands, but the control of accent on individual notes interspersed throughout the generally lively pattern.

Chopin is well known for his complicated passages, among which musicians frequently mention the *presto* from the B flat minor Sonata. This passage has 1760 notes, and, as played for Victor Recordings by either Sergei Rachmaninoff or Artur Rubinstein, requires 1 minute and 16 seconds. This is a speed of 23 notes per second. Chopin's Etude OP. 25, NO. 11 in A minor (the "Winter Wind" Etude), exclusive of the first four slow measures, has 2043 notes in the right hand and 1081 in the left. In Dr. Saperton's recording (Command Performance Record NO. 1203), this work requires 3 minutes and 1 second, a speed of 11 notes per second for one hand, and 16 notes per second for both—the speed is here limited by wide excursions of the hand and a relatively slow bass, but the over-all pattern is one of great complexity.

Schumann's C major Toccata, OP. 7 (Columbia Record ML 4375), has 6266 notes and, as played by Simon Barère without the repeat, requires 4 minutes and 20 seconds—a speed of 24.1 notes per second. The third movement of Weber's Sonata NO. 1 in C major, OP. 24, contains 4700 notes and was played for the writer by Mr. Randol Masters in 3 minutes and 50 seconds, or at a rate of 20.4 notes per second.

In such works as are cited above, the impediments to speed are great, and as Dr. Saperton demonstrated for the writer, there are several fairly complicated passages of piano music that can be executed at 29 to 33 notes per second, though this speed is not compatible with their good musical interpretation.

The examples cited show, however, that the upper range of

fingering is the order of 20 to 30 notes per second. We believe that Sir James Paget, in assigning three muscle movements to each note, underestimated the complexity of the problem. Practically all movements of a finger involve all three joints, so that a single note involves at least three motor nerve volleys for flexion, three for extension, and at least one for lateral movement. Moreover a finger that is motionless is not in a state of inactivity but is tensed into position by the opposition of flexor and extensor muscles, and for any finger to go into action, at least two fingers must be moved out of the road, involving another fourteen motor actions. So without counting the motions of the wrist, forearm, shoulder, and trunk, or those involved in the use of the pedals, a speed of 20 to 30 notes per second may involve 400 to 600 separate motor actions—all effected by a competent musician with such automatism that he can give his attention to the overall effects, rather than to the mechanical details.

Despite the fact that so much of this complicated muscular activity is at the level of automatism, complete automatism constitutes an inferior performance in no way above the level of a mechanical piano. In this instrument the limited expressive devices do not include the many artifices which the artist uses with such variety. The artist achieves his interpretation by minute deviations from uniformity and regularity: one note is held longer than the metronome permits, another is hurried; one note is struck firmly, another only lightly touched; a succession of notes each having equal paper value may be played with uneven tonal emphasis, or slurred deliberately, or made to parade in a presumptuous or sensuous manner. Huneker, in his introduction to the Chopin mazurkas, tells a story about someone accusing Chopin of writing in 3/4 time and playing in 4/4 because he prolonged the second beat. Chopin merely shrugged his shoulders and replied that it was a national trait. The stressing of the second beat is a characteristic of the mazurka, a Polish national rhythm.

Conversely, in reducing a melody to paper, the theme, which may be nascently tenuous and undisciplined, must be rigidly molded into measures, beats, and rests, and made to ascend and descend on the limited ladder of the conventional octave—interpretation is, in part, a matter of liberating Orpheus's inspiration from this regimentation between vertical and horizontal lines.

The "meaning" of music is carried by a variety of elements: melody, rhythm, pitch, timbre, sequence, harmony, anticipation, suspension, and fulfillment. Its essence is tonal form, and is not necessarily related to our experience of words, things, or events. Much good music is programmatic, but music need not be programmatic to be good. Nor is good music necessarily descriptive of any one of the emotions, or intended to evoke any particular emotional response: on the contrary, some critics hold that music is at its best when, in composer, artist, and auditor alike, it has been filtered by psychic distance and detachment until its affective qualities are uniquely its own. Then it is that it conveys—or perhaps elicits is a better word, because it is hard to say what a composer intends to convey—its own semantics, its own affirmations and denials, syntheses and antitheses, in pilasters and arabesques of sound, substituting myth for reality, complementing, not imitating, other forms of perceptual experience with values of its own.

But these musical values are not absolute, in the sense of having the same significance for all individuals—as is witnessed by the changes in musical style with the passage of time, and the wide and sometimes vehement division of opinion with respect to style and content. These values, both in respect to creation and reception, vary in different individuals with their emotional make-up, their musical experience and ability, their prevalent interest and emotional set, their intellectual maturity, and perhaps with such fundamental psychological matters as how they hear music—as a plastic flow of sound, as an increase or decrease of intensity, or as isolated notes like blocks of stone placed at different elevations. It is the ever-conscious task of the artist to preserve such values from being lost in automatism, and to infuse new values stemming from his own interpretation.

11.

Agnosticism versus Atheism

Smith's position on the subject of religion was that of the "agnostic." In the first selection below, "Agnosticism versus Atheism," delivered as a lay sermon in 1956 at the White Plains Community Church, he elaborates upon agnosticism as being for him an inescapable point of view. The second, "Objectives and Objectivity in Science," was published in the Yale Scientific Magazine *in October, 1949, in juxtaposition with two other articles on the general subject of religion and modern science. Father John C. Murray contributed the Roman Catholic interpretation, and Dr. Theodore M. Greene spoke for liberal protestantism. Smith's article sets forth again the agnostic (or naturalistic) view, which maintains that only the utmost objectivity in observation and verification can provide the basis for belief in the modern world. Even in matters of religion, the inquiring mind rejects inspiration and revelation, he tells us, as leading only into the "blind alley of self-deception."*

Agnosticism and atheism invite discussion because these words are frequently misused, and their meaning is anything but clear. Perhaps you will think that adequate definitions could be obtained from any good dictionary, but there are dictionaries and dictionaries, and definitions are altered by local usage and even the intent of the speaker; and in this particular instance a dictionary is not very useful.

Even if a man does not know the meaning and history of the word agnosticism, he doubtless thinks that he knows what atheism means, and accordingly he gives it whatever meaning he wishes. But if he tells me that atheism means simply "to deny the existence of God," I will thereupon look up "God" in my dictionary, and then where am I?

You will recall Humpty Dumpty's assertion that "glory" means "a nice knock-down argument." When Alice objected to this equation, Humpty Dumpty replied, "When *I* use a word it means just what I choose it to mean—neither more nor less." To Alice's question whether one *can* make words mean so many different things, Humpty Dumpty replied, "The question is, which (of us) is to be master—that's all." After this experience Alice must have had some appreciation of the art of argument, as well as some insight into the difficulties of philosophy, and we could believe that she might understand our predicament with respect to "atheist" and "agnostic."

We can best understand words by examining their origins and the meanings which have been given to them in the past. Because it has a longer history, let us take atheism first. It is a distinguished word, in that it bears the scars of many battles, it has been bathed in blood and tears, and countless men have suffered and many have died because of it. And some of those who were about to die even thought that they were dying for God.

Its composition, from the Greek α, "without," + *theos*, "god," supplies the literal meaning "without god," and supports the preferred meaning now given in *Webster's Collegiate Dictionary* of "disbelief in, or denial of, the existence of a supreme being." But on etymological grounds the editors of the thirteen-volume *Oxford English Dictionary* can equally defend their definition as "disbelief in, or denial of, the existence of a God."

Both definitions clearly refer to some presumably supernatural being or beings (as distinct from known animals and mythological creatures such as unicorns, leprechauns, and elves), the existence of which is denied; but a moment's consideration shows that "a supreme being" cannot be equated with just any "God." This ambiguity reveals the difficulties which the word atheism has always encountered: that which is to be denied must first be defined, and to define "God" is very difficult if not impossible. Hence for most purposes atheism may be taken to mean a categorical denial of deism, theism, polytheism, or any other belief in supernatural beings, and also a denial of any assertions, positive or negative, concerning the attributes of such beings.

The earliest utterance approaching an atheistic statement that I can find dates from about 2400 B.C., in the bleak Feudal Period which succeeded the magnificence of the Old Kingdom in Egypt, when Khati II, a king of the IXth Dynasty, wrote, ". . . the gods . . . have hidden themselves"—truly a masterpiece of understatement. Khati nevertheless had quite a bit to say about the gods, things which he had learned from the words of the ancestors; and he was perhaps better justified in asserting that "More acceptable is the virtue of the upright man than the ox of him that doeth iniquity" than was Herbert Spencer, who asserted forty three centuries later that God was "absolutely Unknowable." If God is Unknowable, how did Spencer know that he exists?

The first recorded charge of atheism in the West was levelled against Anaxagoras about 434 B.C., who was tried in Athens for denying the divinity of the sun and moon, which he held to be natural bodies like the earth, and for sundry other naturalistic propositions. Saved by the eloquence of Pericles, Anaxagoras fled to Lampsacus in Asia Minor where on his death, it is said, he was honored by altars and a public funeral. The law under which Anaxagoras was tried, probably the first law in the West against atheism, and hence against freedom of inquiry, had been passed by Pericles' opponents in order to injure him politically, because Pericles was something of a radical himself. It permitted the impeachment of anyone who did not practice "religion" (as the party in power defined it) or promulgated theories about "the things on high."

About 411 B.C., Protagoras, an older contemporary of Socrates, was indicted for atheism under this same law but escaped from Athens, to be lost at sea on his way to Sicily. In a book called *Truth* Protagoras maintained that "Man is the measure of all things," meaning possibly that man's knowledge is strictly limited by experience, and all moral ideas and principles are necessarily empirical. The charge of atheism against Protagoras was possibly also based on statements in a lost work entitled *On the Gods*, which opened with the declaration, "Of the gods, I can know nothing, neither that they are, nor that they are not."

Critias, who maintained that the gods were an invention of some clever man who used the fiction as a protection against secret wrong-doing, escaped punishment. This synthetic theory of the gods, as we might call it, came to be widely accepted in Graeco-Roman times when freedom of opinion was better tolerated than in the day of Pericles.

The outstanding victim of politico-religious prosecution was, of course, Socrates, who chose death to banishment in 399 B.C. when he was found guilty, first, of denying the gods recognized by the state and introducing new divinities, and second, of corrupting the young. Socrates' teaching was basically monotheistic and in conflict with the deities of the sun and moon. His "new divinity" was probably what he called his "dæmon," or conscience. Starting with the argument advanced by Burnet in 1920, I have elsewhere developed the thesis that Socrates was the inventor of the immortal, incorruptible soul of Plato and later philosophers. The charge of corrupting the young seems to have been mostly a legalistic tag which rounded out the indictment politically and identified him firmly as an enemy of the state.

I mention these early examples of atheism chiefly to note that in the first great age of rationalism, antirationalism on occasion also had its way.

If the meaning of atheism in Athens appears to have been a trifle astigmatic, this astigmatism in no way diminishes in later times. "Away with the atheists! To the lions with the *Christiani!*" opened the era of that bloody battle that was to engulf the whole of Europe and to last for eighteen centuries as Christianity fought its way, first against polytheism, then against its own sectaries and dissenters, and later against rationalism, scepticism, and general disbelief. The early Christians were denounced as atheists because they denied the authority (not the existence, which they never doubted) of the multitudinous gods of the Greeks and Romans, and refused to pay obeisance to the statue of the living Caesar, as to a god. But when the Christian church had secured a fair political and economic foundation, it turned the weapon of prosecution on unbelievers with a viciousness equal to that of the best wild lions in the arena, and persisted in this prosecution until disbelief (atheism in the historical meaning of the word) within the framework of the Christian community itself destroyed its organized and calculated powers to harm. Throughout most of the Christian period its victims were not called atheists but heretics, infidels, agents of Satan, or, more specifically, enemies of God. When the word atheist reappears in modern usage, it is in the sceptical milieu of the philosophic renaissance.

As early as 1348 one Nicolaus de Autricuria of Paris was compelled to recant several doctrines, among which was this, that in the processes of nature there is nothing to be found but the motion of the combination and separation of atoms; only here it was the authority of Aristotle rather than that of Christian dogma which certified the condemnation. Giordano Bruno, honored today as an original philosopher with whom we would all agree on certainly many matters, was burned as an atheist in Venice in 1600. Lucilio Vanini, another learned Italian dissenter, had his tongue torn out and was strangled and burned at Toulouse in 1619, condemned as an atheist. Descartes, generally recognized as the founder of modern philosophy, was looked upon as an atheist and possibly escaped prosecution only because, observing Galileo's fate, his more radical essays in philosophy remained to be published after his death. By Descartes' time the word "atheist" had become part of the common language, and it is related that Mersenne, a friend of Descartes, said that there were as many as 50,000 atheists in Paris alone. What Mersenne meant we cannot be sure; but writing in 1604, Rowlands admonishes, "Thou damned Atheist . . . that dost deny his power which did create thee," which indicates that to Rowlands an atheist was one who denied, among other things, the verity of the first chapter of Genesis.

In 1605 Francis Bacon noted that "A little or superficial knowledge of philosophy may incline the mind of man to atheism." At first sight this sounds like a warning against some grave danger; but in retrospect where one knows more about Francis Bacon, one can easily read into it the opposite meaning, i.e., a cautious encouragement to scepticism—cautious because scepticism was not popular in Bacon's day. John Knox, the reformer, who would not worship the mother of Jesus or the saints; Hobbes, the political philosopher (remember, you who live in the United States under a Constitution whereby state and church are held apart, that in Hobbes's day the state and church, and the theory of both, were inextricably mixed); Spinoza, for whom God was equivalent to both nature as we comprehend it and the ultimate reality behind nature which we do not comprehend, were every one of them called atheist by responsible thinkers of their time. The poet Marlowe was accused of atheism, but while awaiting trial he disappeared (tradition has it that he was killed in a tavern in 1593), and his friend, the dramatist Kyd, was implicated in the charge and put to torture. Sir Walter Raleigh was also tried for unbelief, but not convicted.

Throughout the seventeenth, eighteenth and nineteenth centuries Christian literature is as crowded with "atheism" as it is with God, an atheism that is, for the most part, a continuing effort to redefine "God." The nineteenth century is in many ways the most interesting in respect to the history of atheism because the rapiers of doubt had been considerably sharpened by the expansion of the geological and biological sciences, but only one more incident can be recounted here, and that is from the eighteenth century. It is told that David Hume, who in rebuttal of Berkeley's idealism had denied the reality of mind as something existing apart from individual sensations and thus had, in effect, pulled the foundations out from under not only Berkeley's "mental" universe but from the traditional Christian God, was once dining in a party of eighteen at the house of the declared French atheist, d'Holbach. Hume had expressed his doubt that it was possible to find any person who would avow himself dogmatically to be an atheist, to which his host replied, "My dear sir, you are at this moment sitting at table with seventeen such persons."

Truly, were we to call forth all the books wherein atheism is explicitly named or is clearly implied as belief opposed to some current variety of polytheism, deism, or theism, the four walls of the library would all but empty themselves. Let us leave these volumes on the shelves for the historically minded student who has the time and patience to bear with their repititiousness, and sum up succinctly. By the touchstone of usage, "atheism" as a denial of some or all of the attributes of a transcendental being, whether it be one god or the attributes of three gods and sundry subordinate sprits, is not a very useful word in informative discourse. We cannot know what it means until its antithesis is defined.

As opposed to "atheism" in this sceptical or critical sense, which is historically the more general usage, we can consider another meaning in which the word is trimmed to dimensions by common sense, namely, "dogmatic atheism," which denies the existence of any god or gods categorically. The irrefragable answer to dogmatic atheism was apparently first framed by a dissenting Baptist minister, John Foster, who held the opinion that "churches are useless and mischievous institutions, and the sooner they are dissolved the better." In a volume of essays published in 1806 Foster pointed out that dogmatic atheism is an untenable position because it implies infinite knowledge. On this point there seems to be no more that can be said, except to affirm that no scientist or philosopher would presume to deny that which lies beyond empirically ascertained and empirically verifiable knowledge, which at best is finite, partial, and incomplete. As Protagoras said, and as Hume pointed out in refuting Bishop Butler, no argument from experience can carry us beyond experience. For all I know to the contrary, there may be millions of gods, good, bad or indifferent, hovering beyond the periphery of the observable cosmos. I am not in a position dogmatically to affirm their existence or to deny it.

In shutting the door on dogmatic atheism, however, Foster also shut the door on dogmatic deism. Even as the atheist cannot deny that which is not known, the deist cannot dogmatically affirm that which is not known without laying claim to knowledge of it. The critical word here is "knowledge," because mere "belief" is not enough: you may "believe" that the moon is made of green cheese, but what man who is on his guard will not distinguish between your "belief" in the moon's composition and your "knowledge" with respect to it? To support your assertion you must advance evidence which can be examined by others, and then your assertion will stand or fall on the validity and verifiability of the evidence in the opinion of others. Failing to establish your point, you will be charged with indulging in futile prattle about the moon.

In the last two centuries the "evidence" that long supplied the foundations of Christianity, namely, revelation and authority, have either been shown outright to be unreliable (as, for example, the Mosaic account of the creation of the earth and man, the inspired nature of the Old and New Testaments, their miracles, episcopal authority, etc.), or have been brought into such serious question (as in the case of the historical nature of the New Testament, including the synoptic gospels) that these "foundations" have proved, for an ever-increasing number of people, insufficient to bear the weight of the traditional conclusions. And thus it has come about that the liberal "Christian" churches have been forced to abandon one after another of their traditional positions until some of them are largely, and some of them wholly, free of supernaturalism. In such institutions a qualified atheism, better informed and in most respects even more sceptical than that of the eighteenth and nineteenth centuries, is the accepted working philosophy. Since dogmatic atheism is philosophically an untenable position, this progressive catharsis of supernaturalism invites a redefinition of the sceptic's position.

AND THUS we come to the word "agnosticism." This word has a much shorter history and much clearer meaning than has any variety of atheism. The word was coined by Thomas Henry Huxley in 1869, and for definition we need examine only what Huxley meant by it. The immediate circumstance behind Huxley's invention of the word was the Metaphysical Society, founded in 1869 by Alfred Lord Tennyson and James Knowles, the architect who designed Tennyson's house and the liberal editor of the *Contemporary Review*. England had recently been rocked by Darwin's *Origin of Species*, by new discoveries in all areas of science and particularly in geology, and by what was called the "Higher Criticism" of the biblical texts. The Poet Laureate, despite the fact that he was the son of a vicar of the Established Church, sang that "There lives more faith in honest doubt, believe me, than in half the creeds."

The Metaphysical Society was a convivial effort to bring believers and unbelievers together on some common ground. Among its members were Archbishop Manning and two Protestant bishops; Hutton, editor of the *Spectator* and Arian by faith; Father Dalgairns, an able Roman Catholic priest; Lord Arthur Russell, a deist; two Scottish freethinking metaphysicians; W. G. Ward, who had abandoned the Established Church to follow Newman into Catholicism; Gregg, a deist and author of *The Creed of Christendom;* Froude, decan-historian, now a deist; Roden Noel, a declared atheist; Martineau, the Unitarian; Henry Sidgwick, philosopher; John Ruskin, writer and critic; and sundry other clerics, essayists and freethinkers. Only a Jew and a Mohammedan were wanting to complete a roster of Western metaphysics. It was surmised by some that this mixture of incompatibles could end up only in explosive mayhem, but, as Huxley said later, "Charity, brotherly love, were [its] chief traits; we all expended so much charity that, had it been money, we should all have been bankrupt." After ten years of harmony born of charity and self-restraint, the "Society passed away quietly, as it were, in its sleep." Tennyson said that it expired because "after ten years of strenuous effort no one had succeeded in even defining metaphysics." The Dean of Westminster wistfully mourned, "We all meant the same thing, if we only knew it." Huxley was more succinct: "The Society," he said, "died of too much love."

According to Hutton's recollection, it was at Knowles's house in 1869 that Huxley first used the word "agnostic," but there is no reason to accept Hutton's assertion that Huxley took it from Paul's mention of the altar to "the Unknown God." Huxley no more esteemed an Unknown God than he esteemed Spencer's Unknowable God. However, it was nearly a decade after the Metaphysical Society had passed away before Huxley took occasion to reconstruct the history of the word. At an annual church congress in Manchester, in 1888, in an afternoon session devoted to "Atheism, Agnosticism and Pessimism," Dr. Henry Wace of St. Paul's and King's College had seen fit to call Huxley an infidel, and Bishop Magee of Peterborough had expressed the belief that the intellectual unrest of the time all reduced to "cowardly agnosticism." "Infidel" Huxley did not mind so much, but the charge of cowardliness stung him to a rebuttal ("Agnosticism," *Coll. Essays*, v, pp. 209–262) which he published early in 1889 in *The Nineteenth Century*. Here he mentioned, apropos of the nature of evidence as to the unseen world and as an instance involving the physiology and pathology of the nervous system, an area in which he pretended to some competence, namely, the episode of the Gadarene swine as recounted in *Mark V*. This miracle, in which Jesus exorcises devils out of a man and transfers them into "about two thousand" swine belonging to an innocent neighbor, whereupon the swine run violently down a steep place into the sea, and are choked in the sea, would scarcely be advanced today by any informed person as evidence of the miraculous power of the founder of Christianity. It remains of interest chiefly because it reveals the superstitious and credulous nature of the author of the gospel of *Mark*, and because it was still accepted at its face value in the nineteenth century. Huxley, however, on biological grounds rejected the miracle of the Gadarene swine as a fiction. This in turn led him to ask himself just what he did believe. He told the story as follows:

"When I reached intellectual maturity and began to ask myself whether I was an atheist, a theist or a pantheist, a materialist or an idealist; a Christian or a freethinker; I found that the more I learned and reflected, the less ready was the answer; until, at last, I came to the conclusion that I had neither art nor part with any of these denominations, except the last. The one thing in which most of these good people were agreed was the one thing in which I differed from them. They were quite sure they had attained a certain 'gnosis'—had, more or less successfully, solved the problem of existence; while I was quite sure that I had not, and had a pretty strong conviction that the problem was insoluble. . . .

"This was my situation when I had the good fortune to find a place among the members of that remarkable confraternity of antagonists, the Metaphysical Society. Every variety of philosophical and theological opinion was represented there, and expressed itself with entire openness; most of my colleagues were -ists of one sort or another; and I, . . . the man without a rag of a label to cover himself with, could not fail to have some of the uneasy feelings which must have beset the historical fox when, after leaving the trap in which his tail remained, he presented himself to his normally elongated companions. So I took thought, and invented what I conceived to be the appropriate title of 'agnostic.' It came into my head as suggestively antithetic to the 'gnostic' of Church history, who professed to know so much about the very things of which I was ignorant; and I took the earliest opportunity of parading it at our Society, to show that I, too, had a tail, like the other foxes. . . ." (*Coll. Essays*, v, p. 237–8).

Thus, unlike "atheist," which I have noted is a messy word of many meanings, agnostic is a nice, clean-cut word the meaning of which we can discover from the intent of its author.

So much for its origin. On looking in the dictionary we find that "agnostic" is the equivalent of the Greek *agnostos*, meaning "unknowing" (and hence derivatively, "unknown" or "unknowable"). Thus, where atheism means "no god," agnosticism means "no knowledge"–not of god alone but possibly of many things.

As Huxley implies, this word was not the product of sudden inspiration, but the fruit of many years of deep thinking. It could be traced in part to his training and experience as a scientist, but it also has its roots in his profound knowledge of history and philosophy. But it is enough to note here that Huxley's agnosticism was fully formed and clearly visible nearly a decade before he wrote this essay, and it is particularly evident in a series of letters to the Reverend Charles Kingsley, in which he searched out his philosophy of life. In one of these (1863) he had said to Kingsley, "I know nothing of Necessity [and] abominate the word Law. . . . I don't know whether Matter is anything distinct from Force. . . . I don't know that atoms are anything but pure myths. . . . *I think, therefore I am,* is to my mind a ridiculous piece of bad logic [because] all I can say at any time is *I think.* . . . My fundamental axiom of speculative philosophy is that *materialism and spiritualism are opposite poles of the same absurdity*–the absurdity of imagining that we know anything about either spirit or matter." By "anything" he clearly meant that we do not know anything *absolute* about either spirit or matter.

It has been said that on occasion Huxley and others used the word "agnosticism" "to avoid wasteful discussion of the unknown while they applied themselves to the ascertainable facts of nature"; and Huxley himself may at times have used it in slightly different senses. But it is not true, as Dr. Wace as much as said to the church congress, that it was simply an attempt on Huxley's part to evade important issues in relation to Christianity. Nor is it true, as one biographer says, that "agnosticism was a white flag which he and his small company carried as they walked through the country of orthodoxy and placed dynamite under offensive buildings"; this is only a facetious way of looking at an issue that is anything but facetious. It is true that for the churchmen the word indicated every variety of scepticism; while for many

Christians it only designated rejection of certain specific articles of the Christian creed. And there exists today the notion that "agnostic" means one who wants to straddle the fence, who is afraid to stand up and be counted. But to treat agnosticism as meaning a qualified deism, a nonagressive sceptical atheism, or a position of philosophical vacillation or cowardice is not to know the man who coined it, the way he used it, or the full force of the word. On the contrary, Huxley challenged all unsubstantiated propositions, pro or con. "Of all the senseless babble I have ever had occasion to read," he said at Belfast in 1874, "the demonstrations of these philosophers who undertake to tell us all about the nature of God would be the worst, if they were not surpassed by the still greater absurdities of the philosophers who try to prove that there is no God." If this is rhetorically violent rather than philosophically sophisticated, at least it makes its point.

Again, in his essay on Hume (1879) Huxley identified agnosticism as the admission of our incapacity to discover the indispensable conditions of either positive or negative knowledge; or to put it in current terms, the admission that we cannot attain to absolute knowledge, either positive or negative, thus excluding both dogmatic atheism and dogmatic deism. And I have already argued that critical scepticism with respect to either of these dogmatic positions has in the past (whatever may be the future) led the sceptic to precisely Huxley's position, namely, that agnosticism is the abandonment of metaphysical speculation by the substitution of a *method*.

Agnosticism, Huxley said, is as old as Socrates, as old as the writer who said, "Try all things, hold fast to that which is good." It is the method of Descartes and the fundamental axiom of science: follow your reason and evidence as far as they will take you, and do not pretend that conclusions are certain which are not demonstrated or demonstrable. Note that for Huxley reason was not an instrument for discovering "truth" but an instrument for discovering error in terms of evidence.

Lastly, Huxley once described agnosticism as meaning "that a man shall not say he knows or believes what he has no scientific ground for professing to know or believe." A clerical antagonist cogently replied that this would merely be "a definition of honesty; in that sense we ought all to be agnostics." And so we should, but certainly most of the clerics of the nineteenth century fall far short of the mark. This definition, however, suffers the fault that it fails to distinguish between "knowledge" (of the composition of the moon, for example, as supported by objective, verifiable evidence) and "belief" on the other. This distinction was first made in Greek philosophy and, after suffering eclipse for some centuries, has been re-emphasized in the philosophy known as naturalism or empiricism, the development of which can be traced through Hume, Bain, John Stewart Mill, William James, Pierce and Dewey, until it constitutes the cornerstone of contemporary science.

Spencer wanted to be an agnostic, but he slipped in an unguarded and enthusiastic moment when he declared that the "deepest, widest and most certain of facts [is] that the Power which the Universe manifests to us is utterly inscrutable." Huxley, as I have noted, passed off Spencer's "utterly inscrutable Power" with a shrug—whether it exists or not, he said, "I am quite clear I have no knowledge either way. I neither affirm or deny."

As for the future, Huxley believed that if the Christian creed "should prove to be incompatible with our knowledge, or necessary want of knowledge, some other hypostasis of men's hopes, genuine enough and worthy enough to replace it, will arise." By this hypostasis he did not mean the religion of Humanity—"the incongrous mixture of bad sciences with eviscerated papistry, out of which Comte manufactured the Positivist religion." For Positivism, the adoration of Humanity, he had only scorn, and called it "Catholicism minus Christianity." Agnosticism was in no sense a religion or an imitation ecclesiasticism. Nevertheless, he said, if "a man should determine to devote himself to the service of humanity (spelled with a lower case h)—including intellectual and moral self-culture under that name; that this should be, in the proper sense of the word, his religion—is not only an intelligible, but, I think, a laudable resolution. And I am greatly disposed to believe that it is the only religion which will prove itself to be unassailably acceptable so long as the human race endures."

When we turn to the *Oxford English Dictionary* we find

agnostic defined as "One who holds that the existence of anything beyond and behind material phenomena is unknown and (so far as can be judged) unknowable, and especially that a First Cause and an unseen world are subjects of which we know nothing."

So much for the dictionary definition, which is clear except for the word "material"; and if you can get any physicist to define "matter," please tell me what his definition is. But the definitions of both matter and agnosticism will improve with time, because definitions, like knowledge, do not come to us by revelation but by empirical trial and error in our exploration of the cosmos. If I were to venture a redefinition of Huxley's word, I would say that an agnostic is one who demands verifiable evidence as the only acceptable grounds for belief; lacking that evidence, the agnostic holds belief to be inconsequential, or as a jurist would say, irrelevant. In a philosophical sense, then, agnosticism may be equated with the empiric naturalism, which confines itself to the study of the observable cosmos, including the earth and man and all his hopes and fears, his highest aspirations.

I see in agnosticism a scientifically and philosophically defensible position, and it is the only scientifically and philosophically defensible position I can see. Good old Humpty Dumpty! Huxley's word means just what *I* choose it to mean, and *glory* means *a nice knock-down argument!*

12.

Objectives and Objectivity in Science

THE ANCIENT EGYPTIANS BELIEVED that over the desert's edge were the four mountains that upheld the sky, the cardinal points that gave direction to all events in the Kingdom of Ra, and hence to all events in the Valley of the Nile. They never seriously challenged the fiction, because as the explorer went farther and farther afield it was easy to push the traditional mountains over the horizon.

So the explorer in education, raising his sight above his own immediate hills and valleys, looks about for the mountains that uphold our personal heavens and give direction and meaning to our lives. One meaning of the word "profession" is devotion to higher ends than merely earning a livelihood. The use of the term "higher" in this definition permits me to designate these ends as values. Our grandfathers frequently used this term, and usually spelled it, along with various individual values, with capital letters.

I would like, therefore, to discuss the question of "values" as it appears to a scientist.

Science occupies a rather unique position in society. It has so proved itself, by the repeated verification of its conclusions, by the integration of seemingly unrelated observations, and by the practical control of nature, that no informed person presumes to challenge its pronouncements within the limitations which the scientist properly imposes upon his own conclusions. Society recognizes the fact without exactly understanding how science has come to occupy such a preeminent position.

The layman is apt to think of a scientist as one who possesses some magic gift for discovering truth. Every scientist will hasten to reply that he has no such gift, that indeed there is no touchstone of any kind for the discovery of truth. Science discovers truth the hard way: entertaining no *a priori* certitudes, she starts from ignorance and, by tested and critical procedures, little by little wrests from nature successive fragments of information which prove to be verifiable by competent observers at all times and in all places. This body of verifiable knowledge is what the scientist means by truth, and the process by which science extracts it from nature is called the scientific method. The scientific method has been tried and tested for some three

Reprinted from the Yale Scientific Magazine, *23: 2, 1949.*

centuries and remains inviolate as the only reliable method for discovering something, or anything, that can be called "truth."

Scientific research is directed at the whole of nature, at its most minute events and its farthermost galaxies. There is no special "scientific field"; no aspect of the atom, no aspect of life, no aspect of time or space, can be conceived as lying outside its purview. Science would cease to be science, and its victories over the unknown would decrease were it to fail to explore the whole of nature for exploration's sake. But no interpretation of the atom or life or of time or space can be accepted as other than mere speculation until it has been verified by acceptable scientific methods.

The layman endorses science because science pays, meaning that when put into practical application it adds to man's comfort, wealth, or health. This is not invariably true. To cite just one example—gunpowder; and it is yet to be determined whether the release of atomic energy is, in the net, going to be conducive to good or ill for the human race. Sometimes science pays and sometimes it does not, but science is not concerned with whether it pays or not. The true explorer of the cosmos is not an accountant of human gains and losses; when Galileo studied the swinging pendulum, when Copernicus formulated the heliocentric theory, when Einstein wrote an equation coverting matter into energy, these explorers were not particularly interested in either the practical or humanitarian consequences of their work.

Why, then, does the scientist work? He is in the main motivated by curiosity, a restless psychologic state frequently experienced by the fishes, birds and mammals, and particularly by the anthropoid apes and man. History reveals that most of science and indeed most intellectual advance has come from this impulse of the inquiring mind to explore the universe. It is a corollary that to be successful scientific exploration must be uninhibited by or must challenge all opposing preconceptions. It has been thus that all great discoveries have been made. Galileo, Copernicus, Harvey, Hutton, Darwin, Freud—all moved against a stream of opposing belief. The first lesson of science is that every man must be free to explore the cosmos in his own way, which is to say that he must avoid all *a priori* certitudes.

The second lesson of science is that no certitudes have been discovered *a posteriori.* Scientific truth itself is spelled with a lower case "t"; it is to be defined as a body of belief which has been repeatedly tested and found to be verifiable, but which is none the less always held subject to re-examination and re-interpretation. No scientist ever permanently makes up his mind on any subject, which is why science is ever achieving new victories. And beyond the boundaries of scientific exploration there is only the unknown, about which we know absolutely nothing. A proper scientist does not talk about that of which he knows absolutely nothing.

Since science recognizes neither *a priori* nor *a posteriori* certitudes, she spells none of her values in upper case type. I want to emphasize that by values I mean pretty much the same thing as our grandfathers meant. What were the Values they spelled with capital letters? Truth was one of them, truth that transcended both human error and the flux of cosmic change. Man wants certitude, and he is always tempted to accept some of his immediate beliefs as irrefragable. But certitude he has not found. Least of all can he attribute certitude to his undisciplined personal beliefs or intuition. It was one thing to assess the great Victorian "intuitionalist," Lord Balfour, by intuition, and another to examine his background, his history, his psychology, his logic, all the pertinent details, in order to understand him as a man. Lord Balfour's naive intuition, as does my own, remains a mixture of error and irrationality not necessarily corresponding in any way with reality, as science uses that word.

That special kind of certitude or Truth identified as Inspiration or Revelation, which did so much to shape the Medieval World, began to crumble in the eighteenth century and by the end of the nineteenth lay in ruins. With revealed Truth went Faith, since Faith in the last analysis is either an attribution of transcendental significance to the ecstasies and miseries of the ephemeral biological organism, or else an apotheosis of the unknown, and history reveals that neither equation has been fruitful. For over fifty centuries man has repeatedly sought values through faith of one kind or another, only to find himself in a blind alley of self-deception. Like beauty, Faith is in the eye of the beholder and is no more reliable as a higher end.

Another Value of recent date was Natural Law (I use the

word in the sense of the natural sciences, though the jurists will recognize a close parallel in jurisprudence). It was possibly Thucydides who first spoke of the "law of nature" as a divine edict written into the heart of things; and, after Galileo, Kepler, and Newton, the regularities of nature came to be viewed as divine decrees by which the universe was operated, possibly, as one of Newton's contemporaries opined, to relieve God of the necessity of giving it his constant, personal attention. Then Hume pointed out that all we can discover in the cosmos is regularity, a series of apparently repetitive sequences, and that we cannot assign metaphysical significance to mere repetitiousness. In Nietzsche's words, "the laws of nature are the remains of mythological dreaming."

Then there was Love. It was presumably Paul, the founder of Christianity, who first said that "God is love" and made it possible for Dante to identify Love as the dynamic force that turned the celestial spheres. The poets of the nineteenth century rhapsodized at length on Paul's divine equation, or on the derivative idea that the incandescence of human love had at least been lit by a spark from the divine emotion. But, long since, the equation of God and Love has been erased and the word love has been decapitalized. As Plato recognized, the less the student of the transcendental says about love, the better. The contemporary philosopher recognizes the essential indignity of man and his emotions.

Our grandfathers also believed in something called Progress. The ancients conceived that culture was subject to successive cycles of growth and decay, and most of them looked back nostalgically upon a Golden Age from which their own had retrogressed. Then through the centuries there developed a belief in the perfectibility of man and the conviction that history revealed a continuous movement towards that impeccable state. By the middle of the nineteenth century progress was frequently spelled with a capital letter, and Spencer conceived it to be the *vis a tergo* of his particular and optimistic brand of evolution, while Tennyson epitomized it by the notion of creation moving more or less continuously toward some far-off Divine Event. Progress came to be accepted as an intrinsic principle of nature, until a reinterpretation of Darwinian evolution suggested that man might not be perfectible, that progress, however defined and towards whatever goal, was not inevitable, and that what we observe in nature is only process, an arrow pointed at both ends.

And so it went. Darwin's century was a tragic one for man. Truth, Revelation, Faith, Natural Law, Love, Progress were degraded to lower case type and survive only to enrich our language, even as the words bewitch, beguile, enchant, fascinate, natural, and supernatural, survive from the ancient lore of witchcraft. The transcendental values of the past are gone.

Proud man, who always imagined that he was specially beloved by the gods, has discovered himself to be a creature struggling to live in a world from which has faded the last faint ray of transcendental light. He now faces the task of spelling out his destiny in lower case type. He must reconcile himself to being merely one among earth's many creatures, with no unique destiny reserved for him. At the moment he is confused and unhappy, unhappy in a personal way. Ingenious as he is, he has failed as yet to invent a mechanical device which will manufacture happiness, or one which will instill meaning into life. He has answered many questions, but not the $64 one, Why live at all? Granted that many of us, perhaps most of us, are unwanted accidents, what are we to do about it now? Without some place to go, to harness the forces of the sun and stars is an empty victory. Without meaning in life, education verges on a futile rat race. There is, of course, the Freudian idea of sublimation—that great artists, great musicians, great lawyers, great engineers, great business men, great scientists, are distilled through the retort of escapism over the fires of misery and discontent. The idea is biologically sound and probably true in many instances, but why keep such a bootleg industry in operation?

A contemporary Swedish writer, Soderberg, has one of his characters say, "I believe in the lust of the flesh and the incurable loneliness of the soul." I am inclined to affirm this epitome. I see our problem in these general terms: it is in the nature of the living organism to resist the forces that tend to destroy it, to avoid pain and disability and death, to feed itself and satisfy its physical and emotional needs, and to seek a state of optimal integration with its environment. That state is an ideal which is never quite achieved, yet in its partial achievement the organism must find its satisfactions. To this end it is required not only that the organism have air, food, and water, but that it maintain some sort of balance between itself and other organisms and, as far as possible, that it understand its situation and be prepared to reinterpret it from time to time. Medicine, engineering, business, law, and philosophy are useful to the human organism because they help it to meet these basic biological requirements. On this basis we can reexamine the word "value."

The first requirement in this process of integration is honesty. Honesty is not a supernatural Value but only the best expedient if we are to deal effectively with nature and with each other; for when we deceive others, we deceive ourselves. It pays to be honest insofar as we can know what honesty is. Science is reasonably honest with itself and with society because it is constantly self-critical. In order to be honest, we must pursue ruthlessly all that we conceive to be false. To paraphrase Ambrose Bierce, nothing is more logical than persecution, and tolerance is itself a kind of infidelity. We must be militantly intolerant of what we believe to be false, intolerant of unsupported tradition and uninformed consensus, intolerant of intuitionalism and sentimentality. Tolerance is today perhaps our greatest infidelity to ourselves.

But in being intolerant of tolerance we must not be intolerant of liberty, the essence of all inquiry, of all exploration and advance. Science (and incidentally our democratic Constitution) is based on the premise that every man is entitled to complete freedom of the intellect; every individual is entitled to be let alone, to think and do as he pleases so long as he does not impinge upon the rights of others. Santayana has said that morality is a worse enemy of the spirit than any immorality, implying that those who would reform me for my own good are offenders not only against science but against the Bill of Rights. Science is not a reformer. It entertains no anticipated exploitation of the individual or of the human race; it has no humanitarian ends in view, and that is in part why it has achieved its victories. Morality must be left to moralists, who remain beyond the pale of both science and the Bill of Rights.

Law and science are closely related in their philosophy: law stands in the role of mediator, negotiating the rights of the individual against all other individuals. Like science, it entertains no absolutes but operates primarily from the premise of the right of the individual to maximal freedom of thought and action. The equation which Plato attempted to write, relating Truth to Justice, finds a solution not in Plato's Universal Ideas but in the individual which, as a philosopher, he despised. Justice can only be defined as a reasoned compromise.

And what, in this amoral scheme, has become of Righteousness? One frequently hears the expression "the climate of belief"; it is permissible perhaps to speak also of the "paleontology of belief." When one digs into the past, one finds morality imbedded like a fossil jawbone between supernatural myth and tribal fears: the gods, or God, would have it Thus and So. It was Amos, probably the greatest of the Old Testament Prophets, who, speaking as for the Lord, said, "I hate, I despise your feast days, and I will not smell in your solemn assemblies. Though ye offer me burnt offerings, I will not accept them; neither will I regard the peace offerings of your fat beasts. Take thou away from me the noise of thy songs; for I will not hear the melody of thy viols. But let judgment run down as waters, and righteousness as a mighty stream."

To Amos, the feast day, the solemn assembly, the burnt offering of the fat beast, had become old-fashioned. What his God wanted was Righteousness, Amos's idea of righteousness. But even in Amos's time this supernatural talisman was nearly thirty centuries old. On the so-called Memphite stone of Egypt is inscribed an aphorism that antedates the Pyramids of Sakkara and is dated by Breasted as about 3300 B.C., which in effect says, "He who does what is loved (by the gods) is given life; he who does what is hated, is given death." The early Egyptians had hit upon the belief that immortality could be purchased by doing what is loved by the gods, and had added Righteousness to red ochre, green malachite, cowie shells, hieroglyphic verses and other amulets in their armamentarium of magic. The civilized world has worn that talisman around its neck for 50 centuries. What immortality it has purchased elsewhere I have no way of knowing, but I stand on good ground in saying that it has purchased little for anyone in the here and now. I must reject the supernatural potency of Amos's Righteousness, just as I must reject the legend of Creation as it appears in Genesis, the moral strictures of Numbers and Deuteronomy, the whole maze of Judaic Law, on the grounds that they are folklore and not fact. So too, because the evidence is unconvincing, I must reject the New Testament, its miracles, and all the metaphysics extrapolated from these foundations, as unhistoric and unreal.

As this metaphysical castle tumbles, I find not one stone left in place. I am left with a cosmos billions of light years in extent, and beyond it with an Unknown the dimensions of which I have no idea. I know nothing about the Unknown. I know nothing about God (nor do I believe that anyone else does), and therefore as a scientist I cannot discuss him any more than I can discuss the Unknown. I cannot even deny the existence of God or of a dozen gods—how can I when I am completely ignorant on the subject? But as a fanciful philosophical exercise, I find that to equate the word God with the whole of nature in all its detailed parts (pantheism) is an empty tautology. I prefer the word nature. If the word God is to be significant at all, it must mean something more than nature, and to step outside the bounds of nature takes me into a series of dilemmas not the least of which is the paradox of Good and Evil. God is either Good or Evil, or Both. If God is Good (as Christian doctrine has so rigorously contended), then Evil (accidental injuries, catastrophies, cancer, heart disease, mosquitoes, death, etc., etc.) must either issue from him with his consent or else stem from an independent source of Evil, let us say, Satan. Since I must reject the legend, Babylonian in origin, that man is a fallen angel who was driven from the Garden of Eden for the Affair of the Apple, I must also reject the theory of Evil which stems from this legend, and which was propounded by Augustine, based upon the notion of Original Sin transmitted through concupiscence to all of Adam's progeny. Nor can I accept a modernized version of the ancient doctrine of Divine Punishment, and suppose that Evil is inflicted on man because at some point in his evolution from anthropoid ape to *Homo sapiens* (he or his helpmeet, Eve) sinned against some Commandment of the deity. In short, I do not see how one can talk about God without defining the word, and the definition cannot avoid the problem of Good and Evil, and any consideration of this problem other than in naturalistic terms leads to such a hopeless metaphysical morass that I prefer not to talk about God at all, the more so since I do not know anything about him. To me it seems that that line of philosophical speculation has long since been shown to be a blind alley, and a very dangerous one. Science and Theology are and ever have been in conflict with each other, and they will remain so until one or the other succumbs, or until science adduces evidence that the cosmic Unknown is something other than the cosmic known.

The logical application of any theology which posits a Beneficent Deity who is not responsible for evil requires that the theologians condemn me as a heretic who, by my heresies, is tempting men to risk the Eternal Damnation of their Immortal Souls, and who therefore should be forthwith burned at the stake by the "secular arm," as countless witches and heretics have logically been condemned and burned or otherwise punished since the Christian metaphysicians were conceded the power of punishment and of life and death by the Roman emperors of the fourth century of the Christian era. In the interests of justice (by my own definition), it is better that I should die than that many men, misguided by my heresies, should risk the eternal torment of God's Punishment.

I have my own theory of evil. As I have said, I believe in the essential indignity of man. He is on his way up, I hope, from some remote ancestor of the anthropoid apes, who are the only ones who have reason to resent my remarks. He is part of the natural universe, and his problem, like that of every other natural organism, is to seek the maximalization of his individual freedom against storms and droughts, depressions, parasites, plagues, and, not least of all, other men.

Do you recall Francis Bacon's Atlantis? A shipwrecked sailor came ashore on an island where there was no poverty, no crime, no hunger, no sickness except unavoidable old age, but only happy people. The island was tenanted by architects, astronomers, geologists, physicians, chemists, engineers, psychologists, and philosophers (I do not recall whether there were any lawyers present or not); there were certainly no politicians and no government of any kind, for these wise men were wholly engaged in controlling nature, rather than in ruling man. "The End of our Foundation is the Knowledge of Causes and secret motions of things; and the enlargement of the bounds of human empire, to the effecting of all things possible." There is one of my values, that we may replace the essential indignity of man by some increased measure of dignity. Bacon's society is one of my values, that form of society which is achieved by reasoned compromise. The "effecting of all things possible" is a value to which I can sincerely dedicate myself.

Medicine is an application of knowledge which may aid man to achieve his Atlantis. It has certain functions for the adequate discharge of which the physician is paid in social esteem and in the coin of the realm. The functions of medicine are to allay pain, to prevent disability, to postpone death, and to enhance human happiness, just as it is the function of the iceman to bring ice and of the shoemaker to repair shoes.

The expectation of life for a male baby born in the United States has increased from 39 years in 1850 to 64 years in 1945. Is this of value? No, if we want to go on having the largest possible number of babies, for it is clear that biologically there is not room for more people on the face of the earth; yes, if we prefer that a relatively few babies should have a superior opportunity to achieve maturity and enjoy life. Is medicine concerned with these *if's*, *and's* and *but's* as Values? No, only as values. When society wants fewer babies, medicine will apply itself to that problem. When society wants life to be shortened instead of lengthened, medicine will get to work on the task.

An increase in life expectancy of 25 years since 1850 reflects a reduction in deaths from such diseases as typhoid fever, measles, scarlet fever, whooping cough, diptheria, influenza, pneumonia, and tuberculosis. How did medicine reduce these deaths? Not by talking metaphysics, but by subjecting the human organism and its parasitic invaders to critical examination in order to understand how they operate. One of my colleagues has chided me that I am now spelling the words "critical examination" with capital letters. No, I mean only that critical examination is the best means so far discovered for promoting the integration of the organism with its environment. Without the aid of capital letters, medical science in one century has added 25 years to the life span, it has stripped living of many if its minor miseries, it has contributed its modicum to the one and only biological goal. I contend that it is thus that man has crept his small distance out of the shadows of the Old Stone Age.

Viewed biologically, the maximalization of human satisfactions (with deference to the rights of others) is the only ultimate goal of life, the fine art of attaining that goal the only morality, and confidence in the potential effectiveness of conscious effort, the only faith. If we view education as a means of discovering a better equation for living, then disciplined doubt is its only higher end.

13.

"The Ethic of the Individual"

If the naturalistic point of view rejects man's traditional religious beliefs, what remains, if anything, to provide a basis for judging right from wrong? Is morality to be considered as having gone the way of revealed Truth and Faith? Smith treats of this problem in the "Epilogue" which we here reproduce from Man and His Gods.

As "a little lower than the angels," man would be ludicrous. As an animal, he has reason to be proud because he is the first who can ask himself, "Whither, Why, and Whence?" and confident because he can know himself as a creature of earth who has risen by his own efforts from a low estate. If he would rise higher, he must be true to earth, he must accept that he is its creature, unplanned, unprotected, and unfavored, co-natural with all other living creatures and with the air and water and sunlight and black soil from which their dynamic pattern has been fabricated by impersonal and indifferent forces. In every wish, thought, and action he is seeking to escape the same protoplasmic disquietude that impels the meanest flesh crawling beneath his feet. He must find his values and his ends entirely within this frame of reference.

As an intelligent creature he explores his world, and here is the first value that is uniquely his: he is more intelligent than any other creature, and from intelligence fired by curiosity comes knowledge, and from knowledge come power and the manifold satisfactions by which he surpasses all his fellow creatures. This sequence has led him to abandon the forest and the cave for purposes and plans. But the need for knowledge has burdened him with the ethic of truth: to lie willingly to himself or others, to adhere to that which is suspect, however tentatively he holds to truth, is to forfeit his opportunity and jeopardize his dreams. This is the essence of all philosophy: to cherish truth for its uniquely human value, to search for it, to test and retest it by conscious effort, to communicate it, to be guided by it, to base upon it all purposes and plans.

But he who has purposes and plans must make a choice; no other can make it for him. A proper view of man finds no place for *a priori* "should" or "ought" or any categorical imperative, but only for this, that if a man so acts, that is *his* action, and his alone. This is the essence of all morality: a man is responsible for the consequences of whatever choice he makes. The degree to which he recognizes this and acts accordingly is a measure of his biological maturity.

Man is an animal for whom life is more than an experience

to be passively endured. Below his bare perception he feels the resonances of the affections, joy, love, wonder, fear, anger, sorrow, which color every wish and vision until he can scarcely think but his thought is reinforced by feeling. His history is unimaginable except as impelled by emotional reverberations, and that is one reason why he has become man, the creator of a world that is uniquely human and shot through and through with uniquely human values. That is why he creates beauty to express the inexpressible, to sing his joy, to ease his pain, to mitigate his loneliness—a black statue of a mighty king, a polychrome frieze of wild ducks feeding among the rushes, a marble temple, a pigment transposed to canvas, a string to give off rhythmic melodies, beauty that is personal in creation and possession, beauty that is a measure of his own disquietude. If revealing his melancholy vision that tragedy is truer to life than other moods, it also reveals that life is many moods.

To neglect the creative dynamic of the emotions is to neglect the essence of human nature. Fear, anger, and exhilaration move man as they move the denizens of forest, sky, and stream, but the emotion that is uniquely his, is pride. He will risk his life in combat rather than suffer loss of his self-esteem; and honor, jealousy, and indignation contribute to the determination of his rights and duties, and elicit courtesy and consideration for the pride and privileges of others. He who is sensitive to shame will not be insensitive to the judgment of his fellows, careless of decorum, unappreciative of convention. He who through imagination can suffer another's pleasures and pains—his fear, anger, pride, and even his prejudices and hatreds—will build a family, tribe, and nation, and fabricate a moral code.

The remark that no individual can make a conscience for himself, that he needs a society to make it for him, is true only in part—true, because man is a social creature and a creature of tradition; his self-judgment is not of himself alone but importantly concerned with himself as identified with his fellows; but false, in that society is but an aggregate in which the individual remains an independent organism enjoying a private life of sensory and affective experiences, hopes and despairs, and exultations, and for whom public life is an additional and contingent experience. Man is individualized to a greater degree than any other creature. Apart from the simple calculation that from twenty-four chromosomes in the paternal and maternal germ cells, the total number of different combinations of chromosomes in the potential offspring of one man and one woman is nearly three hundred thousand billions—one hundred and fifty thousand times the population of the earth—the possibility for infinite diversification through the family and through personal experience warrants the conclusion that no two men are ever exactly alike, and most of them are very different. Consequently no one individual carries all possible potentialities or knows all the answers, and it is to man's collective advantage, both biologically and sociologically, to foster this diversity. Whence comes the ethic of the individual: the individual's integrity, dignity, and potentiality issue from the most basic biological mandate and comprise the basis from which all strictures of existence relative to morals, society, economics, law, and government must be derived.

To analogize between the human organism, the individual, the highest court of appeal in all human affairs, and the aggregate of individuals that comprises society is to fall into a grave biological error. No value, right, or virtue can be discovered in any pattern of living that does not stem from the individuals concerned. The argument that some essential superiority is inherent in the "state" is both biologically indefensible and dangerous because it runs counter to the indefeasible autonomy of the individual. Individual men must dictate their Bill of Rights, and not "society." But appended to the Bill of Rights is an unwritten Bill of Duties: sharing the benefits of collective effort in no measure abrogates man's individual responsibility. What man does, he does as an individual, what he would do, men as individuals must do. Nor can he expect others to do for him what he is not prepared to do for others.

All human history reveals that transcendental metaphysics is not only futile but dangerous. Those who have, frequently by dishonest means, foisted upon the naïve and gullible their own unsupported speculations have served to retard man's self-realization more than any other misfortune that has ever befallen him. History also reveals that man does not need any brand of transcendental metaphysics—his lasting contentments and achievements he has found wholly within the frame of reference that takes things as they are in the here and now. No pattern of living is written in the stars; each may be tried and esteemed according to the individual. No principle of justice is foreordained; justice must be realized between individuals as a reasoned compromise. No value can be capitalized; all values are fluxions in vital dynamics. No supernal power can aid him. He must find within himself the creative vision, the courage, and the will for his fulfillment.

Unhappiness, whether avoidable or not, too frequently comes in large pieces. But happiness is generally as fine-grained as life itself, and so intimately intermixed with living that it can be extracted from breathing, eating, sleeping, waking, from the humblest labor, from all achievement and creation and understanding, and few men need fail to accumulate a goodly store of it; all men can accumulate a larger store. Man does not need a machine to manufacture happiness, nor an oracle to tell him where to find it. It is a by-product of life, needing only to be separated from a dross of want and pain. When the scales weigh down beneath the latter, his self-reliance will not fail him; he will fall back on that most elemental of animal virtues—courage. A man can lose his god, but he cannot lose himself.

His fate was not decreed in the temple of Osiris, or written on the tablets of Marduk, or settled by Olympian conclave, or predestined by a righteous Yahweh. He has always had it clutched in his own hands; he need but open his fingers to read his lifeline; he need but close them resolutely upon the task in order to turn his dreams into reality. Then he will pronounce life good and cease to worry about that which at present lies beyond his ken, nor look back at the phantasmagoria that mark the past.

It is up to him. He alone by his own efforts can enlarge the bounds of empire, to the effecting of all things possible, to remolding this sorry scheme of things nearer to the heart's desire. He alone can see himself and his world in width and depth. He alone can choose, out of his vision of the present and the past, his future course.

14.

" Landfall "

Smith's only full-length novel, The End of Illusion, *was published by Harper and Brothers in 1935. The youthful hero goes off to Malaya in quest of an illusory personal freedom, resolved to avoid entanglement in matters of worldly concern. But the human involvement in which he finds himself from the moment of landing on the shores of the China Sea dispels any such illusion.*

Like most first novels, this one did not prove to be popular and Smith never tried another, but it is not too much to suppose that he could have achieved success as a novelist had he persisted. As a writer whose scientific wanderings took him about the world he successfully conveyed to the reader the feel of ships and the smell of the sea.

In the first of the two selections following, his hero finds himself at the sea's edge, on the brink of inescapable and tragic events.

THE SUN'S RAYS FELL ALMOST PERPENDICULARLY upon the white ship *Suddahdib* as she moved slowly off across the China Sea, towing an empty lighter behind her. For a moment the man watching from the shore wished he were back on board. He had looked her over a little disdainfully in Singapore, but now she was homely and familiar; she had little, comfortable places into which he fitted and a steady routine to which he had become accustomed; she had supplied him with the necessities, and not a few of the luxuries, of life; and she had carried him safely over many unseen miles, past unknown dangers, and had set him down where he wanted to be. He was a landlubber, yet he could understand why a sailor was enamoured of his ship—leaving her was leaving a familiar world, was a little like leaving some one you had loved. He sighed deeply. But why be sentimental over that tub? In truth, he was mightily relieved to be ashore, with the *Suddahdib* metaphorically behind him, and Batu Batu ahead.

He looked about him. The sand-spit upon which the *Suddahdib's* launch had landed him (the tide was out and Captain Sorenson had been wary of having the launch cross the bar at the river's mouth) was a narrow crescent thrown up by the wide and sluggish Sungai. At its outer end it disappeared so gradually beneath the water that its submerged contour could be followed far out to sea, while in the other direction it broadened slowly towards a far-off line of close-set palms. In the intervening distance the expanse of sun-lit sand was broken only by the cluster of casuarinas a hundred yards inland. He started to walk up the spit towards the mainland, but when he reached the trees he was tempted to linger beneath them, and took off his jacket and sat down in the shade. A long blast on the whistle told him that the *Suddahdib* was moving on; Captain Sorenson was telling him good-bye. He walked back into the sun and waved his helmet, suspecting that the captain would be watching him through the glass. When a second blast answered him, he returned to the shade and sat down again, leaning against a tree.

He lit a cigarette and stretched himself out to watch the *Suddahdib* move away towards the north, a small speck at the bottom of a high apostrophe of smoke. He wondered idly what would come next. Here he was in an unknown land, literally sitting on the end of a barren sand-spit with his luggage scattered about as though it had been dropped by the winds of heaven. He felt that he should get his things tucked decently under cover, but he was loath to hurry away–it was so delightful in the shade of the trees, whose feathery boughs arched down and, with their long annulated needles cast delicate kaleidoscopic patterns against the sky. The stillness of air and water, the contrast of blues and greens, lights and shadows, filled him with contentment and matched perfectly his moment of repose.

Yes, he was a happy man–probably, he thought, the happiest man in the world. His life was like the scene about him in its perfection. It was good to be away from routine and responsibility, and from people–particularly from people. It was all scarcely the less miraculous because it had sprung from Uncle John and a wholly unexpected bundle of gilt-edge bonds thick enough to keep away all earthly cares. Yet, having enough to eat, being able to buy a steamship ticket where and when one wanted it–those were but the first degrees of freedom. Personal alliances and social obligations could entangle a man as much as promissory notes. To be absolutely free required an isolation impregnable to the world, yet one that could be dissolved at will; and on the other side it required an inner contentment that in no way derived from outside oneself. To be perfectly free, in short, demanded that one be an agent of nothing but oneself. He was, in a sense, indebted to John Kerlow, cynic, bachelor, and philosopher, for that freedom, too.

He looked around the glaring sand beyond the shadow in which he sat and counted his luggage to make sure it was all there. The stuff was scattered from one side of the spit to the other. The devil take it, he thought; where had he picked it all up? China, Java, Singapore? He'd have to give half of it away or it would become a nuisance. The warm air seemed to bear a faint perfume of grass and flowers–faint indeed, but enough, when he shut his eyes, to evoke the fancy that he was lounging in an Oriental garden. He was sipping wine from an earthen cup the while he listened to a bearded poet reading from a scroll of ivory-tinted parchment embellished with red and blue ornaments and flecked with gold; the ground around the poet's feet was covered with petals where a dancing girl in passing had impertinently flicked a blossom-loaded rosebush with her hand. The rhythm of the verses half concealed the true import of the words, that dealt with love and destiny and death, and he vacillated between metre and meaning, captivated by the one and seeking the other. The words rose and fell like a pulse from the garden about him, compounded of wine and roses and nightingales, and then became words again, expressing in matched measures the sweet and bitter essences of aspiration and defeat—the twin elements of life that no alchemy could separate. "Ah, Love! could you and I with Him conspire to grasp this sorry Scheme of Things entire——"

The verse slipped away, and before he could recapture it he was in a Bedfordshire paddock green with spring grass and spattered with yellow buttercups, beside a poet of another day who was turning over and over on his lips the rough jewels of the Naishápúr philosopher and polishing them to precise and priceless gems, casting them into quatrains of eternal beauty. A dainty racing filly belonging to W. Browne came up to wonder and sniff at him, and when he broke off a long-stemmed buttercup and held it against her quivering nostrils she nibbled at it with an air of appreciation, then galloped down the hill, alarmed by his laughter. He was laughing at the tricks that memory played. For confounding time and space, he was at the next moment dreaming of one winter's day when he had sat before a fire while his Uncle John, staring out of the window at snow beating before a sharp wind off the Adirondacks, had, as the old man put it, tried to give him some good advice. "The greatest difficulty a man has is to get rid of his illusions. Some people *want* to believe that the moon is made of green cheese." What the advice may have been, Heaven only knew, but he smiled now at the ironic comment of the kindly man who for so many years had been his friend and mentor. And who by his death had become his unexpected benefactor. . . . A wish half-formed itself in his thoughts: if only one of those boxes were filled with books from Uncle John's library. . . . Then he laughed at the impracticability of it. No, if he had not acquired in all the years he had spent thumbing those heavy volumes some key to wisdom, some touchstone to carry in the wallet of common sense, there was not one of the books that could help him now. He was ashore at Batu Batu, on his own.

He opened his eyes to the blue sea. Only a wisp of smoke marked the *Suddahdib*. Yes, he was ashore at Batu Batu for better or for worse. He had whimsically chosen Batu Batu on the map because from there, it appeared, he could cross the mountains of Kelantan and thus enter Perak by an unbeaten track. It had seemed a sporting thing to do, not so much to venture into the jungles of the Peninsula as to test his power to go wherever he might choose. It was the sort of thing that John would have liked. And having brought a nephew up to be master in a boys' school, having educated him too generally and generously, perhaps, and having as much as said, "Take this, my boy, and buy that which your heart desires," he must certainly have seen the outcome. It was strange enough to be a dream. But it was no dream. He was free to take *his* world, at least, and, without shattering it to bits, "re-mould it nearer to his Heart's Desire." This was the goal and the reward of freedom. He was free to enjoy the kind of happiness that is compounded of the pleasure of sense, the appreciation of value, and the peace of tranquillity. Like an alchemist of old he could put into his pot such odds and ends as a stretch of blue sea with a smudge of smoke from the *Suddahdib*, a patch of paler blue sky with a wisp of cloud and a fringe of long down-curving boughs that gave off a faint odour in the tropic heat; from the mixture he could distil an ecstasy of bliss! Old John had always wanted a potto for a pet, a potto was such a queer animal; but he had died without getting it. Were the old man alive now, it would be a pleasure to go to Africa just to get him one. Poor old John. . . . Thus musing beneath the casuarina trees he fell asleep.

He was awakened by some one shouting "Hello!" He was so startled that he jumped up in confusion, his eyes half-blinded by the sudden influx of light from the white sand. A short, brown-haired, sunburnt man, dressed like himself in khaki shorts and jacket, was standing half a dozen paces off, laughing at him.

The man, seeing his confusion, held out his hand apologetically and made an evident effort to be hospitable.

"Excuse me for laughing, but you *were* comical. Did you doze off? David MacBride's my name. I heard the *Suddahdib* whistle, and I came down to see what it was all about. They just did put you ashore, heh? You look like Captain Kidd with all these boxes scattered over the sand. I hope you've pieces of eight in them."

He ignored the man's allusion and shook hands while explaining briefly who he was.

"So you're Ceylon Kerlow, the chap who is going over to Perak. Bence-Jones is expecting you. Why didn't you let him know when you were coming? He would have sent a boat down to take you up to the village."

Kerlow said that he himself had not known when he would arrive at Batu Batu, and asked who Bence-Jones might be and how he happened to be expecting him.

"Bence-Jones is the Commissioner of Kelantan. He had a telegram some time ago from a friend of yours in Government House saying you were on the way and giving you a royal sendoff. He's been looking for you ever since. This is a peculiar way to get to Perak from Singapore—something unusual afoot?"

Kerlow had not expected that anyone would be forewarned of his arrival. Apparently that friend of his, who was an Under Secretary at Singapore, had sent the telegram in a kindly but misadvised effort to help him out. He assured the stranger, who was carefully eyeing him up and down, that he would not think of troubling anyone to meet him. He was two days late, anyway; the *Suddahdib* had a lighter in tow, manned by a nit-wit crew, and she had stopped to pick it up a number of times after the tow-line had parted. Then a cylinder head had cracked, and once they had lost six hours down the coast, waiting for a consignment of three bags of rice. What with one thing and another, he couldn't expect to be met.

"I suppose Bence-Jones is accustomed to that. People never look for a coasting-vessel until they see her or hear her whistle. At that, I'll bet the Old Man will have the *Suddahdib* in Bangkok on time. Well, let's get your boxes into town. *Engkau*"—the man called an order in Malay to some one behind Kerlow's back, and when Kerlow looked around he was surprised to find a group of natives grinning and bowing good-naturedly to him. At a word from his companion they went after his luggage. "These boys followed me down to see the excitement. Now we'll put them to work."

"That's hardly fair," Kerlow remonstrated. "Perhaps they don't want to carry my stuff."

"They'll carry it if you tell them to. Why worry whether they want to or not? You can settle with one of the lot after we get to Mr. Bence-Jones's. He is expecting you to stay with him."

"But"—Kerlow hesitated a moment at this unexpected news—"the captain of the *Suddahdib* told me there was a rest-house here."

"Yes, there is a rest-house, but it's used mostly by Indians, and it's down in the mud. The mosquitoes are terrible. You wouldn't want to stay there."

"I think I would prefer—if I may—" Kerlow covered his hesitancy by stooping for his helmet and jacket.

"Very well—if you wish. Come along, then." There was a tone of injury in the man's words that was emphasized by a sudden elevation of the eyebrows; it might have induced Kerlow to make an apology for his iciness had it not been for the extraordinary manner in which the concluding command was given. It was virtually just that! Kerlow found himself standing alone, his helmet and jacket in his hands, staring with rising irritation at the back of this David MacBride. But after a moment he laughed at himself, and with an affectionate look at the casuarinas, hurried after the brown-haired stranger who had descended so abruptly into his life.

15.

“An Experience with Nakedness”

In the second selection from End of Illusion, *Smith expounds a religious motif, a theme of major interest in his nonscientific writings. His description of the religious eccentricities of a native Asian tribe again reveals his intense interest in the mysterious relationship between man and his gods.*

WHILE HE WAS RESTING FROM A LONG HUNT WITH Saladi—a hunt that had been wholly in vain, for not so much as a bird had they found in the valley where they had hoped to kill mouse deer—Kerlow lay on the ground, listening to the half-idle chatter of Chebubn and Pa Moa, occasionally aware of the pungent odour of *duryon* wafted downward from the near-by tree. In the tangle of dark-green leaves above he could make out one of the fruit, a brownish-green sphere larger than a coconut and covered with thick spikes giving it the appearance of a giant's mace. He had sat first at the foot of the tree, but the Orang-Utan had warned him to move away lest one of the *duryons* drop and drive its spikes into his skull. The fruit were ripe, and the heavy odour they gave off was like nothing, he thought, so much as a mixture of onions and limburger cheese. A *duryon* tree was one of the Orang-Utan's most cherished possessions, and they had to defend it not only against the marauding Malays, but against wild animals as well. Guided by the scent and sound of a falling fruit, the pig and the elephant would rush to the spot to devour the creamy meat inside, and unlucky was the *duryon*-owner who did not get there first, or pick his fruit in advance of its natural detachment.

"But what if you should find *rimau* there?" Kerlow asked in fun, knowing that they held the tiger in greater dread than any other beast.

The Orang-Utan admonished him to silence; it was dangerous, they said, to mention that name, for he might hear them and grow angry. They never let the dreadful word pass their lips above a whisper, but substituted for it a manual sign, a gesture of a striking paw with claws extended, and when Saladi gave a silent illustration Chebubn and Pa Moa looked timidly away. The tiger, they explained, usually hunted them in the dead of night and leaped upon them without warning, and in any case they were helpless before him because their poison darts could not penetrate his thick skin. The elephant, the venomous snake, the saladang were dangerous, too; yet they knew how to outwit or avoid these, but when the tiger roared in the forest the best the Orang-Utan could do was to flee. The tiger was *Karei's* policeman, sent to wreak vengeance upon them for their *lawaids*—and what man had no *lawaids* against him?

Kerlow realized now why the Orang-Utan, who had never seen a glove, who could scarcely imagine anything paler than his own tanned fingers, had been frightened beyond belief by his clawing gesture with a white cotton-covered hand. He was thankful that he had restrained an impulse to laugh at them.

Of what else were they afraid? Of the thunder, because it was *Karei's* voice roaring in anger at them. And of the other punishments that *Karei* inflicted upon them. He might strike a man down quickly with the storm or lightning, as a father might strike a child for disobedience, or he might send a slow pain to gnaw in the chest or groin until it killed.

It was *lawaid* to laugh at an animal in pain; to eat a cat, which was a sacred animal beloved by *Karei* even as the tiger, his own policeman; to kill certain kinds of monkeys; to marry blood relations; to throw a spear before noon; to express joy on returning to the encampment; to approach or address your mother-in-law if you were a man, or your father-in-law, if a woman; to look into a mirror under the open sky. And there were many others. *Karei*, it seemed, was a very jealous and arbitrary god. . . . Once upon a time, so the Orang-Utan related, they had been the only people in the forest. They had been happy then, with no pains in their bodies; there had been just as many women as men, fruit had been abundant, and there had been neither floods to drown them nor storms to strike them down. The trouble had come when the coconut monkey stole a brand of fire and with it kindled the grass so that the conflagration swept the land and the people fled in panic before the flames. Some went down the rivers to the sea, and these became the Malays who lived thenceforth by fishing or stealing. Others sought refuge in the mountains, where their hair was singed and became curly, and these were the ancestors of the Orang-Utan.

Since this separation the Malays had never been their friends. Once, not many years ago, the Malays had come to capture the Orang-Utan by driving them into a gorge pitted with elephant traps; they had taken most of the women away to a place where there was a big hole in the mountain and had given them to labourers, while the men had been tied up and left to the merciless beasts. Sometimes the Orang-Utan gathered resins and fruits and took them to the *kampongs* to trade, but they usually left their wares at the edge of the forest and returned later to collect whatever the Malays wished to give in exchange. The latter too often forced them to labour in the rice-fields, only to cheat them out of their honest pay when the work was done, and nothing less than starvation could drive them to work in the Malay *kampongs* for a scant handful of rice a day.

In these and many other ways *Karei* punished them, they knew not why. Perhaps a man in the beginning had offended him. His son, *Ta Pedn,* had made the earth and the fruits and flowers and animals upon it, for *Karei* himself was too great a lord to stoop to so lowly a task, but although *Ta Pedn* loved his earth, *Karei* was displeased with it and killed *Ta Pedn's* men with lightning, floods and sickness. It was clear he had no love for them. He made *lawaids* and punished men if they committed them, and he demanded the blood sacrifice to appease his wrath. *Karei* looked like a man, only he was big and terrible and shone with a bright, fiery light, so that no man could come near him without being burnt. To amuse himself he spent his time turning the table of the heavens from which six lianas hung down to earth, bearing at their ends the fruits and flowers of the seasons. Thus, rather indifferently, he provided fare for men. He ruled the kingdom of the dead, and the Milky Way was a girdle on his *sarong.*

Timidly, as though he were afraid the question might involve some heresy, Pa Moa interrupted to ask, "Why is *Karei's* girdle twisted upon itself?"

Kerlow shook his head and repressed a smile, though on the way home he thought, it is not a bad cosmology because it shifts responsibility. But *Karei's* little game of watching men trying to catch the fortune of life from a liana wheel as it swung by was something like teasing trapped animals, or laughing at one in pain. He had the Orang-Utan trapped between his thunder and lightning, his storm and flood; he had them hiding among the trees, not knowing which way to run to escape the prowling cat that he had set loose in the forest to watch them.

When he got to his shelter he took a mirror from his kit and asked Chebubn to show him how it could be used without *lawaid*.

Chebubn carefully held it face down and carried it under cover before he looked into it. When he returned it and Kerlow brazenly examined his own reflection under the sky, asserting that no harm befell him, the old man shook his head.

"It is *lawaid*, Tuan. You will be punished by the tiger, or sickness will take you and you will die."

"Why is it *lawaid*, Chebubn?"

"It always has been *lawaid*, Tuan, ever since *Ta Pedn* created the earth. It angers *Karei* to have us take the sky as a frame for our faces, for it is his, it is from there that he looks down."

Kerlow laid the mirror on the grass and leaned over it, marvelling. A great bank of white cloud floated below him—or so it seemed in the mirror—and beyond was an unending space of blue into which he might have toppled and fallen were he not braced by his hands upon the ground. What greater conceit could there be than to see one's face peering down from the very clouds and framed by the blue vault of heaven? From such an aspect an humble man could readily believe himself omnipotent and freed of all mortal chains! It was too tempting, too beautiful, too awful a sin to be played with lightly, so he turned the mirror face downward on the grass, nodding his head.

When Chebubn had gone away he returned to his shelter, to sit facing the setting sun. In the crescentic clearing that nestled at the far side of the mountain before him they would just now be gathering on the veranda for *pahits*. He wondered why he could not keep his eyes away from the direction of Kuala Lapan; he did not want to think about the people he had left there, but he found his glance always shifting towards the river valley as though he were expecting some apparition to rise from it to dispel the sense of incompleteness possessing his mind. Or was it a sense of apprehension? MacBride would call it conscience. He drove the questions away by telling himself that he was done with Kuala Lapan. It would be only two more days until he would meet K'he-at at the junction of the trail and, with his retinue behind him, turn his back upon the place for ever. . . .

He climbed down from the shelter and walked to the fire, where he stood watching the Orang-Utan cooking their evening meal. The more he grew accustomed to the black bodies and enigmatic faces of the dwarfs the more like himself they seemed to become. Could he cast off his superficial shell of rationalized belief, he would be as one of them. MacBride's words came back to him: an armour to insulate oneself from the world and ward off the trauma that it would otherwise inflict. The Doctor had been right, there: that armour was real enough; the trouble was that it was all inside, an armour of ideas. His newly made friends were an experience with nakedness. Their cosmology was as primitive as the primeval world in which they lived, and their character was moulded to fit as unobtrusively within that world as possible. Nature was more frequently an enemy than a friend. They could not hope to master it with bamboo knives and poison darts; and the maze of great trees, ferns, and lianas through which they penetrated impressed upon them constantly the ruthless and indomitable insurgence of its vitality. Against it a man had to pick his way as best he could, disturbing his environment little, but having his own plastic being shaped to accord with the pressing, entangled forest about him. And yet, though fear might seize him when the storm uprooted the aged monarchs and sent them to the ground, crushing everything beneath them, that fear gave way to joy and confidence when the storm had passed and the sunlight, warm and vitalizing, shone down upon the prostrate trees and stirred new plants to life. Then, his spirit quieted by the serenity of solitude, he took new courage, rebuilt the shelters that the storm destroyed, and went on with the business of living.

And through it all things had to be explained. The Orang-Utan said that the dead went to a far-away country, called *Talogn,* lying beyond the mountains where the sun went down. Men's joints were dislocated when they entered the kingdom of the dead because they no longer needed to use them, and they ate only the shadows of fruits and tubers succulent beyond belief.

Talogn was a far journey, so the living buried food and water with the dead to help them on their way, or, as sometimes happened, to nourish them in case they decided to return to the haunts of men. It was not uncommon, Pa Moa insisted, for the dead to return; he had pointed out an old, shrivelled woman who had died and come back twice. On one of their walks they passed an empty grave, a shallow hole covered with boughs and light earth, with a lateral recess for the body so that it should not be pressed upon. It had probably been raided by a jackal, but as Kerlow eyed the dried fruit and water-cup, he thought how frequently, with no sure criterion of death, the apparently dead might rise from their shallow graves and, partaking of the fare intended for their journey elsewhere, seek to rejoin those who had left them prematurely in the earth. Though no spark of comprehension of that dark hour might linger in their memories, what tales the imaginative could tell if prompted to talk by pride, or jealousy, or some other all too human stimulus.

Death was constantly before their eyes, but they wanted to go on living. So they avoided it and planned against it as best they could, and in the end they refused to believe that it was final. They refused to believe that life could end, so they said that the dead went to the land of *Talogn*, to be ruled by the powerful and fearful princeling called *Karei*—how powerful and fearful you could better understand if you had experienced the terrifying violence of the lightning that seared the mountain-sides, or run from the sudden flood that carried everything before it; if you had lived in the shadows of the forest always alert for the strike of the tiger, or suffered the pain of disease in your loins or chest and knew not which way to run to escape the death that pain foreboded, then you feared not only *Karei*, but all the *lawaids* that might evoke his wrath. And you respected his favourite animal, the cat, propitiated his policeman, the tiger, or you paid *Karei* his blood sacrifice to save your life. . . .

Kerlow had tried to get the Orang-Utan to tell him about the blood sacrifice, but they evaded all his questions. He had learned that the sacrifice was made when *Karei* roared in violent anger and his voice echoed among the hills. This was all he knew until his last night in Kampong Tajong, when he was awakened by the roaring of a storm far off in the valley of the Sungai. The sequence of flashing light and clap of thunder recurred at diminishing intervals as the storm moved up the mountains, and the constant repetition of its threat was enough to fill the bravest with alarm. He peered out from behind his *rotan* mat and saw that the dwarfs were terrified beyond words; the embers in the centre of the *kampong* had been fanned to flames and piled with wood, and by the light he could see men and women slipping out of their shelters after fuel and darting to the fire with it, imploring *Karei,* as they stoked the flames higher and higher, to stay his wrath. At last, with a sudden chilling of the air, the electrical storm engulfed them. Peal after peal of thunder exploded so near that it seemed to threaten physical violence by its detonation. The Orang-Utan, driven now to the extremity of fear, rushed about the *kampong,* stabbing their legs and groins with sharp splinters until the blood spurted out in freely-flowing streams; they caught the warm, precious fluid in receptacles and tossed it into the air and sprinkled it over the ground—for was not red blood the very substance of life, and could not life be saved by offering some of its substance to the vengeful god of death to appease his thirst, that he might return to his kingdom of the dead and leave the living alone? . . .

The storm broke at last and the Orang-Utan stumbled back to their shelters through the perpendicular streams of rain that quenched the fire and washed the blood stains from the trees and ground. The water soaked through the *hapoi* leaves and dripped onto the bodies of men and women trembling with joy because *Karei* had spared them the destruction of his wrath. Into the downpour that lasted for an hour Kerlow once had thrust his hand to make certain that it was colourless water and not red blood drenching the earth. He shivered in his dripping shelter, not with cold, but with horror of this ritual to which men were driven by their fear of death and by which they sought to ward off destruction by the payment of a price. And he saw for the first time how an atavistic cycle of supernal life—god—sin—fear—and atonement had been spun around the fact of death and so implanted in the thoughts of men that it persisted into their enlightened days and dominated their way of thinking long after their primitive cosmology had been outgrown.

After the storm had passed he found that he could not sleep; he was oppressed by the memory of the violent disturbance of nature that had engulfed him, by the memory of the sacrificial rites, and by the sound of water dripping monotonously on his shelter-roof. At last he took a blanket and went to a rocky shelf outside the *kampong*, where he lay upon his back and watched the sky through the breaking clouds around the mountain-top. It was not long before the stars, the spangles on *Karei's sarong*, showed in a wide expanse above his head, each star twinkling as though it hung loosely by a thread from the princely garment of black velvet.

Words. . . . Words were such empty things until experience filled them with meaning. Take that word star, for an example: a bright object just too far away for a child to reach; or a spangle on a royal gown; or a heavenly body inconceivably remote, gigantic, torrid, and moving through space with an inconceivable velocity to fill an astronomer's dreams with puzzling computations; or only one in a cluster of countless stars, a single point in a cloud that was itself but a minor condensation in a galaxy apart from other galaxies without ultimate number or ultimate meaning—all to perplex philosophers who would grasp the whole in one inadequate word. . . . Across the widening rift the nebulous band of the Milky Way stretched like a richly embroidered girdle twisted upon itself: the great Galaxy of Sagittarius, an incandescent, spiralling pinwheel of a million stars whirling in the immensity of black space and holding in its midst, halfway towards its outer edge, a meagre sun shining upon nine dark satellites; from one of which (the third, counting from the centre, according to Copernicus) men looked forth in one direction and saw nothing but their own small star because it filled the sky with its golden light, while in the other direction they looked into the night and saw the flattened Galaxy of which they were a part as a luminous band across the heavens, a girdle on *Karei's sarong*, a Milky Way. . . .

Or take the word God. The Orang-Utan, out of love of life and fear of death, had invented *Talogn*, where their beings, as shadowy images of flesh and desire, could be perpetuated when life was ended; and they had set up in this domain a prince to personify the fearsome world against which they had to spend their strength, fashioning him in their own image, and calling him *Karei.* Civilized man had softened the features of the phantom ruler by endowing him with a measure of benevolence, but he was still delineated in the likeness of the male of the biped animal, man; he still possessed animal faculties—omniscience, an infinite expansion of the animal faculty for knowing, and omnipotence, an infinite expansion of the animal faculty for doing; he was all-loving, yet he demanded submission and delighted in obeisance as any Malay princeling solicitous of his selfish power; and he still created the world by blowing a bubble of a universe, and watched its evolution even as *Karei* amused himself by turning a liana wheel, for apparently no better reason than to pass away the tedium of time. . . .

Such was the Divine Idea. Poetically, it envisaged a wizardry spinning planet-dust and sun-fire into loving human eyes; and poetically, it neglected to explain why life and its history, and all the history of the cosmos, was a battle such as the Orang-Utan had to fight against *Karei.* Planet-dust and sun-fire might do well enough for a beginning, but it was another matter to have the stroke of the lightning and the tiger's paw, the sweep of famine and the scythe of plague, shrouded forever in the densest mystery. To the adolescent child, loving human eyes might seem ideal; but he for one rebelled against enthroning a half-witted and irresponsible affection over the entire universe. No, the Divine Idea was of little use in life, and as for death, what logic or recompense was there in having a single mortal passion paradoxically immortalized?

One felt so much safer believing that causes resided in things themselves, and not in some mystical heaven. He was glad for himself, Kerlow thought, that men had had the courage to wrest their fortunes from the empyrean and examine them on a mundane plane.

When the sun's rays, filling the sky with opalescent pink,

cut off the light from the stars Kerlow shook the wet leaves from his blanket and returned to the *kampong*. Under an old mat he found dry wood, and with it kindled a fire, realizing that this was the last time he would ever cook a meal among the Orang-Utan, for he was scheduled to meet K'he-at at the junction of the trails in the afternoon.

16.

"The Whirlpool of Life"

Kamongo, *which Smith wrote in 1930 to occupy his time during the boredom of a Pacific crossing was first published in 1932. It is probable that more of his contemporaries knew him as the author of this successful book than for any other achievement. Written in the form of a novel, it could hardly be called one, being more of a philosophical dialogue with two characters and no plot. And yet Smith has penned a narrative that will not soon be forgotten, the story of two men aboard ship, one a priest, the other a scientist, and their talk of life, of God, and of man's beliefs. In the hands of a lesser writer,* Kamongo *would probably not have survived the handicap of its own form, for the reading public dislikes "talk pieces." The many editions through which this book has gone, however, amply attest the artistry and skill of the man who wrote it. Smith's style is unobtrusive and at the outset calls no attention to itself. Only after some acquaintance with it does the reader become conscious of the simplicity and poetic imagery with which Homer Smith put words together. This propensity shows itself in all he ever wrote; it can certainly be credited, in part, with the success of* Kamongo.

As our final selection from the writings of Homer Smith, we reprint the chapter from Kamongo *in which the life process is likened to a whirlpool. This now famous discourse broaches many of the philosophical problems which concerned Smith throughout his life.*

JOEL TOSSED THE KEY-RING with which he was playing into the air, and thrust it back into his pocket. He turned to the bulwark and leaned over to watch the series of smooth waves that marched alongside at the foot of the steep prow.

"What a pessimist you are, Joel! . . . Though I must say you do talk well for the first cousin of an anthropoid ape."

The Padre squirmed himself into a more comfortable position, half on his back.

"But you *are* discouraging. I still think there is some loophole in your damnable mechanistic doctrine through which I can escape. Life and evolution must have some meaning for me as well as for you, but as you interpret it, it is meaningless.

"Even if I grant that my emotional instincts are—what shall I say, animalistic reactions?—and therefore unworthy of an ultimate appeal, I still am not satisfied on the grounds of pure reason with your explanation of things. Beyond the realm of the phenomena which we can see and measure, behind the whole process of evolution and within the warm pulse of life itself, there is an Unknown which neither you nor I nor any man can ever fully comprehend. You as a scientist have your attention fixed upon the known while I, being what my sounding-board has made me, prefer to turn my eyes toward that more distant horizon.

"I cannot remain content with a philosophy that is out of step with science; I want to go along with science and understand it. The scientific spirit is one aspect of life which has proved its worth, both pragmatically and intellectually—yes, and aesthetically, too. There is grandeur and beauty in your scientific saga as in the Psalms of David—I love them both. I am a man of two parts: a man of faith and a man of action. It is not enough for me to say, 'God made it thus'; for I must always ask myself, 'Do I see it as God made it?' So I would step closer and obtain a nearer vision of the Unseen by treading the path of reason, by walking along with you. . . .

"At night, after the African drum which does duty for a church bell has rolled out its summons to prayers, I ponder on it; when the village is safely asleep under the heavy-eyed and misty stars and there is no sound except the incessant whirring of cicadas or the occasional bark of a stray ape up to some mischief in the maize, I walk among the acacias with evolution in one hand and astronomy in the other. I am lost, not in a web of emotional confusion, but in the sheer tangle of my reason trying to put them all together and to make them fit into a coherent whole. I go from a theory of Special Creation to one of Evolution without finding any that satisfies me, and without finding a God Who is compatible with either. . . . What you say about man is true, he is a beast; and life is filled each day, as throughout its evolution, with pitfalls, with blind alleys. The bitter cruelty of man, the hardness of his lot, his hapless fate, are difficult to reconcile with the smooth orbits of the stars, the geometry of a crystal. Life alone seems to be devoid of order. Only in us is God incomprehensible . . . but surely He has not so hidden His countenance that we cannot obtain some little light to guide our steps. . . . Only by seeing God in us are we comprehensible. I do not ask to know the ultimate beginning and the ultimate end of life, but only how to find the open road. . . . Which way, O Life, shall I turn now?"

"I cannot help you." Joel turned back from the water. "Isn't it said that you can only find God by faith alone? . . . Modern science cannot take you any nearer your unseen horizon than could the science of ancient Greece or Babylonia. Some scientists think that it can, but they are only fooling themselves. Scientific knowledge comprises the world of the known and the knowable, and hypotheses based upon the known are scientific hypotheses; the validity of science and its hypotheses rests upon proof by correspondence with reality. Beyond these there is only the great vacuity of the unknown, and science cannot stop you, and fundamentally is not interested, if you as a man of faith or as a philosopher wish to jump off into that vacuity; except to say that there is nothing in history to indicate that you will accomplish anything by doing so. . . . Special Creation is as good a doctrine to jump into as any other, for all those who would instil something into matter in order to make life are only Special Creationists squeezed out of shape by trying to square themselves with experience. Whenever they come to a tempting gap in our knowledge—whether it be vital spirits and animal heat or the limitations of physical measurement—they put their fingers on it and say: 'Here is God.' At heart, what they want to do is to put into the Universe *purpose* where there is only *process;* to put plan *before* the even rather than *after.* They want to mark the sparrow's fall, not by the laws of Chance, but by the Hand of God. So they peer out past the outlying ramparts of science to discover if there is a Deity hovering near; not realizing, when they find Him, that either He must devour them or they must devour Him—either they must post a sign toward science saying, 'Here is where you get off!' or they must be prepared to amputate a slice off their Deity at any future time and to graft it on to the body of verifiable knowledge. . . . No, you can never find God by walking with me. . . . When you start back for your temple in the jungle, you should leave your biology at home. For life is a phenomenon of Nature, and the more we dig into natural law the more we find of the laws of chance."

The Padre shook his head, and held up a hand as though to stop Joel from talking. After a moment he got up and rested his elbows on the opposite bulwark, staring into the darkness ahead.

"You cannot so lightly discount the Unknown, Joel. As a scientist you do not neglect the unknown. You calculate on it in every step you take. You extrapolate from the known to the unknown every day, and, if I understand correctly, that is in great part how you make progress. You do not speak of 'Jumping off into the unknown' when you speculate, as I presume you must, on matters pertaining to geology, or to your lungfish. You speculate in part because you want everything to be reasonable, to fit together, to make sense.

"Yet when you add it all together, in your total philosophy you dismiss the greatest unknowns of all—the Beginning and the End of things, the Whence and Whither—with a shrug. Almost a contemptuous shrug. You speak of the laws of chance with respect, but you are almost resentful of what I call God. Are you afraid of Him? Is it such a small gap in your knowledge that you do not know why evolution has come about, why we and the sun, moon, and stars are here, that you can ignore it as unworthy of your consideration?

"I suspect you are overlooking a great many Unknowns. You know a lot about that lungfish of yours, but come with me up the Ruvuma River and see something with which you are possibly not so familiar. See my boys clearing the jungle to set out plantains and maize in long, straight rows. See their woodworking shops where they make baskets and tables and chairs. Watch them in their homes, see how they love their children, see their courage against adversity, their fortitude against suffering. See how grateful they are not only for the quinine and little medicines we give them, and the occasional surgery, but for every new thing we bring them—for the schools where they cannot only study their own dialects but learn Swahili and English, if they have a talent for it; for their increasing knowledge of themselves and of the outside world. Yes, and for the Golden Rule. Oh, they are bad, sometimes, very bad, but they can also be very good. Sometimes I am very angry with them, but mostly I love them, lowly creatures that they are. . . . Did the lungfish evolve new eyes when it crawled out upon the land? I do wish you could come up the Ruvuma River with me, Joel; you would enjoy my black boys."

"They aren't 'lowly creatures,' Padre. I don't like that expression. There is a wide range of individual aptitude in every race, but there is no convincing evidence that intrinsic aptitude differs significantly among the major races of mankind. Send them to college and they will be teaching biology and physics. And theology, I dare say. Only I wish they'd stick to biology and physics."

"You really think they are capable of going that far? I don't mean theology—" the Padre laughed, "—I mean just biology and physics?"

"Of course they are. It's largely a matter of background and training just as in any animal stock.

"Of course you love them, and they love you. . . . And I am not resentful of your God. Neither am I afraid of Him or of the Unknown, and neither do I dismiss the Unknown with a contemptuous shrug. Only as a scientist I am convinced that I do not know anything about God, and I cannot talk about something that I know nothing about. He may be there, but I cannot accept as proof any of the evidences that have hitherto been presented, and, as the astronomer La Place told Napoleon *à propos* of astronomy, one has no need of that hypothesis. As a scientist I do extrapolate into the unknown, yes, but only where I can test the extrapolation. One cannot test your hypothesis, and however well it may satisfy your hunger for an answer to the Great Unknowns, it does not satisfy mine. It is, in fact, no answer at all. It will not jibe with the lungfish, with any of the verifiable facts of this admittedly grotesque scheme of things. I would rather say that I don't know, and stick to what I do know. It is one thing to speculate about the Unknown–it is another to let it shape the pattern of your life in any way. The one is harmless, the other dangerous. You would still be in Tanganyika whatever kind of God you believed in, a good God, an evil God, or one who was both good and evil, or no God at all."

The Padre laughed. "Yes, I think you are right. . . . And you can't prove the existence or nonexistence of God by argument. It is a matter of faith–I choose to believe, and you do not."

"Just a moment." Joel interrupted. "I have not denied the existence of any one or an infinite number of deities. I simply choose not to talk about that about which I know absolutely nothing. You would, I take it, persuade me to take your God into my scheme of things. Now, I ask you, Is your God Good, or is He Evil, or is He both? We can start from there. . . ."

The Padre laughed again, roguishly. "No, Joel, we are not going to start from there. We are going to start from your lungfish. I think you contradict yourself! You say that life is a phenomenon of Nature; yet life has risen in spite of Nature; it has risen above her until it over-rides her, uses her, dominates her. You can't do that with a *part* of Nature without adding something to it. You talk about life flowing on through new forms, trying to keep alive. Almost waiting until accidental mutations come to its advantage, yes, but all the time there is this will to live. And yet you do not know what life is, this life that flows through bird and beast and man. The biologists, I think, talk about protoplasm as the 'physical basis of life,' which implies to me that protoplasm is the machinery by which something that

I call 'life' carries on this business of living. Can your protoplasm explain the insurgence that has carried life over obstacle after obstacle in its evolution? Can it explain the sentience that every organism shows to some degree? Can it explain the fight that every organism puts up to keep on going?

"Perhaps we cannot see ourselves clearly because of our emotional confusion, but we should certainly be able to see an amoeba, let us say, without prejudice. Yet your protoplasm does not tell you why an amoeba grows, why it reproduces itself, why it is so nicely adjusted to its environment, or why it goes on being an amoeba instead of turning suddenly into something else. Life is different from the rest of Nature because it is forever pushing uphill in its search for freedom, while the universe is forever cooling off, running down."

"No, there is something wrong with your cave-man's picture. There is something missing from it; something that not only supplies the will to live but pushes forward, even when it gets itself into blind alleys! That is why I say that you don't know what life is—you only know *how* it lives, and there is a big difference."

Joel turned back to the yellow, fan-shaped beam that cut sharply through the surrounding blackness and illuminated the water and the sandy shore ahead. It seemed to possess some tangible golden substance which it sprayed like paint over the landscape, and as it crept forward at a steady pace the formless shadows which it engulfed became stones, or posts, or eerie masses of machinery that were sharply defined in scintillating radiance. He straightened up and ran his hands along the cold iron edge of the bulwark.

"No, we don't know what life is, but we must find out what it is from how it works. I admit, so far as protoplasm is concerned, that there may be something wrong with the picture. . . . I sometimes wonder if we don't look at life, at protoplasm, in the wrong way. I wonder if we do not see it backwards, upside down, wrong side out! Perhaps that slimy jelly is not really the 'physical basis of life,' as Huxley called it, but merely a pile of driftwood, a mantle of debris thrown up around the centre where life is. If so, perhaps it obscures the living centre from our view. We would have to tear the jelly away, as you tear away the slime from around a spitbug, to find the living focus at its heart."

The Padre squatted on the floor again and thrust his hands into his coat pockets.

"Are you going over to a dualistic theory of mind and matter?" he asked, looking up at Joel with an amused smile.

"No," Joel answered, "nothing like that. I remain a mechanist, I am only going consistently back along the course of mechanistic evolution. We have asked ourselves, Did the reptile exist before the mammal, the invertebrate before the vertebrate, the protozoan before the metazoan; why not ask, Did not life exist before the mantle of flesh in which we now find it clothed? I was thinking that perhaps it did. I was thinking—if I may indulge in pure fantasy—that at the heart of that gelatinous blob of protoplasm there may be something utterly primitive and simple—something, say, like a whirlpool."

"Heavens!" the Padre interjected. "Isn't protoplasm complex enough without putting a whirlpool inside it?"

Joel shrugged his shoulders. "That's the trouble—it's too complex. It has the complexity of a multitude of effects that can issue from a single source. I was looking for the source, something that is simplicity itself. That is why I chose a whirlpool—a whirlpool of sunlight, if you wish, or, if you prefer a more technical term, call it an eddy in the Second Law of Thermodynamics."

The Padre laughed. "I'm worse off now than I was before."

Joel flashed a smile at his companion, then jumped down from the bracket and paced back and forth along its edge.

"What I mean is"—he stopped suddenly to make a gesture with his hand—"did you ever have among your toys a gyroscope? Do you remember, when the wheel was spinning rapidly, how the thing felt in your hand? How it resisted you when you tried to turn it over, pushing back against your fingers with such uncanny power? And when it was forcibly laid on its side, how it straightened itself up at once? Well, life is something like that. . . .

"It's a crude analogy, but try to imagine a flowing river and note where it strikes against a sandbar of just the right shape." Joel pointed his fingers at the Padre's feet and began to make rapid, circular motions. "Part of the water is deflected from its course and thrown into a whirling motion. That whirlpool is a dynamic entity, a thing apart from the smoothly flowing river in which it has its being."

He waved his hand toward the brilliant stars above them.

"Now turn from the river of water to the universe around us: you say the universe is running down. I would put it another way—I would say that we live in a river of free energy that tends to flow from a higher level to a lower one. The living organism is an arrangement of matter engaged in absorbing, storing, and spending a little of this energy. By doing so, it seems to swim against the major stream.

"Perhaps life is to this river of energy what the whirlpool is to the flowing water, a consequence of sunlight striking upon the dust and being deflected into some special motion, just as the whirlpool is a consequence of water striking upon the sand-bar."

Several minutes passed before the Padre spoke. The silence was broken only by the notes of the ship's bell striking the hour, and the lower tones of the forecastle bell echoing back a few seconds later.

"But life has a purpose, it has power and knowledge—there must be something to it besides a mere spin of energy like a whirling dervish in the wind——"

"Right!" Joel interrupted him. "That is just why I called it a whirlpool. . . . A whirlpool, you see, when once set in motion tends always to continue in that motion, and it opposes destruct-ion with an almost intelligent resistance. If friction wears the whirlpool down, then the river speeds it up again so that it is always whirling, whirling. It has a will to live that is born of its momentum. And it has power, borrowed from the river, to resist invasion or deflection from its course. And it has knowledge, for it tends always to right itself if it is pushed out of a position of equilibrium.

"Life is like a whirlpool in many ways. . . . When once set a-going, it spins on and on. It is not self-sustained because its energy is but borrowed from the river, being constantly renewed upstream and discharged below. If you deprive it of that energy it dies. In its tendency to spin on forever there is life's purpose—to go on living. So long as the sunlight flows, the whirlpool is charged with power, for the energy which is turned into it can reappear as force to resist invasion or deflection from its course. But most importantly, the whirlpool is intelligent, for it is endowed by its dynamic nature with discrimination toward the world about it, and with the tendency to seek those states which disturb it least. When it is disturbed, it automatically reacts to bring itself back into a balanced state, into a condition of well-being. It is that dynamic balance which is life's sentience; it is the prompt reaction, when that balance is upset, that is life's activity. To paraphrase an old law of physiology, 'Life never acts; it only reacts. . . .'

"There are the cardinal features of life, born of the momentum of a whirlpool: a will to live, power to live, intelligence to live. There is no cell, there is no protoplasmic jelly, yet life is on its way. Before it is ever clothed in that jelly it wants to live and it has the power to live, and within limits it knows how to go about living. And all that it wants is to go on living!"

"Then what is the protoplasmic jelly for?"

"It is not *for* anything. It is a pile of debris around the whirlpool. . . . See how the leaves and twigs float into the whirlpool in the river and are picked up and hurled about until they are thrown out upon the shore: so molecules float into our whirlpool in the sunlight and are momentarily caught up in the vortex of its activity and get battered about until they are broken and rearranged into complex organic compounds before they are shot out at the periphery. Some of them stick together and form a jelly that is pushed out and out as far as the whirlpool can push. . . . Thus is your protoplasmic mantle spun and you have a cell—an extraordinarily complex mass which the organic chemist hasn't unravelled yet, and the physical chemist is jolly well lost in the intricacies of its enzymes and surface tensions; but who ever saw a junk pile that wasn't a bewildering conglomeration?

"Watch how it works. Our whirlpool is surrounded by an environment that bombards it continually and tends to choke it up with indigestible debris. It must do battle with that environment every second, matching only its momentum against whatever obstacles it meets. With good luck, the battle may be drawn out endlessly, while the whirlpool cries, 'Won't die!' and environment cries, '*Must die!*' . . . '*Won't die!– Must die!–Won't die!–Must die!*' . . . There is the pulse of life that beats in every cell–there is the pulse by which life has beat its way up the long road of evolution–and the first protoplasm was the first beat of that pulse, it was born of the first battle.

"I say with luck, for just as life came into being by the chance encounter of sunlight and matter, so its continued existence from hour to hour hangs on the chances that it can keep on going in the face of injury, that it won't be suffocated by its own cellular debris. The evolution of the first cell was an infinitely bigger jump than the evolution of ape to man. That cell is a dynamic mass of enzymes and reactive compounds so equilibrated with each other that, if pressed upon at any point, the impulse is transmitted inwardly and answering forces from within are carried back. If the mantle is bruised, fresh materials are forced into the hole and the wound heals.

"The protoplasmic mass is itself an encumbrance. By shutting out the sunlight it tends to pull the whirlpool down; as the pile of debris grows bigger the dynamic center spins more slowly, until it all but dies. . . . But in dying, it divides into two cells. Look at how a whirlpool dies–you can watch the process in your bathtub, or in a whirlwind or a waterspout. Viewed from the side, a symmetrical whirlpool looks like two cones meeting at their points. So long as it is going at full speed these cones adhere together, but as it slows down they pull apart so that there is only half a whirlpool above and half a whirlpool below, separated by a more or less inactive region in the middle. As the pile of debris around our whirlpool of sunlight increases in size, it is retarded until it breaks into two parts; in the centre the forces which push out the protoplasmic jelly are diminished, and this jelly, falling back through instability and disintegration, shrinks into the cell—and itself divides into two parts—into two equal daughter cells each having one half a whirlpool. But in the matter of whirlpools a part is as good as a whole and, as soon as the retarding effect is removed, the missing halves restore themselves and begin to throw up new piles of protoplasmic jelly, continuing until they themselves, choked down again and dying, divide; thus one cell into two, two into four, four into eight, *ad infinitum.* So the whirlpool escapes from the pile of debris which accumulates around its edges by dividing and starting over.

"It is, by the laws of chance, impossible for a single whirlpool to last forever because sooner or later some accident would inevitably destroy it. But by multiplication of its numbers its chances of survival are also multiplied; and so our would-be immortal whirlpool escapes the threat of death that lurks in the laws of chance even while it is escaping the threat of death that lurks in the accumulation of debris around it. . . .

"It has won three battles, it is three paces nearer to realizing its innermost wish for immortality. It has escaped the threat of death that lurks in its random encounters with environment; it has escaped the threat of death that lurks in the debris piled up as a result of these encounters; and it has escaped the threat of death that lurks in the very laws of chance by multiplying itself into a large number of individuals. It has become an organism that grows spontaneously to a fixed size and shape, and that heals itself after injury; it has a rudimentary perception of the world about it and the necessary intelligence to interpret the information in relation to its own well-being; it has power to gain its ends, and power stored away in fuel for those hours when the river is not flowing; it undergoes spontaneous and perfect division when it reaches maturity, and thus tends to multiply itself in numbers and to spread into all the habitable parts of the earth. And it has a will to live that carries it on and on!

"We need not worry yet about the complexity of the sandbar upon which our whirlpool spins; for in these days our ideas of matter, like real sandbars, are shifting overnight. There are several different kinds of life—perhaps the green plants and the animals, the sulphur bacteria, the filterable viruses, and many other kinds of living things have each had a different origin, or perhaps they are only different habits of the same life stream. But they are all just local eddies in the river of energy that flows around them. The apparent complexity of the higher animals tends to obscure life's real simplicity, for out of its long history it has acquired a manifold design. There have come to be cells which, though dividing, yet remain together in delicate balance to make a multicellular organism. These cells have come, through the potentialities of the mother cell, to be differentiated into a body of highly specialized parts—skin, muscles, nerves, glands, receptors, bones—so that by this division of physiological labour the efficiency of each is increased; but these cells have no powers or properties that are not inherent in the fundamental plan.

"During this evolution into a body of specialized parts it has come to pass that certain cells have been set aside to carry on the stream of life—the germ cells—by beginning anew and spinning another body. Perhaps this is because the great specialization of the body cells renders them unfit to serve a genetic role, and perhaps there is an advantage to be gained by putting the germ cells away where they will not be bruised by a rude world. But it is thus that death finally came about. The lower animals that multiply by division are immortal for, as someone has said, you cannot speak of death where there is nothing left to bury. But the flesh of the higher animals is too specialized, this pile of debris is too cumbersome, to be of further use; so after it has matured and been given an opportunity to pass on the seed of life, it is thrown aside. And the whirlpool escapes through the germ cell, to fight another battle. . . .

"It has come about that organisms have learned to draw the energy to keep their whirlpools going not directly from the sunlight but from the dead substance of other organisms; until the fisherman lives upon fish which live upon crustaceans which live upon infusorians which live upon diatoms, while only the diatoms still live directly in the sunlight stream. Life has gained, perhaps, its greatest freedom by this cannibalistic habit, but it has not changed its nature, for, fisherman or diatom, it is still sunlight spinning within the cell.

"It has come about that the natural forces of that primordial organism are made manifest in ways that are variegated beyond belief;

"Until life lives in bodies that are big and small, in bodies that are born from a spore, from an egg, or from a mother's womb; in bodies that last a week, a month, or threescore years and ten; in bodies that are of two sexes or only one; in bodies that have long noses, short noses, or no noses at all;

"Until life has broken itself into hundreds of thousands of species and has spread itself into the depths of the ocean, the heights of the mountains, the air, into caverns, coal mines, icebergs, hot springs;

"Until the scorpion has poison on the tip of its tail and the cobra poison at the roots of its fangs; until the flower has honey in its heart and the bee honey in its comb;

"Until the spider revels in the shadows and the bird in the sunshine and the biologist in all of them!

"Yes, life has spun itself into a web that is infinitely complex with interrelations, interdependencies—but it makes no difference; it is the same sunlight spinning the same matter in all of us—in you and me, the bird, the tree, the worm, the diatom; only the life-habit of the whirlpool, the number of whirlpools in our bodies, and the intricate pattern of their arrangement are in each of us a little different. . . .

"One should not be surprised that there is a remarkable 'fitness' between life and the world it lives in, for the fitness of the living organism to its environment and the fitness of environment to the living organism are as the fit between a die and its mould, between the whirlpool and the river bed. What we should note is that the fit is neither perfect nor permanent, because environment is not constant in its character for a fleeting instant; it changes with every breeze and sound, with every light and shadow. The battle is never finished and the pulse of life beats on . . . *Won't die!—Must die!—Won't die!—Must die!* . . . It throbs anew each second into the substance of its flesh, into its healing, its reproduction, its rhythms, its activities, its further evolution–into its innermost wish. . . . But still it is not intelligent enough to keep itself out of blind alleys–of mud or philosophy, or of speculating about its own nature!"

Joel laughed and shook his head. "No, I do not know what life is. But I think that it is something like that; like a whirlpool stirred up in the dust by sunlight that, spinning on and on, of its own momentum presses always against its environment where the blind alleys are cut off and the rest escapes through different ways of spinning."

APPENDICES

APPENDIX A

Bibliography of the Writings of Homer W. Smith from 1918 to 1962

On dichlorethylsulphide (mustard gas).

I. The systemic effects and mechanism of action. V. Lynch, H. W. Smith, and E. K. Marshall, Jr. *J. Pharmacol. and Exper. Therap.*, 12: 265, 1918.

II. Variations in susceptibility of the skin to dichlorethylsulphide. E. K. Marshall, Jr., V. Lynch, and H. W. Smith. *J. Pharmacol. and Exper. Therap.*, 12: 291, 1918.

III. The mechanism of absorption by the skin. H. W. Smith, G. H. A. Clowes, and E. K. Marshall, Jr. *J. Pharmacol. and Exper. Therap.*, 13: 1, 1919.

A relation between the volume and the velocity of some organic ions. Homer W. Smith. *J. Phys. Chem.*, 24: 540, 1920.

Quantitative studies in chemotherapy.

I. The trypanocidal action of antimony compounds. Carl Voegtlin and Homer W. Smith. *J. Pharmacol. and Exper. Therap.*, 15: 453, 1920.

II. The trypanocidal action of arsenic compounds. C. Voegtlin and H. W. Smith *J. Pharmacol. and Exper. Therap.*, 15: 475, 1920.

III. The oxidation of arsphenamine. C. Voegtlin and H. W. Smith. *J. Pharmacol. and Exper. Therap.*, 16: 199, 1920.

IV. The relative therapeutic value of arsphenamine and neoarsphenamine of different manufacture. C. Voegtlin and H. W. Smith. *J. Pharmacol. and Exper. Therap.*, 16: 449, 1921.

V. Intravenous versus intramuscular administration of arsphenamine. Curative power and minimum effective dose. C. Voegtlin and H. W. Smith. *J. Pharmacol. and Exper. Therap.*, 17: 357, 1921.

The nature of secondary valence. Homer W. Smith.

I. The concept of secondary valence—Preliminary communication. *J. Phys. Chem.*, 25: 160, 1921.

II. Partition coefficients. *J. Phys. Chem.*, 25: 204, 1921.

III. Partition coefficients in the system water: ether. Supplementary note on the method of correction. *J. Phys. Chem.*, 25: 616, 1921.

IV. Partition coefficients in the system glycerine: acetone. *J. Phys. Chem.*, 25: 721, 1921.

V. Partition coefficients in systems containing water as one component

with special reference to the absolute values of the series constants. *J. Phys. Chem.*, 26: 256, 1922.
VI. Summary and discussion. *J. Phys. Chem.*, 26: 349, 1922.

Arsenic therapy. Homer W. Smith. *J. Am. Pharm. A.*, 11: 423, 1922.
The biochemical differentiation of bacteria. Homer W. Smith. *Am. J. Hygiene*, 2: 607, 1922.
The influence of hydrogen ion concentration on the fertilization and growth of certain marine eggs. G. H. A. Clowes and Homer W. Smith. *Am. J. Physiol.*, 64: 144, 1923.
The influence of carbon dioxide on the velocity of division of marine eggs. Homer W. Smith and G. H. A. Clowes. *Am. J. Physiol.*, 68: 183, 1924.
The influence of hydrogen ion concentration on unfertilized Arbacia, Asterias, and Chaetopterus eggs. Homer W. Smith and G. H. A. Clowes. *Biol. Bull.*, 47: 304, 1924.
The influence of hydrogen ion concentration on the development of normally fertilized Arbacia and Asterias eggs. Homer W. Smith and G. H. A. Clowes. *Biol. Bull.*, 47: 323, 1924.
The influence of hydrogen ion concentration on the fertilization process in Arbacia, Asterias, and Chaetopterus eggs. Homer W. Smith and G. H. A. Clowes. *Biol. Bull.*, 47: 33, 1924.
The action of acids on cell division with reference to permeability to anions. Homer W. Smith. *Amer. J. Physiol.*, 72: 347, 1925.
The action of acids on turtle heart muscle with reference to the penetration of anions. Homer W. Smith. *Am. J. Physiol.*, 76: 411, 1926.
Note on the nitrogen excretion of camels. Homer W. Smith and H. Silvette. *J. Biol. Chem.*, 78: 409, 1928.
The excretion of ammonia and urea by the gills of fish. Homer W. Smith. *J. Biol. Chem.*, 81: 727, 1929.
The composition of the body fluids of the goosefish (*Lophius Piscatorius*). Homer W. Smith. *J. Biol. Chem.*, 82: 71, 1929.
The inorganic composition of the body fluids of the Chelonia. Homer W. Smith. *J. Biol. Chem.*, 82: 651, 1929.
The distribution ratios of some organic acids between water and organic liquids. Homer W. Smith and T. A. White. *J. Phys. Chem.*, 33: 1953, 1929.
The composition of the body fluids of elasmobranchs. Homer W. Smith. *J. Biol. Chem.*, 81: 407, 1929.
Metabolism of the lungfish (*Protopterus Aethiopicus*). Homer W. Smith. *J. Biol. Chem.*, 88: 97, 1930.

The glomerular development of the vertebrate kidney in relation to habitat. E. K. Marshall, Jr., and Homer W. Smith. *Biol. Bull.*, 59: 135, 1930.

Lungfish. Homer W. Smith. *Scient. Month.*, 31: 467, 1930.

The absorption and excretion of water and salts by marine teleosts. Homer W. Smith. *Am. J. Physiol.*, 93: 480, 1930.

Observations on the African lungfish (*Protopterus Aethiopicus*) and on evolution from water to land environments. Homer W. Smith. *Ecology*, 12: 164, 1931.

The regulation of the composition of the blood of teleost and elasmobranch fishes, and the evolution of the vertebrate kidney. Homer W. Smith. *Copeia*, 4: 147, 1931.

The absorption and excretion of water and salts by the elasmobranch fishes. Homer W. Smith.

I. Fresh water elasmobranchs. *Am. J. Physiol.*, 98: 279, 1931.
II. Marine elasmobranchs. *Am. J. Physiol.*, 98: 296, 1931.
III. The use of xylose as a measure of the glomerular filtrate in Squalus Acanthias. Robert W. Clarke and H. W. Smith. *J. Cell. and Comp. Physiol.*, 1: 131, 1932.

Water regulation and its evolution in the fishes. Homer W. Smith. *Quart. Rev. Biol.*, 7: 1, 1932.

On the use of sodium bicarbonate and calcium in the rectification of sea-water in aquaria. C. M. Breder, Jr., and H. W. Smith. *Jour. Marine Biol. Assoc. Unit. Kingdom*, 18 (1): 199, 1932.

The excretion of urine in the dog.

I. The urea and creatinine clearances on a mixed diet. N. Jolliffe and Homer W. Smith. *Am. J. Physiol.*, 98: 572, 1931.
II. The urea and creatinine clearance on cracker meal diet. N. Jolliffe and Homer W. Smith. *Am. J. Physiol.*, 99: 101, 1931.
III. The use of nonmetabolized sugars in the measurement of the glomerular filtrate. N. Jolliffe, J. A. Shannon, and H. W. Smith. *Am. J. Physiol.*, 100: 301, 1932.
IV. The effect of maintenance diet, feeding, etc., upon the quantity of glomerular filtrate. J. A. Shannon, N. Jolliffe, and H. W. Smith. *Am. J. Physiol.*, 101: 625, 1932.
V. The effects of xylose and sucrose upon the glomerular and urea clearances. N. Jolliffe, J. A. Shannon, and H. W. Smith. *Am. J. Physiol.*, 101: 639, 1932.
VI. The filtration and secretion of exogenous creatinine. J. A. Shannon, N. Jolliffe, and H. W. Smith. *Am. J. Physiol.*, 102: 534, 1932.

Kamongo. New York: The Viking Press, 1932; revised edition, 1949.

The action of phlorizin on the excretion of glucose, xylose, sucrose, creatinine, and urea by man. H. Chasis, N. Jolliffe, and H. W. Smith. *J. Clin. Invest.*, 12: 1083, 1933.

The functional and structural evolution of the vertebrate kidney. H. W. Smith. *Sigma XI Quarterly*, p. 141, 1933.

Lungfish. Homer W. Smith. *Aquarium*, 1: 241,1933.

The metabolism of the lungfish. H. W. Smith.

I. General considerations of the fasting metabolism in active fish. *J. Cell. and Comp. Physiol.*, 6: 43, 1935.

II. Effect of feeding meat on metabolic rate. *J. Cell. and Comp. Physiol.*, 6: 335, 1935.

The excretion of inulin, xylose, and urea by normal and phlorizinized man. J. A. Shannon and H. W. Smith. *J. Clin. Invest.*, 14: 393, 1935.

The evolution of the kidney. Homer W. Smith. *Bul. N.Y. Zool. Soc.*, 38: 120, 135.

Excretion of inulin, creatinine, xylose, and urea in the normal rabbit. B. I. Kaplan and H. W. Smith. *Am. J. Physiol.*, 113: 354, 1935.

The excretion of the nonmetabolized sugars in the dogfish, the dog, and man. H. W. Smith. In H. Berglund and G. Medes, Eds., *The Kidney in Health and Disease*, (Philadelphia, Lea and Febiger), 1935.

The End of Illusion. New York: Harper and Brothers, 1935.

The retention and physiological role of urea in the elasmobranchii. Homer W. Smith. *Biol. Revs.*, 11: 49, 1936.

The composition of urine in the seal. Homer W. Smith. *J. Cell. and Comp. Physiol.*, 7: 465, 1936.

The phenol red clearance in normal man. W. Goldring, R. W. Clarke, and H. W. Smith. *J. Clin. Invest.*, 15: 221, 1936.

Inulin and its suitability for intravenous administration in man. W. Goldring and Homer W. Smith. *Proc. Soc. Exper. Biol. and Med.*, 34: 67, 1936.

Error in physiology. H. W. Smith. In J. Jastrow, Ed., *The Story of Human Error* (New York: Appleton-Century Co., Inc.), 1936.

The diffusion coefficient of inulin and other substances of interest in renal physiology. J. J. Bunim, W. W. Smith, and H. W. Smith. *J. Biol. Chem.*, 118: 667, 1937.

Differentiation of glomerular and tubular function in glomerular nephritis. W. Goldring and H. W. Smith. *Proc. Soc. Exper. Biol. and Med.*, 37: 180, 1937.

The Physiology of the Kidney. New York: Oxford University Press, 1937.

Suitability of inulin for intravenous administration to man. H. W. Smith, H. Chasis, and H. A. Ranges. *Proc. Soc. Exper. Biol. and Med.*, 37: 726, 1938.

The excretion of inulin and creatinine by the anthropoid apes and other infrahuman primates. H. W. Smith and R. W. Clarke. *Am. J. Physiol.*, 122: 132, 1938.

The measurement of the tubular excretory mass, effective blood flow, and filtration rate in the normal human kidney. H. W. Smith, W. Goldring, and H. Chasis. *J. Clin. Invest.*, 17: 263, 1938.

The excretion of urea in normal man and in subjects with glomerulonephritis. H. Chasis and H. W. Smith. *J. Clin. Invest.*, 17:347, 1938.

Protein binding of phenol red, diodrast, and other substances in plasma. W. W. Smith and H. W. Smith. *J. Biol. Chem.*, 124: 107, 1938.

The control of renal blood flow and glomerular filtration in normal man. H. Chasis, H. A. Ranges, W. Goldring, and H. W. Smith. *J. Clin. Invest.*, 17: 683, 1938.

Kidney. Homer W. Smith. *Ann. Rev. Physiol.*, 1: 503, 1939.

The effects of spinal anesthesia on the circulation in normal, unoperated man with reference to the autonomy of the arterioles, and especially those of the renal circulation. H. W. Smith, E. A. Rovenstine, W. Goldring, H. Chasis, and H. A. Ranges. *J. Clin. Invest.*, 18: 319, 1939.

New aspects of renal physiology. Homer W. Smith. *J. Urol.*, 41: 867, 1939.

Studies in the Physiology of the Kidney. Lawrence: University Extension Division, University of Kansas, 1939.

Renal excretion of hexitols (sorbitol, mannitol, and dulcitol) and their derivatives (sorbitan, isomannide, and sorbide) and of endogenous creatinine-like chromogen in dog and man. W. W. Smith, N. Finkelstein, and H. W. Smith. *J. Biol. Chem.*, 135: 231, 1940.

Relations of effective renal blood flow and glomerular filtration to tubular excretory mass in normal man. W. Goldring, H. Chasis, H. A. Ranges, and H. W. Smith. *J. Clin. Invest.*, 19: 739, 1940.

Glomerular dynamics in the normal human kidney. H. W. Smith,

H. Chasis, W. Goldring, and H. A. Ranges. *J. Clin. Invest.*, 19: 751, 1940.

Physiology of the renal circulation. Homer W. Smith. Harvey Lectures, 35: 166, 1939–40.

Reduction of blood pressure associated with the pyrogenic reaction in hypertensive subjects. H. Chasis, W. Goldring, and H. W. Smith. *J. Clin. Invest.*, 21: 369, 1942.

The removal of diodrast from blood by the dog's explanted kidney. A. C. Corcoran, H. W. Smith, and I. H. Page. *Am. J. Physiol.*, 134: 333, 1941.

Note on the interpretation of clearance methods in the diseased kidney. Homer W. Smith. *J. Clin. Invest.*, 20: 631, 1941.

Effective renal blood flow in subjects with essential hypertension. W. Goldring, H. Chasis, H. A. Ranges, and H. W. Smith. *J. Clin. Invest.*, 20: 637, 1941.

Role of the kidney in the genesis of hypertension. H. W. Smith, W. Goldring, and H. Chasis. *Bull. N.Y. Acad. Med.*, 19: 449, 1943.

The application of saturation methods to the study of glomerular and tubular function in the human kidney. H. W. Smith, W. Goldring, H. Chasis, H. A. Ranges, and S. E. Bradley. *J. Mt. Sinai Hosp.*, 10: 59, 1943.

Lectures on the Kidney. Homer W. Smith. Porter Lectures, Series 9, (Univ. Ext. Div., Univ. of Kansas), 1943.

I. The evolution of the kidney, p. 1.
II. Newer methods of study of renal function in man, p. 25.
III. The renal blood flow in normal subjects, p. 47.
IV. Renal physiology between two wars, Wm. Henry Welch Lecture, p. 63.
V. Application of saturation methods to the study of glomerular and tubular function in the human kidney, Wm. Henry Welch Lecture, p. 83.

The renal clearances of substituted hippuric acid derivatives and other aromatic acids in dog and man. H. W. Smith, N. Finkelstein, L. Aliminosa, B. Crawford, and M. Graber. *J. Clin. Invest.*, 24: 388, 1945.

The use of sodium p-aminohippurate for the functional evaluation of the human kidney. H. Chasis, J. Redish, W. Goldring, H. A. Ranges, and H. W. Smith. *J. Clin. Invest.*, 24: 583, 1945.

Hemodynamic alterations in normotensive and hypertensive subjects during the pyrogenic reaction. S. E. Bradley, H. Chasis, W. Goldring, and H. W. Smith. *J. Clin. Invest.*, 24: 749, 1945.

Statement on the question of similarity in pathogenesis of experimental renal hypertension and human hypertension. W. Goldring, H. Chasis, and H. W. Smith. *Experimental Hypertension* (special publication of the N.Y. Acad. Sc.) 3: 177, 1946.

The excretion of water. Homer W. Smith. *Bull. N.Y. Acad. Med.*, 23: 177, 1947.

Plato and Clementine. Homer W. Smith. *Bull. N.Y. Acad. Med.*, 23: 352, 1947.

Studies on the mechanism of death in dogs after systemic intoxication by the intravenous injection of methyl-bis (β-chloroethyl) amine or tris (β-chloroethyl) amine. C. R. Houck, B. Crawford, J. H. Bannon, and H. W. Smith. *J. Pharmacol. and Exper. Therap.*, 90: 277, 1947.

The toxicity and pharmacological action of the nitrogen mustards and certain related compounds. W. P. Anslow, Jr., D. A. Karnovsky, B. Val Jager, and H. W. Smith. *J. Pharmacol. and Exper. Therap.*, 91: 224, 1947.

Glomerular filtration rate, effective renal blood flow, and maximal tubular excretory capacity in infancy. J. R. West, H. W. Smith, and H. Chasis. *J. Pediat.*, 32: 10, 1948.

The clinical and pathologic effects of the nitrogen and sulfur mustards in laboratory animals. I. Graef, D. A. Karnofsky, B. V. Jager, B. Krichesky, and H. W. Smith. *Am. J. Path.*, 24: 1, 1948.

Hypertension and urologic disease. Homer W. Smith. *Am. J. Med.*, 4: 724, 1948.

Present status of national science foundation legislation. Homer W. Smith. *J.A.M.A.*, 137: 17, 1948.

The intravenous, subcutaneous, and cutaneous toxicity of bis (β-chloroethyl) sulfide (mustard gas) and of various derivatives. W. P. Anslow, Jr., D. A. Karnofsky, B. V. Jager and H. W. Smith. *J. Pharmacol. and Exper. Therap.*, 93: 1, 1948.

Studies on the mechanism of action of the nitrogen and sulfur mustards *in vivo*. D. A. Karnofsky, I. Graef, and H. W. Smith. *Am. J. Path.*, 24: 275, 1948.

The excretion of strong electrolytes. L. G. Wesson, Jr., W. P. Anslow, Jr., and H. W. Smith. *Bull. N.Y. Acad. Med.*, 24: 586, 1948.

Effects of salt and protein restriction on blood pressure and renal hemodynamics in hypertensive patients. H. Chasis, W. Goldring, E. Breed, A. Bolomey, and H. W. Smith. *J. Clin. Invest.*, 28: 775, 1949.

Organism and environment: dynamic oppositions. Homer W. Smith. In J. Romano, Ed., *Adaptation*, (Ithaca, Cornell Univ. Press), 1949, p. 25.

Religion and modern science: three interpretations. H. W. Smith, T. M. Green, and J. C. Murray. *Yale Scientific Mag.*, 23: 2, 1949.

Significance of the renal juxtamedullary circulation in man. M. H. Maxwell, E. S. Breed, and H. W. Smith. *Am. J. Med.*, 9: 216, 1950.

Science versus metaphysics. Homer W. Smith. *Ohio State Law J.*, 12: 53, 1951.

The Kidney: Structure and Function in Health and Disease. New York: Oxford University Press, 1951.

The distribution of sodium and potassium in man. N. Deane and H. W. Smith. *J. Clin. Invest.*, 31: 197, 1952.

The distribution of total body chloride in man. N. Deane, M. Ziff, and H. W. Smith. *J. Clin. Invest.*, 31: 200, 1952.

Biology and government. Homer W. Smith. *Phi Chi Quart.*, April, 1952, p. 1.

Renal excretion of sodium and water. Homer W. Smith. *Fed. Proc.*, 11: 701, 1952.

Man and His Gods. Boston: Little, Brown and Company, 1952, revised edition, 1955.

The kidney. H. W. Smith. *Scient. Amer.*, 188: 40, 1953.

Effects of epinephrine and typhoid vaccine on segmental vascular resistances in the human kidney. M. H. Maxwell, D. M. Gomez, A. P. Fishman, and H. W. Smith. *J. Pharmacol. and Exper. Therap.*, 109: 274, 1953.

Evaluation of renal function tests; Renal excretion of sodium and water. H. W. Smith. In *Renal Function in Infants and Children*, Report of the Eighth M. and R. Pediatric Research Conf., March, 1953.

Comparative physiology of the kidney. Homer W. Smith. *J.A.M.A.*, 153: 1512, 1953.

From Fish to Philosopher. Boston: Little, Brown and Company, 1953.

Effect of unilateral splanchnic nerve resection on the renal excretion of sodium. L. B. Page, C. F. Baxter, G. H. Reem, J. C. Scott-Baker, and H. W. Smith. *Am. J. Physiol.*, 177: 194, 1954.

The mechanism of formation of osmotically concentrated urine during the antidiuretic state. G. A. Zak, C. Brun, and H. W. Smith. *J. Clin. Invest.*, 33: 1064, 1954.

On a proper knowledge of man. Homer W. Smith. Lecture before the Univ. of Washington Research Society, April 21, 1955.

Fate of inulin and sucrose in normal subjects as determined by a urine reinfusion technique. N. Deane and H. W. Smith. *J. Clin. Invest.*, 34: 681, 1955.

The elaboration of osmotically concentrated urine in renal disease. D. S. Baldwin, H. J. Berman, H. O. Heinemann, and H. W. Smith. *J. Clin. Invest.*, 34: 800, 1955.

Notes on the history of renal physiology. H. W. Smith. *Dept. Med. and Surgery, Vets. Adm. Tech. Bull.* TB10–110, 1955, p. 1.

Urine pH and carbonic anhydrase activity in the marine dogfish. J. Hodler, H. O. Heinemann, A. P. Fishman and H. W. Smith. *Am. J. Physiol.*, 183: 155, 1955.

Reassurance in the management of benign hypertensive disease. W. Goldring, H. Chasis, G. E. Schreiner, and H. W. Smith. *Circulation*, 14: 260, 1956.

Unilateral nephrectomy in hypertensive disease. Homer W. Smith. *J. Urol.*, 76: 685, 1956.

Interpretation of observations of renal hemodynamics in preeclampsia. H. W. Smith. In *Toxemia of Pregnancy*, Report of First Ross Obstetric Research Conf., April, 1956.

The apparent first dissociation constant, pK_1, of carbonic acid in the human erythrocyte. N. Deane and H. W. Smith. *J. Biol. Chem.*, 227: 101, 1957.

Salt and water volume receptors. An exercise in physiologic apologetics. Homer W. Smith. *Am. J. Med.*, 23: 623, 1957.

On the reading of scientific papers. Homer W. Smith. *Tr. A. Am. Physicians*, 70: 41, 1957.

Renal concentrating operation at low urine flows. S. Boyarsky and H. W. Smith. *J. Urol.*, 78: 511, 1957.

Acute renal failure. H. W. Smith. *Kaiser Foundation Med. Bull.*, 6: 18, 1958.

De Urina. Homer W. Smith. *Kaiser Foundation Med. Bull.*, 6: 1, 1958.

Principles of Renal Physiology. New York: Oxford University Press, June 1956; revised edition, November 1956.

The fate of sodium and water in the renal tubules. Homer W. Smith. *Bull. N.Y. Acad. Med.*, 35: 293, 1959.

The biology of consciousness. Homer W. Smith. In C. McC. Brooks and P. F. Cranefield, Eds., *The Historical Development of Psysiological Thought.* (New York: Hafner Publ. Co.), 1959.

Highlights in the history of renal physiology. Homer W. Smith. *Bull. Georgetown Univ. Med. Center,* 13: 4, 1959.

A knowledge of the laws of solutions . . . H. W. Smith. *Circulation,* 21: 808, 1960.

Evolución del medio interno (Estudio filogenético del riñón). H. W. Smith. *Principia Cardiologica,* 7: 103, 1960.

Negative pressure respiration, water diuresis and natriuresis in normotensive, hypertensive, and prehydrated normotensive subjects. H. W. Hulet and H. W. Smith. *J. Clin. Invest.,* 38: 1972, 1959.

Postural natriuresis and urine osmotic concentration in hydropenic subjects. W. H. Hulet and H. W. Smith. *Am. J. Med.,* 30: 8, 1961.

The kidney. H. W. Smith. In D. W. Richards and A. P. Fishman, *The Fabric of Cardiovascular Concepts,* (New York: Oxford Univ. Press).

The plasma membrane. With notes on the history of botany. H. W. Smith. *Circulation,* 26 (2): 987, 1962.

Urea and the renal concentrating operation in man. P. R. Steinmetz and H. W. Smith. *Amer. J. Med.* 35: 727, 1962.

APPENDIX B

Awards and Honors Received by Homer W. Smith

AWARDS

1937 Honorary Degree Master of Science, Yale University
1948 Lasker Award
1948 Presidential Medal of Merit
1954 Passano Award
1958 Harlow Brooks Medal, New York Academy of Medicine

LECTURESHIPS

1936 Visiting Lecturer, Yale Medical School
1938 Belfield Lecturer, Chicago
1939 Porter Lecturer, Kansas City
1940 Harvey Lecturer, New York
1942 Welch Lecturer, New York
1946 Herzstein Lecturer, San Francisco
1948 Millikan Lecturer, Nashville
1948 Rothschild Lecturer, New York
1949 Barlow Lecturer, Los Angeles
1950 Sommer Lecturer, Portland
1950 McGuire Lecturer, Richmond
1950 Visiting Lecturer, Hadassah University School of Medicine, Jerusalem
1951 Martland Lecturer, Newark
1952 Freiberg Lecturer, Cincinnati
1952 Sherwood Lecturer, Lawrence, Kansas
1952 Rockwood Lecturer, Iowa City
1952 Musser Lecturer, Tulane University
1953 Brown Lecturer, Baltimore
1953 Ballenger Lecturer, Havana
1953 Bernard Lecturer, Winston-Salem
1955 Comroe Lecturer, Philadelphia
1955 Tritt Lecturer, St. Louis

1955 Walker Ames Visiting Professor, University of Washington

1958 George Cyril Graves Visiting Professor, University of Indiana School of Medicine

1958 Kober Lecturer, Association of American Physicians, Georgetown University Medical School

1960 National Institutes of Health Lectureship, United States Public Health Service

ADVISORY APPOINTMENTS

1930–1938 Research Associate, American Museum of Natural History

1935–1955 Medical Fellowship Board, National Research Council

1936–1945 Assistant Editor, *Chemical Abstracts*

1936–1956 One of founding editors, *Journal of Cellular and Comparative Physiology*

1938–1962 Research Associate, New York Zoological Society

1938–1953 Member, Postdoctoral Fellowship Board in the Medical Sciences, National Research Council

1941–1954 Associate Editor, *American Journal of Physiology*

1942–1946 Division Member, National Defense Research Committee

1943–1944 Member, Committee on Medicine, in preparation of Bush report, *Science—the Endless Frontier*

1943–1949 Scientific Advisory Committee, Memorial Hospital, New York

1946–1950 Secretary, Bowman Committee Supporting the Bush Report, seeking effective legislation for the creation of the present National Science Foundation

1947–1950 Scientific Advisory Board, Sloan-Kettering Institute for Cancer Research

1948–1951 Chairman, NRC-AEC Postdoctoral Fellowship Board (Medicine)

1949–1951 Member, Fellowship Board, Oak Ridge Institute of Nuclear Studies

1950–1953 Scientific Board, Jackson Memorial Laboratory, Bar Harbor, Maine

1951–1954 Chairman, NRC-Fulbright Advisory Committee on Medicine (Conference Board of Associated Research Councils)

1952–1962 Scientific Advisory Committee, Russell Sage Institute of Pathology, N.Y.

1956–1962 Member, Cardiovascular Study Section, National Institutes of Health

EXTRAMURAL OFFICES

1938–1962 Trustee, Bermuda Biological Station for Research

1951–1962 President, Mount Desert Island Biological Station

APPENDIX C

Library on Man's Place in Nature

Homer Smith conceived and initiated at New York University School of Medicine in 1955 an important area of education by establishing a special library designated the "Library on Man's Place in Nature." In consequence of the rapid advances of technical knowledge in medicine and related fields, neither medical students nor the instructional staff have adequate opportunity to keep informed on the humanistic and philosophic implications of modern science. He therefore proposed to place in the newly formed Library selected books and journals which dealt with such subjects as cosmogony, physics, biology, philosophy, semantics, comparative religion, and social anthropology. He intended that the library should offer regular seminars in areas of timely interest and regular lectureships by which distinguished extramural speakers would be brought to the Medical Center. The following books were selected by Smith himself as the initial collection. The annotations are his.

E. T. Bell, *The Queen of the Sciences* (1931). Mathematics; what she is and what she isn't; by the famous Professor at California Institute of Technology.

———, *Numerology* (1933). The same Professor gives the lighter side of the Queen the once-over.

J. Bronowski, *The Face of Violence, An Essay with a Play* (1955). Motives and manifestations of violence in human history; a remarkable study in literature and anthropology.

Arturo Castiglioni, *Adventures of the Mind* (1946). Discourses on magic and its manifold manifestations throughout human history. By the eminent Italian historian of science.

Giorgio de Santillana, *The Crime of Galileo* (1955). Fascinating, realistic, and historically accurate analysis of the tragedy of Galileo.

JOHN WILLIAM DRAPER, *History of the Conflict between Religion and Science* (1874; 1896). By the first Professor of Physiology at this medical school. Preceded White's more famous book (*vide infra*) by 21 years.

A. DUPONT-SOMMER, *The Jewish Sect of Qumran and the Essenes: New Studies on the Dead Sea Scrolls* (1955). By the eminent French scholar who has translated much of this material. Technically more difficult than Edmund Wilson's popular volume (*vide infra*).

BENJAMIN FARRINGTON, *Science and Politics in the Ancient World* (1939). A fresh look at ancient thought.

———, *Francis Bacon, Philosopher of Industrial Science* (1949). A provocative and stimulating reinterpretation.

PHILIPP FRANK, *Modern Science and its Philosophy* (1941; 1955). The philosophy of logical empiricism.

SIGMUND FREUD, *The Future of an Illusion* (1928; 1949). One of Freud's most provocative essays.

GEORGE GAMOW, *Biography of the Earth* (1948). By the Professor of Theoretical Physics at George Washington University and an eminent student of cosmogony.

CHARLES COULSTON GILLISPIE, *Genesis and Geology: A Study in the Relations of Scientific Thought, Natural Theology, and Social Opinion in Great Britain, 1790–1850* (1951). A lively account of the impact of science and Mosaic cosmology prior to the *Origin of Species*.

ETIENNE GILSON, *History of Christian Philosophy in the Middle Ages* (1955). One of the most authoritative works in this area.

MICHIHIKO HACHIYA, *Hiroshima Diary: The Journal of a Japanese Physician August 6–September 30, 1945* (1955). An eyewitness account of the greatest man-made catastrophe in history.

PHILIP HUGHES, *A Popular History of the Catholic Church* (1949; 1954). Brief but complete, by an outstanding historian of the Catholic Church.

ALDOUS HUXLEY, *The Devils of Loudun* (1953). A brilliant historical study of alleged demonic possession in a 17th century convent.

THOMAS HENRY HUXLEY, *Man's Place in Nature* (1863). Includes the three famous essays, first published in 1863, which definitively applied Darwin's theory of evolution to man.

WILLIAM IRVINE, *Apes, Angels, and Victorians: The Story of Darwin, Huxley, and Evolution* (1955). A fascinating portrait of an age and the two men who stood at the center of its intellectual and moral turmoil.

WILLY JOHNS, *The Fabulous Journey of Hieronymous Meeker* (1954). One of the better books of science fiction, loaded with philosophic dynamite.

JOSEPH WOOD KRUTCH, *The Voice of the Desert* (1955). A noted writer and critic describes the life on the Sonoran Desert of the American Southwest, and ends on a philosophic note.

WESTON LA BARRE, *The Human Animal* (1954). A remarkable synthesis of man's intellectual and social efforts in the light of their biological origins.

W. E. H. LECKY, *History of the Rise and Influence of the Spirit of Rationalism in Europe* (1865; 1955). The scope and significance of reason in religion, morality, politics, and economics. Historically important.

———, *History of European Morals from Augustus to Charlemagne* (1869; 1955). A brilliant study of the origins and development of Western moral beliefs and conduct. Also historically important.

EDWARD MACCURDY, ed., *The Notebooks of Leonardo Da Vinci* (1939; 1955). The most comprehensive approach to the character and thought of Leonardo in the English language.

M. F. ASHLEY MONTAGU, *The Direction of Human Development: Biological and Social Bases* (1955). An analysis of the biological, social, and cultural bases of human nature and its development.

HERBERT J. MULLER, *Uses of the Past* (1954). History as reread by an alert student of contemporary philosophy. A must book for those who want to understand what the Iron Curtain signifies.

DAVID SAVILLE MUZZEY, *Ethics as a Religion* (1951). A statement of creed, by a leader of the Ethical Society.

RICHARD NEUTRA, *Survival Through Design* (1954). An architect looks at the two billion people now living on this planet and cogitates on the physical "how" and the humanistic "why."

RALPH BARTON PERRY, *The Thought and Character of William James* (1935; 1954). Briefer version of the Pulitzer Prize-winning biography. A vivid panorama of New England thought and imagination.

CHARLES FRANCIS POTTER, *The Faiths Men Live By* (1954). Short accounts of the origins and beliefs of fifty different religions, by the dean of humanism.

HANS REICHENBACH, *Rise of Scientific Philosophy* (1951). An excellent, up-to-date recapitulation.

OSCAR RIDDLE, *The Unleashing of Evolutionary Thought* (1954). A trenchant account of our contemporary schizophrenic culture, by a distinguished biologist.

JOHN ROMANO, ed., *Adaptation* (1949). Lectures by Weiss, Smith, Liddell, Kubie, and Kluckhohn.

JOSIAH ROYCE, *The Spirit of Modern Philosophy* (1892; 1955). A great American philosopher presents the history of modern thought, with discussions of the problems of evolution, freedom, and moral attitudes. Historically important.

GEORGE SANTAYANA, *Character and Opinion in the United States* (1955). A brilliant study of the American scene, its great minds, popular beliefs, moral dilemmas, and political commitments.

GEORGE SARTON, *Galen of Pergamon* (1954). By one of the greatest of historians in the field of science.

GEORGE GAYLORD SIMPSON, *Life of the Past* (1953). An introduction to the study of fossil life. Readable and scientifically authoritative. By one of our leading palaeontologists.

ANDREW D. WHITE, *History of the Warfare of Science with Theology* (1895; 1955). A monumental study by the President and Professor of History at Cornell University. Recognized as one of the greatest creations of American scholarship and as a landmark in the history of human ideas. Has been through many editions. Here republished in one volume.

EDMUND WILSON, *The Scrolls from the Dead Sea* (1955). A popular account, more readable if less authentic than Dupont-Sommer's work. First printing sold out immediately.

APPENDIX D

Associates

Appended below is a partial list of scientists who were associated with Homer Smith between the years 1928 and 1962. His far reaching influence on the preclinical and clinical sciences is evident from the productivity, in diverse areas of medical science, of those who had been exposed, through him, to the basic principles of the scientific method.

John Adriani
Professor of Clinical Anesthesiology
Tulane University
School of Medicine
New Orleans, Louisiana

John D. Alexander
Assistant Professor of Medicine
University of Pennsylvania
School of Medicine
Philadelphia, Pennsylvania

W. Parker Anslow, Jr.
Professor and Chairman,
Department of Physiology
University of Virginia
School of Medicine
Charlottesville, Virginia

David S. Baldwin
Assistant Professor of Medicine
New York University
School of Medicine
New York City

James H. Bannon
Veteran's Administration Hospital
Tupper Lake, New York

John W. Bauman, Jr.
Bureau of Research
in Neurology and Psychology
New Jersey Neuro-Psychiatric
Institute
Princeton, New Jersey

E. Lovell Becker
Associate Professor of Medicine
Cornell University Medical College
New York City

Adolph R. Berger
Associate Professor
of Clinical Medicine
New York University
School of Medicine
New York City

Robert W. Berliner
Director of Intra-Mural Research
National Heart Institute
Bethesda, Maryland

Albert Biggs
Assistant Professor
of Urological Surgery
University of Tennessee
College of Medicine
Memphis, Tennessee

Richard J. Bing
Professor and Chairman,
Department of Medicine
Wayne State University
College of Medicine
Detroit, Michigan

Richard A. Bloomfield
Clinical Associate in Medicine
Harvard Medical School
Harvard University
Cambridge, Massachusetts

Alfred A. Bolomey
Chief, Cardiovascular Division
Kaiser Foundation Hospital
Oakland, California

J. G. G. Borst
Professor of Medicine
University of Amsterdam
Binnengasthuis, Amsterdam
The Netherlands

Saul Boyarsky
Professor of Urologic Surgery
Duke University Medical Center
Durham, North Carolina

Stanley E. Bradley
Bard Professor and Chairman,
Department of Medicine
Columbia University,
College of Physicians and Surgeons
New York City

Ernest Breed
Associate Professor of Surgery
New York University
School of Medicine
New York City

Emanuel H. Bresler
Associate Professor of Medicine
Tulane University
School of Medicine
New Orleans, Louisiana

Jan Brod
Professor of Medicine
Institute for Cardiovascular
Research
Prague, Czechoslovakia

Dugald E. S. Brown
Professor and Chairman,
Department of Zoology
University of Michigan
Ann Arbor, Michigan

Claus Brun
Director
of Central Clinical Laboratories
Kommunehospitalet
Copenhagen, Denmark

Joseph J. Bunim*
Clinical Director
National Institutes
of Arthritis and Metabolic Diseases
Bethesda, Maryland

Herbert Chasis
Professor of Medicine
New York University
School of Medicine
New York City

Robert W. Clarke
Chief,
Department of Surgical Physiology
(retired)
Walter Reed Army Medical Center
Washington, D.C.

Charles A. R. Connor
Associate Professor
of Clinical Medicine
New York University
School of Medicine
New York City

John S. Cook
Associate Professor of Physiology
New York University
School of Medicine
New York City

Andre Cournand
Professor of Medicine, Emeritus
Columbia University
College of Physicians and Surgeons
New York City

Betty Jane Crawford
New York City

Charles H. Crowder
South Hill, Virginia

Joseph Dancis
Professor of Pediatrics
New York University
School of Medicine
New York City

Norman Deane
Associate Professor of Medicine
New York Medical College
New York City

David P. Earle
Professor and Director,
Department of Medicine
Northwestern University
Medical School
Chicago, Illinois

Robert P. Eisinger
Clinical Investigator
Veterans Administration Hospital
New York City

Doris J. Escher
Physician-in-Charge
Cardiac Catheterization Unit
Montefiore Hospital
New York City

Saul Farber
Professor of Medicine
Acting Dean
New York University
School of Medicine
New York City

Saul H. Fisher
Associate Professor
of Clinical Psychiatry
New York University
School of Medicine
New York City

Alfred P. Fishman
Associate Professor of Medicine
Columbia University
College of Physicians and Surgeons
New York City

Roy Forster
Lecturer in Physiology
Darmouth Medical School
Dartmouth College
Hanover, New Hampshire

Norbert Freinkel
Assistant Professor of Medicine
Harvard Medical School
Harvard University
Cambridge, Massachusetts

N. Mario Gaudino
Associate Medical Director
Pfizer International, Incorporated
New York City

Renato O. Gazmuri
Santiago, Chile

Herbert Gershberg
Assistant Professor of Medicine
New York University
School of Medicine
New York City

William Goldring
Professor of Medicine
New York University
School of Medicine
New York City

David H. Goldstein
Professor of Environmental Medicine
New York University
School of Medicine
New York City

Ervin A. Gombos
Associate Clinical Professor
of Medicine
George Washington University
Washington, D.C.

Domingo N. Gomez
Assistant Professor of Medicine
Columbia University
College of Physicians and Surgeons
Bellevue Hospital
New York City

Irving Graef
Associate Professor
of Clinical Medicine
New York University
School of Medicine
New York City

Jean Hamburger
Professor of Medicine
Université de Paris
Hopital Necker
Paris, France

Chester W. Hampel
Professor and Chairman,
Departments of Physiology
and Pharmacology
New York University
College of Dentistry
New York City

Pinckney J. Harman
Professor and Chairman
Department of Anatomy
Seton Hall College
of Medicine and Dentistry
Jersey City, New Jersey

Jack R. Harnes
Instructor of Clinical Medicine

New York University
School of Medicine
New York City

Henry O. Heineman
Assistant Professor of Medicine
Columbia University
College of Physicians and Surgeons
New York City

Hans Heller
Professor of Pharmacology
University of Bristol
Bristol, England

Edwin P. Hiatt
Professor and Chairman,
Department of Physiology
Ohio State University
College of Medicine
Columbus, Ohio

Tage Hilden
Director,
Department III of Internal Medicine
Kommunehospital
Copenhagen, Denmark

J. E. Hodler
Director of Medicine
Medizinische Klinik
Bern, Switzerland

Bertil Hood
Professor of Medicine
Sahlgren's Hospital
Goteborg, Sweden

C. Riley Houck*
Associate Professor of Physiology
University of Tennessee
College of Medicine
Memphis, Tennessee

William H. Hulet
Associate Professor
of Internal Medicine and Physiology
University of Miami
School of Medicine
Coral Gables, Florida

Blair Valdemar Jager
Associate Professor of Medicine
Washington University
School of Medicine
St. Louis, Missouri

Norman Jolliffe*
Director, Bureau of Nutrition
Department of Health
New York City

Olafur Johnson
Johnson Clinic
Rugby, North Dakota

Bernard I. Kaplan
Director of Medicine
Phelps Memorial Hospital
Tarrytown, New York

David A. Karnofsky
Associate Professor of Medicine
Cornell University Medical College
New York City

Helen Kiegher
Schenectady, New York

Irvin M. Korr
Professor and Chairman,
Department of Physiology
Kirksville College
of Osteopathy and Surgery
Kirksville, Missouri

Michael Ladd*
Instructor in Surgery
Dartmouth Medical School
Dartmouth College
Hanover, New Hampshire

Paul Lambert
Professor of Medicine
Université Libre de Bruxelles
Brussels, Belgium

Henry D. Lauson
Professor and Chairman,
Department of Physiology
Albert Einstein College of Medicine
Yeshiva University
New York City

Marvin F. Levitt
Associate in Medicine
(Mount Sinai Hospital)
Columbia University
College of Physicians and Surgeons
New York City

Henry H. Ludemann
Katonah, New York

Donald J. Marsh
Assistant Professor of Physiology
New York University
School of Medicine
New York City

Morton H. Maxwell
Associate Clinical Professor
of Medicine
University of California
School of Medicine
Los Angeles, California

Alexander J. Michie
Assistant Professor of Urology
University of Pennsylvania
Graduate School of Medicine
Philadelphia, Pennsylvania

Pablo A. Morales
Associate Clinical Professor
of Urology
New York University
School of Medicine
New York City

Joseph Nash*
Assistant Professor
of Clinical Surgery
New York University
School of Medicine
New York City

Eric Ogden
Chief,
Environmental Biological Division
National Aeronautics
and Space Administration
Moffett Field, California

John J. Osborn
Clinical Associate Professor
of Pediatrics
Stanford University
School of Medicine
Palo Alto, California

Lot B. Page
Instructor in Medicine
Harvard Medical School
Harvard University
Cambridge, Massachusetts

Emanuel M. Papper
Professor and Chairman,
Department of Anesthesiology
Columbia University,
College of Physicians and Surgeons
New York City

Barbara Parker
Assistant Professor of Medicine
New York University
School of Medicine
New York City

George A. Perera
Professor of Medicine
Columbia University
College of Physicians and Surgeons
New York City

Robert F. Pitts
Professor and Chairman,
Department of Physiology
Cornell University Medical College
New York City

Robert S. Post
Assistant Professor of Medicine
Western Reserve University
School of Medicine
Cleveland, Ohio

Lawrence G. Raisz
Associate Professor
of Pharmacology and Medicine
School of Medicine and Dentistry
University of Rochester
Rochester, New York

Hilmert A. Ranges
Director of Medicine
New Rochelle Hospital
New Rochelle, New York

Jules Redish*
Assistant Professor of Medicine
New York University
School of Medicine
New York City

Gabrielle B. Reem
Assistant Professor of Pharmacology
New York University
School of Medicine
New York City

Morris Rockstein
Professor of Physiology
University of Miami
School of Medicine
Coral Gables, Florida

Emery Rovenstine*
Professor of Anesthesiology Emeritus
New York University School of Medicine
New York City

Wilbur H. Sawyer
Associate Professor of Pharmacology
Columbia University College of Physicians and Surgeons
New York City

David Schachter
Associate Professor of Medicine
Columbia University College of Physicians and Surgeons
New York City

David E. Schafer
Assistant Professor of Physiology
New York University School of Medicine
New York City

George E. Schreiner
Professor of Medicine
Georgetown University School of Medicine
Washington, D.C.

Irving L. Schwartz
Professor and Chairman, Department of Physiology
University of Cincinnati School of Medicine
Cincinnati, Ohio

John Cameron Scott-Baker
Surrey, England

Ewald E. Selkurt
Professor and Chairman, Department of Physiology
Indiana University School of Medicine
Indianapolis, Indiana

James A. Shannon
Director, National Institutes of Health
United States Public Health Service
Bethesda, Maryland

Jonas H. Sirota
Clinical Assistant Professor of Medicine
Stanford University School of Medicine
Palo Alto, California

Willie W. Smith
Research Physiologist
National Cancer Institute
Bethesda, Maryland

Heinz Specht
Chief, Pacific Office of International Research
National Institutes of Health
San Francisco, California

Samuel Standard
Professor of Clinical Surgery
New York University School of Medicine
New York City

Philip R. Steinmetz
Instructor in Medicine
New York University School of Medicine
New York City

John Taggart
Professor and Chairman, Department of Physiology
Columbia University College of Physicians and Surgeons
New York City

Herman Villarreal
Professor of Cardiology
Postgraduate School
National University of Mexico
Mexico 1, D.F.

Catherine A. Welsh
Glenridge Hospital
Schenectady, New York

Laurence G. Wesson, Jr.
Professor of Medicine
Jefferson Medical College
Philadelphia, Pennsylvania

Joseph R. West*
Palm Beach, Florida

James L. Whittenberger
Professor of Public Health
Head of Department of Physiology
Harvard School of Public Health

Harvard University
Boston, Massachusetts

Heinrich Wirz
Basle, Switzerland

Robert A. Wolbach
Assistant Professor of Physiology
University of Utah
School of Medicine
Salt Lake City, Utah

J. Allen Yager
Director, Department of Health
Paterson, New Jersey

George A. Zak
Assistant Professor
of Clinical Medicine
New York University
School of Medicine
New York City

Morris Ziff
Professor of Internal Medicine
University of Texas
Southwestern Medical School
Dallas, Texas

* Deceased.

PHOTOGRAPHS

Plate 1. Robert Pitts and Homer Smith

Plate 2. Robert Pitts, Homer Smith, Mrs. Robert Berliner, Robert Berliner, and John Taggart

Plate 3. Homer Smith and Herbert Chasis

Plate 4. James Shannon, Homer Smith, and Robert Berliner

Plate 5. George Schreiner, Herman Villarreal, Marvin Levitt, and Chester Hampel

Plate 6. André Cournand and Barbara Parker

Plate 7. Herbert Chasis, Geraldine Bradley, and Stanley Bradley

Plate 8. Currier McEwen, Samuel Standard, Sherwood Lawrence, and Colin MacLeod

Plate 9. George Schreiner and Hilmert Ranges

Plate 10. Willie Smith, Laurence Wesson, Mrs. Henry Lauson, Henry Lauson, and Lovell Becker

Plate 11. Alfred Fishman and Saul Farber

Plate 12. John Cook, Mrs. Erwin Gombos, Erwin Gombos, and John Bauman

Plate 13. George Zak, Ernest Breed, Mrs. David Baldwin, David Baldwin, and Marvin Levitt

Plate 14. Charles Kossmann and William Goldring

Plate 15. Jan Brod

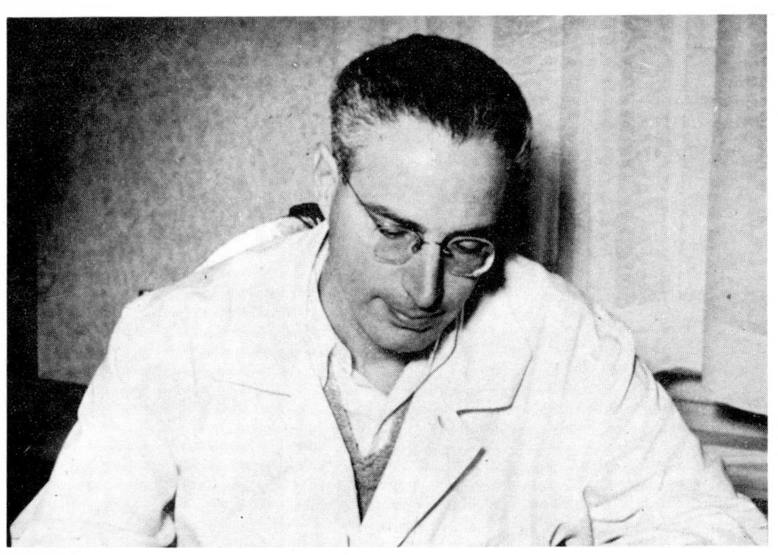

Plate 16. Hilmert Ranges, Herbert Chasis, Homer Smith, and William Goldring

Plate 17. Herbert Chasis, William Goldring, and Homer Smith